Stewart's Greatest Hits

Problems and Worked Solutions for Calculus Test and Exam Prep

Extended Edition

James Stewart

NELSON

NELSON

ISBN-13: 978-0-17-676478-4
ISBN-10: 0-17-676478-X

Consists of Selections from:

Calculus, 8th Edition
James Stewart
ISBN 10: 1-285-74062-9, © 2016

Cover Credit:

Nata-Lia

CONTENTS

1 | FUNCTIONS, LIMITS, AND MODELS

1. If $f(x) = 2x^2 + 3x - 4$, find $f(0)$, $f(2)$, $f(\sqrt{2})$, $f(1 + \sqrt{2})$, $f(-x)$, $f(x + 1)$, $2f(x)$, and $f(2x)$.

2. If $g(x) = x^3 + 2x^2 - 3$, find $g(0)$, $g(3)$, $g(-x)$, and $g(1 + h)$.

3–4 ■ Match each equation with its graph. Explain your choices. (Don't use a computer or graphing calculator.)

3. (a) $y = x^8$ (b) $y = \log_8 x$ (c) $y = 2 + \sin 2x$

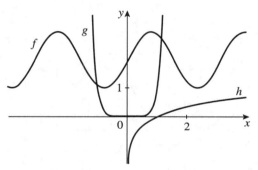

4. (a) $y = x^7$ G (b) $y = 7^x$ F

  (c) $y = -1/x$ g (d) $y = \sqrt[4]{x - 2}$ f

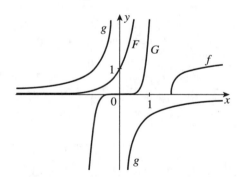

5–11 ■ Find the functions $f \circ g$, $g \circ f$, $f \circ f$, and $g \circ g$ and their domains.

5. $f(x) = \sqrt{x - 1}$, $g(x) = x^2$

6. $f(x) = 1/x$, $g(x) = x^3 + 2x$

7. $f(x) = \dfrac{1}{x - 1}$, $g(x) = \dfrac{x - 1}{x + 1}$

8. $f(x) = \sqrt{x^2 - 1}$, $g(x) = \sqrt{1 - x}$

9. $f(x) = \sqrt[3]{x}$, $g(x) = 1 - \sqrt{x}$

10. $f(x) = \dfrac{x + 2}{2x + 1}$, $g(x) = \dfrac{x}{x - 2}$

11. $f(x) = \dfrac{1}{\sqrt{x}}$ $g(x) = x^2 - 4x$

12–15 ■ Find $f \circ g \circ h$.

12. $f(x) = x - 1$, $g(x) = \sqrt{x}$, $h(x) = x - 1$

13. $f(x) = \dfrac{1}{x}$, $g(x) = x^3$, $h(x) = x^2 + 2$

14. $f(x) = x^4 + 1$, $g(x) = x - 5$, $h(x) = \sqrt{x}$

15. $f(x) = \sqrt{x}$, $g(x) = \dfrac{x}{x - 1}$, $h(x) = \sqrt[3]{x}$

16. The point $P(4, 2)$ lies on the curve $y = \sqrt{x}$.

(a) If Q is the point $(x, \sqrt{x})$, use your calculator to find the slope of the secant line PQ (correct to six decimal places) for the following values of x:

  (i) 5   (ii) 4.5   (iii) 4.1   (iv) 4.01

  (v) 4.001   (vi) 3   (vii) 3.5   (viii) 3.9

  (ix) 3.99   (x) 3.999

(b) Using the results of part (a), guess the value of the slope of the tangent line to the curve at $P(4, 2)$.

(c) Using the slope from part (b), find an equation of the tangent line to the curve at $P(4, 2)$.

17. The point $P(0.5, 2)$ lies on the curve $y = 1/x$.

(a) If Q is the point $(x, 1/x)$, use your calculator to find the slope of the secant line PQ (correct to six decimal places) for the following values of x:

  (i) 2   (ii) 1   (iii) 0.9   (iv) 0.8

  (v) 0.7   (vi) 0.6   (vii) 0.55   (viii) 0.51

  (ix) 0.45   (x) 0.49

(b) Using the results of part (a), guess the value of the slope of the tangent line to the curve at $P(0.5, 2)$.

(c) Using the slope from part (b), find an equation of the tangent line to the curve at $P(0.5, 2)$.

(d) Sketch the curve, two of the secant lines, and the tangent line.

✱18. The point $P(1, 3)$ lies on the curve $y = 1 + x + x^2$.

(a) If Q is the point $(x, 1 + x + x^2)$, find the slope of the secant line PQ for the following values of x:

(i) 2   (ii) 1.5   (iii) 1.1   (iv) 1.01

(v) 1.001   (vi) 0   (vii) 0.5   (viii) 0.9

(ix) 0.99   (x) 0.999

(b) Using the results of part (a), guess the value of the slope of the tangent line to the curve at $P(1, 3)$.

(c) Using the slope from part (b), find an equation of the tangent line to the curve at $P(1, 3)$.

19. The point $P(-1, 3)$ lies on the curve $y = 1 - 2x^3$.

(a) If Q is the point $(x, 1 - 2x^3)$, find the slope of the secant line PQ for the following values of x:

(i) -2 (ii) -1.5 (iii) -1.1

(iv) -1.01 (v) -1.001 (vi) 0

(vii) -0.5 (viii) -0.9 (ix) -0.99

(x) -0.999

(b) Using the results of part (a), guess the value of the slope of the tangent line to the curve at $P(-1, 3)$.

(c) Using the slope from part (b), find the equation of the tangent line to the curve at $P(-1, 3)$.

20. The displacement (in meters) of a certain particle moving in a straight line is given by $s = t^2 + t$, where t is measured in seconds.

(a) Find the average velocity over the following time periods:

(i) [0, 2]   (ii) [0, 1]   (iii) [0, 0.5]
(iv) [0, 0.1]

(b) Find the instantaneous velocity when $t = 0$.

(c) Draw the graph of s as a function of t and draw the secant lines whose slopes are the average velocities found in part (a).

(d) Draw the tangent line whose slope is the instantaneous velocity from part (b).

21. The experimental data in the table define y as a function of x.

x	0	1	2	3	4	5
y	2.6	2.0	1.1	1.3	2.1	3.5

(a) If P is the point $(3, 1.3)$, find the slopes of the secant lines PQ when Q is the point on the graph with $x = 0, 1, 2, 4,$ and 5.

(b) Estimate the slope of the tangent line at P by averaging the slopes of two secant lines.

(c) Use a graph of the function to estimate the slope of the tangent line at P.

22. For the function f whose graph is given, state the value of the given quantity, if it exists. If it does not exist, explain why.

(a) $\lim_{x \to 1} f(x)$ (b) $\lim_{x \to 3^-} f(x)$ (c) $\lim_{x \to 3^+} f(x)$

(d) $\lim_{x \to 3} f(x)$ (e) $f(3)$ (f) $\lim_{x \to -2^-} f(x)$

(g) $\lim_{x \to -2^+} f(x)$ (h) $\lim_{x \to -2} f(x)$ (i) $f(-2)$

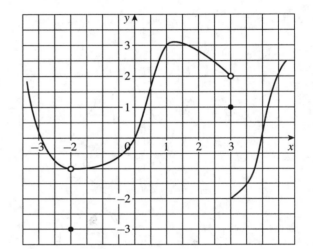

23. For the function f whose graph is given, state the value of the limit, if it exists. If it does not exist, explain why.

(a) $\lim_{x \to 3} f(x)$ (b) $\lim_{x \to 1} f(x)$ (c) $\lim_{x \to -3} f(x)$

(d) $\lim_{x \to 2^-} f(x)$ (e) $\lim_{x \to 2^+} f(x)$ (f) $\lim_{x \to 2} f(x)$

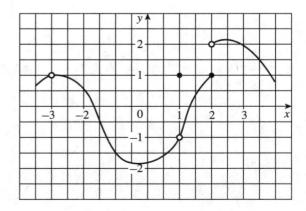

24. For the function g whose graph is shown, state the following.

(a) $\lim_{x \to -6} g(x)$ (b) $\lim_{x \to 0^-} g(x)$

(c) $\lim_{x \to 0^+} g(x)$ (d) $\lim_{x \to 4} g(x)$

(e) The equations of the vertical asymptotes

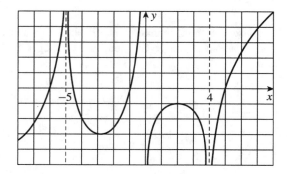

25. For the function f whose graph is shown, state the following.

(a) $\lim_{x \to 3} f(x)$ (b) $\lim_{x \to 7} f(x)$ (c) $\lim_{x \to -4} f(x)$

(d) $\lim_{x \to -9^-} f(x)$ (e) $\lim_{x \to -9^+} f(x)$

(f) The equations of the vertical asymptotes

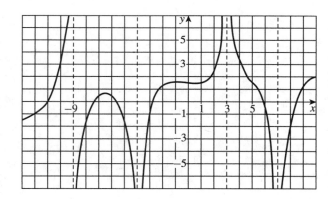

26. State the value of the limit, if it exists, from the given graph.

(a) $\lim_{x \to 1} g(x)$ (b) $\lim_{x \to 0} g(x)$ (c) $\lim_{x \to 2} g(x)$

(d) $\lim_{x \to -2} g(x)$ (e) $\lim_{x \to -1^-} g(x)$ (f) $\lim_{x \to -1} g(x)$

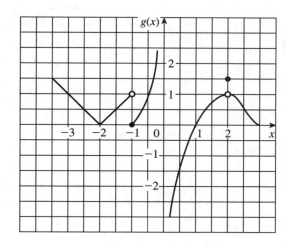

27–28 ■ Determine the infinite limit.

27. $\lim_{x \to 3} \dfrac{1}{(x-3)^8}$ **28.** $\lim_{x \to 1^+} \dfrac{x+1}{x \sin \pi x}$

29. Let

$$f(x) = \begin{cases} x^2 - 2x + 2 & \text{if } x < 1 \\ 3 - x & \text{if } x \geq 1 \end{cases}$$

(a) Find $\lim_{x \to 1^-} f(x)$ and $\lim_{x \to 1^+} f(x)$.

(b) Does $\lim_{x \to 1} f(x)$ exist?

(c) Sketch the graph of f.

30. Let

$$g(x) = \begin{cases} -x^3 & \text{if } x < -1 \\ (x+2)^2 & \text{if } x > -1 \end{cases}$$

(a) Find $\lim_{x \to -1^-} g(x)$ and $\lim_{x \to -1^+} g(x)$.

(b) Does $\lim_{x \to -1} g(x)$ exist?

(c) Sketch the graph of g.

31. Let $g(x) = [[x/2]]$.

(a) Sketch the graph of g.

(b) Evaluate each of the following limits if it exists.

(i) $\lim_{x \to 1^+} g(x)$ (ii) $\lim_{x \to 1^-} g(x)$

(iii) $\lim_{x \to 1} g(x)$ (iv) $\lim_{x \to 2^+} g(x)$

(v) $\lim_{x \to 2^-} g(x)$ (vi) $\lim_{x \to 2} g(x)$

(b) For what values of a does $\lim_{x \to a} g(x)$ exist?

32–34 ■ Prove the statement using the ε, δ definition of limit.

32. $\lim\limits_{x \to 2} \dfrac{x}{7} = \dfrac{2}{7}$

33. $\lim\limits_{x \to 4} \left(\dfrac{x}{3} + 1 \right) = \dfrac{7}{3}$

34. $\lim\limits_{x \to 2} \dfrac{x^2 + x - 6}{x - 2} = 5$

35–43 ■ Use Theorems 4, 5, 7, and 9 to show that the function is continuous on its domain. State the domain.

35. $f(x) = (x + 1)(x^3 + 8x + 9)$

36. $G(x) = \dfrac{x^4 + 17}{6x^2 + x - 1}$

37. $H(x) = \dfrac{1}{\sqrt{x + 1}}$

38. $f(t) = 2t + \sqrt{25 - t^2}$

39. $h(x) = \sqrt[5]{x - 1}(x^2 - 2)$

40. $g(t) = \dfrac{1}{t + \sqrt{t^2 - 4}}$

41. $F(t) = (t^2 + t + 1)^{3/2}$

42. $H(x) = \sqrt{\dfrac{x - 2}{5 + x}}$

43. $L(x) = |x^3 - x|$

44–47 ■ Use the Intermediate Value Theorem to show that there is a root of the given equation in the specified interval.

44. $x^3 - 3x + 1 = 0$, $(0, 1)$

45. $x^5 - 2x^4 - x - 3 = 0$, $(2, 3)$

46. $x^3 + 2x = x^2 + 1$, $(0, 1)$

47. $x^2 = \sqrt{x + 1}$, $(1, 2)$

CHALLENGE

48. Draw the graph of the equation
$$|x| + |y| = 1 + |xy|.$$

1 | ANSWERS TO SELECTED EXERCISES

1. $-4, 10, 3\sqrt{2}, 5 + 7\sqrt{2}, 2x^2 - 3x - 4, 2x^2 + 7x + 1,$
$4x^2 + 6x - 8, 8x^2 + 6x - 4$

2. $-3, 42, -x^3 + 2x^2 - 3, h^3 + 5h^2 + 7h$

3. (a) g (b) h (c) f

4. (a) G (b) F (c) g (d) f

5. $(f \circ g)(x) = f(x^2) = \sqrt{x^2 - 1}, (-\infty, -1] \cup [1, \infty)$

$(g \circ f)(x) = x - 1, [1, \infty)$

$(f \circ f)(x) = \sqrt{\sqrt{x - 1} - 1}, [2, \infty)$

$(g \circ g)(x) = x^4, (-\infty, \infty)$

6. $(f \circ g)(x) = 1/(x^3 + 2x), \{x \mid x \neq 0\}$

$(g \circ f)(x) = 1/x^3 + 2/x, \{x \mid x \neq 0\}$

$(f \circ f)(x) = x, \{x \mid x \neq 0\}$

$(g \circ g)(x) = x^9 + 6x^7 + 12x^5 + 10x^3 + 4x, (-\infty, \infty)$

7. $(f \circ g)(x) = \dfrac{-x - 1}{2}, \{x \mid x \neq -1\}$

$(g \circ f)(x) = \dfrac{2 - x}{x}, \{x \mid x \neq 0, 1\}$

$(f \circ f)(x) = \dfrac{x - 1}{2 - x}, \{x \mid x \neq 1, 2\}$

$(g \circ g)(x) = -\dfrac{1}{x}, \{x \mid x \neq 0, -1\}$

8. $(f \circ g)(x) = \sqrt{-x}, (-\infty, 0]$

$(g \circ f)(x) = \sqrt{1 - \sqrt{x^2 - 1}},$

$$[-\sqrt{2}, -1] \cup [1, \sqrt{2}]$$

$(f \circ f)(x) = \sqrt{x^2 - 2}, (-\infty, -\sqrt{2}] \cup [\sqrt{2}, \infty)$

$(g \circ g)(x) = \sqrt{1 - \sqrt{1 - x}}, [0, 1]$

9. $(f \circ g)(x) = \sqrt[3]{1 - \sqrt{x}}, [0, \infty)$

$(g \circ f)(x) = 1 - \sqrt[6]{x}, [0, \infty)$

$(f \circ f)(x) = \sqrt[9]{x}, (-\infty, \infty)$

$(g \circ g)(x) = 1 - \sqrt{1 - \sqrt{x}}, [0, 1]$

10. $(f \circ g)(x) = \dfrac{3x - 4}{3x - 2}, \left\{x \mid x \neq 2, \dfrac{2}{3}\right\}$

$(g \circ f)(x) = \dfrac{-x - 2}{3x}, \left\{x \mid x \neq 0, -\dfrac{1}{2}\right\}$

$(f \circ f)(x) = \dfrac{5x + 4}{4x + 5}, \left\{x \mid x \neq -\dfrac{1}{2}, -\dfrac{5}{4}\right\}$

$(g \circ g)(x) = \dfrac{x}{4 - x}, \{x \mid x \neq 2, 4\}$

11. $(f \circ g)(x) = 1/\sqrt{x^2 - 4x}, (-\infty, 0) \cup (4, \infty)$

$(g \circ f)(x) = \dfrac{1}{x} - \dfrac{4}{\sqrt{x}}, (0, \infty)$

$(f \circ f)(x) = x^{1/4}, (0, \infty)$

$(g \circ g)(x) = x^4 - 8x^3 + 12x^2 + 16x, (-\infty, \infty)$

12. $(f \circ g \circ h)(x) = \sqrt{x - 1} - 1$

13. $(f \circ g \circ h)(x) = 1/(x^2 + 2)^3$

14. $(f \circ g \circ h)(x) = (\sqrt{x} - 5)^4 + 1$

15. $(f \circ g \circ h)(x) = \sqrt{\dfrac{\sqrt[3]{x}}{\sqrt[3]{x} - 1}}$

16. (a) (i) 0.236068   (ii) 0.242641   (iii) 0.248457

(iv) 0.249844   (v) 0.249984   (vi) 0.267949

(vii) 0.258343   (viii) 0.251582   (ix) 0.250156

(x) 0.250016

(b) $\dfrac{1}{4}$ (c) $y = \dfrac{1}{4}x + 1$

17. (a)   (i) -1 (ii) -2

(iii) -2.222222 (iv) -2.5

(v) -2.857143 (vi) -3.333333

(vii) -3.636364 (viii) -3.921569

(ix) -4.444444 (x) -4.081633

(b) -4 (c) $y = -4x + 4$

(d)

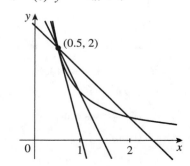

18. (a)   (i) 4   (ii) 3.5   (iii) 3.1   (iv) 3.01

      (v) 3.001   (vi) 2   (vii) 2.5   (viii) 2.9

      (ix) 2.99   (x) 2.999

  (b) 3   (c) $y = 3x$

19. (a)   (i) -14 (ii) -9.5 (iii) -6.62

      (iv) -6.0602 (v) -6.006002 (vi) -2

      (vii) -3.5 (viii) -5.42 (ix) -5.9402

      (x) -5.994002

  (b) -6 (c) $y = -6x - 3$

20. (a)   (i) 3 m/s   (ii) 2 m/s

      (iii) 1.5 m/s   (iv) 1.1 m/s

  (b) 1 m/s

  (c), (d)

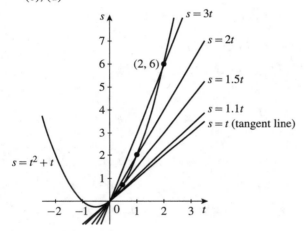

21. (a) $-0.43, -0.35, 0.2, 0.8, 1.1$

  (b) 0.5   (c) 0.57

22. (a) 3   (b) 2   (c) -2

  (d) Does not exist   (e) 1   (f) -1

  (g) -1 (h) -1 (i) -3

23. (a) 2   (b) -1 (c) 1   (d) 1

  (e) 2   (f) Does not exist

24. (a) 0   (b) ∞ (c) $-\infty$

  (d) $-\infty$ (e) $x = -5, x = 0, x = 4$

25. (a) ∞ (b) $-\infty$ (c) $-\infty$ (d) ∞

  (e) $-\infty$ (e) $x = -9, x = -4, x = 3, x = 7$

26. (a) 0   (b) Does not exist   (c) 1

  (d) 0   (e) 1   (f)   Does not exist

27. ∞ **28.** $-\infty$

29. (a) 1, 2   (b) No

  (c)

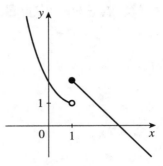

30. (a) 1, 1   (b) Yes

  (c)

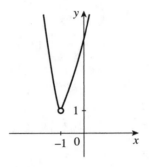

31. (a)

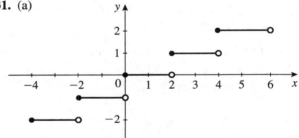

  (b)   (i) 0   (ii) 0   (iii) 0

      (iv) 1   (v) 0   (vi) Does not exist

  (c) All values except even integers

35. $\mathbb{R}$ **36.** $\left\{ x \mid x \neq -\dfrac{1}{2}, \dfrac{1}{3} \right\}$

37. $(-1, \infty)$ **38.** $[-5, 5]$

39. $\mathbb{R}$ **40.** $(-\infty, -2] \cup [2, \infty)$

41. $\mathbb{R}$ **42.** $(-\infty, -5) \cup [2, \infty)$

43. $\mathbb{R}$

48.

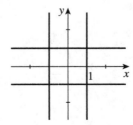

1 | SOLUTIONS TO SELECTED EXERCISES

1. $f(x) = 2x^2 + 3x - 4$, so
$f(0) = 2(0)^2 + 3(0) - 4 = -4,$

$$f(2) = 2(2)^2 + 3(2) - 4 = 10,$$

$$f(\sqrt{2}) = 2(\sqrt{2})^2 + 3(\sqrt{2}) - 4 = 3\sqrt{2},$$

$$f(1 + \sqrt{2}) = 2(1 + \sqrt{2})^2 + 3(1 + \sqrt{2}) - 4$$
$$= 2(1 + 2 + 2\sqrt{2}) + 3 + 3\sqrt{2} - 4$$
$$= 5 + 7\sqrt{2}$$

$$f(-x) = 2(-x)^2 + 3(-x) - 4 = 2x^2 - 3x - 4,$$

$$f(x + 1) = 2(x + 1)^2 + 3(x + 1) - 4$$
$$= 2(x^2 + 2x + 1) + 3x + 3 - 4$$
$$= 2x^2 + 7x + 1$$

$$2f(x) = 2(2x^2 + 3x - 4) = 4x^2 + 6x - 8 \text{, and}$$

$$f(2x) = 2(2x)^2 + 3(2x) - 4$$
$$= 2(4x^2) + 6x - 4$$
$$= 8x^2 + 6x - 4$$

2. $g(x) = x^3 + 2x^2 - 3$, so
$g(0) = 0^3 + 2(0)^2 - 3 = -3,$
$g(3) = 3^3 + 2(3)^2 - 3 = 42,$
$g(-x) = (-x)^3 + 2(-x)^2 - 3 = -x^3 + 2x^2 - 3,$ and
$g(1 + h) = (1 + h)^3 + 2(1 + h)^2 - 3 = h^3 + 5h^2 + 7h.$

3. (a) The graph of $y = x^8$ must be the graph labeled g, because g is the graph of a power function of even degree, as shown in Figure 12.

(b) The graph of $y = \log_g x$ must be the graph labeled h, because h is a graph similar to the graphs of logarithmic functions shown in Figure 21.

(c) The graph of $y = 2 + \sin 2x$ must be the graph labeled f, because f is the graph of a periodic function.

4. (a) The graph of $y = x^7$ must be the graph labeled G, because G passes through the origin.

(b) The graph of $y = 7^x$ must be the graph labeled F, because F appears to be an exponential function with y-intercept 1, increasing, and horizontal asymptote $y = 0$.

(c) The graph of $y = -1/x$ must be the graph labeled g, because g has a vertical asymptote at $x = 0$.

(d) The graph of $y = \sqrt[4]{x - 2}$ must be the graph labeled f, because f has domain $[2, \infty)$.

5. $f(x) = \sqrt{x - 1}, D = [1, \infty); g(x) = x^2, D = \mathbb{R}.$

$(f \circ g)(x) = f(g(x)) = f(x^2) = \sqrt{x^2 - 1},$

$D = \{x \in \mathbb{R} \mid g(x) \in [1, \infty)\} = (-\infty, -1] \cup [1, \infty).$

$(g \circ f)(x) = g(f(x)) = g(\sqrt{x - 1})$
$= (\sqrt{x - 1})^2 = x - 1,$

$D = [1, \infty).$

$(f \circ f)(x) = f(f(x)) = f(\sqrt{x - 1}) = \sqrt{\sqrt{x - 1} - 1},$

$D = \{x \in [1, \infty) \mid \sqrt{x - 1} \geq 1\} = [2, \infty).$

$(g \circ g)(x) = g(g(x)) = g(x^2) = (x^2)^2 = x^4, D = \mathbb{R}.$

6. $f(x) = 1/x, D = \{x \mid x \neq 0\}; g(x) = x^3 + 2x, D = \mathbb{R}.$

$(f \circ g)(x) = f(g(x)) = f(x^3 + 2x) = 1/(x^3 + 2x),$

$D = \{x \mid x^3 + 2x \neq 0\} = \{x \mid x \neq 0\}.$

$(g \circ f)(x) = g(f(x)) = g(1/x) = 1/x^3 + 2/x,$

$D = \{x \mid x \neq 0\}.$

$(f \circ f)(x) = f(f(x)) = f(1/x) = \dfrac{1}{1/x} = x,$

$D = \{x \mid x \neq 0\}.$

$(g \circ g)(x) = g(g(x)) = g(x^3 + 2x)$
$= (x^3 + 2x)^3 + 2(x^3 + 2x)$
$= x^9 + 6x^7 + 12x^5 + 10x^3 + 4x, D = \mathbb{R}.$

7. $f(x) = \dfrac{1}{x - 1}, D = \{x \mid x \neq 1\}; g(x) = \dfrac{x - 1}{x + 1},$

$D = \{x \mid x \neq -1\}.$

$(f \circ g)(x) = f\left(\dfrac{x - 1}{x + 1}\right) = \left(\dfrac{x - 1}{x + 1} - 1\right)^{-1}$

$= \left(\dfrac{-2}{x + 1}\right)^{-1} = \dfrac{-x - 1}{2},$

$D = \{x \mid x \neq -1\}.$

$(g \circ f)(x) = g\left(\dfrac{1}{x - 1}\right) = \dfrac{1/(x - 1) - 1}{1/(x - 1) + 1} = \dfrac{2 - x}{x},$

$D = \{x \mid x \neq 0, 1\}.$

$(f \circ f)(x) = f\left(\dfrac{1}{x-1}\right) = \dfrac{1}{1/(x-1)-1} = \dfrac{x-1}{2-x}$,

$D = \{x \mid x \neq 1, 2\}$.

$(g \circ g)(x) = g\left(\dfrac{x-1}{x+1}\right) = \dfrac{(x-1)/(x+1)-1}{(x-1)/(x+1)+1} = \dfrac{1}{x}$,

$D = \{x \mid x \neq 0, -1\}$.

8. $f(x) = \sqrt{x^2-1}$, $D = (-\infty, -1] \cup [1, \infty)$;

$g(x) = \sqrt{1-x}$, $D = (-\infty, 1]$.

$(f \circ g)(x) = f(g(x)) = f(\sqrt{1-x})$

$\qquad = \sqrt{(\sqrt{1-x})^2 - 1} = \sqrt{-x}$.

To find the domain of $(f \circ g)(x)$, we must find the values of x that are in the domain of g such that $g(x)$ is in the domain of f. In symbols. we have $D = \{x \in (-\infty, 1] \mid \sqrt{1-x} \in (-\infty, -1] \cup [1, \infty)\}$.

First, we concentrate on the requirement that $\sqrt{1-x} \in (-\infty, -1] \cup [1, \infty)$. Because $\sqrt{1-x} \geq 0$, $\sqrt{1-x}$ is not in $(-\infty, -1]$. If $\sqrt{1-x}$ is in $[1, \infty)$, then we must have $\sqrt{1-x} \geq 1 \implies 1-x \geq 1 \implies x \leq 0$. Combining the restrictions $x \leq 0$ and $x \in (-\infty, 1]$, we obtain $D = (-\infty, 0]$.

$(g \circ f)(x) = g(f(x)) = g(\sqrt{x^2-1}) = \sqrt{1-\sqrt{x^2-1}}$,

$D = \{x \in (-\infty, -1] \cup [1, \infty) \mid \sqrt{x^2-1} \in (-\infty, 1]\}$.

Now $\sqrt{x^2-1} \leq 1 \implies x^2-1 \leq 1 \implies x^2 \leq 2 \implies |x| \leq \sqrt{2} \implies -\sqrt{2} \leq x \leq \sqrt{2}$. Combining this restriction with $x \in (-\infty, -1] \cup [1, \infty)$, we obtain

$D = [-\sqrt{2}, -1] \cup [1, \sqrt{2}]$.

$(f \circ f)(x) = f(f(x)) = f(\sqrt{x^2-1})$

$\qquad = \sqrt{(\sqrt{x^2-1})^2 - 1} = \sqrt{x^2-2}$,

$D = \{x \in (-\infty, -1] \cup [1, \infty) \mid$

$\qquad \sqrt{x^2-1} \in (-\infty, -1] \cup [1, \infty)\}$.

Now $\sqrt{x^2-1} \geq 1 \implies x^2-1 \geq 1 \implies x^2 \geq 2 \implies |x| \geq \sqrt{2} \implies x \geq \sqrt{2}$ or $x \leq -\sqrt{2}$. Combining this restriction with $x \in (-\infty, -1] \cup [1, \infty)$, we obtain $D = (-\infty, -\sqrt{2}] \cup [\sqrt{2}, \infty)$.

$(g \circ g)(x) = g(g(x)) = g(\sqrt{1-x}) = \sqrt{1-\sqrt{1-x}}$,

$D = \{x \in (-\infty, 1] \mid \sqrt{1-x} \in (-\infty, 1]\}$. Now $\sqrt{1-x} \leq 1 \implies 1-x \leq 1 \implies x \geq 0$. Combining this restriction with $x \in (-\infty, 1]$, we obtain $D = [0, 1]$.

9. $f(x) = \sqrt[3]{x}$, $D = \mathbb{R}$; $g(x) = 1 - \sqrt{x}$, $D = [0, \infty)$.

$(f \circ g)(x) = f(g(x)) = f(1 - \sqrt{x}) = \sqrt[3]{1 - \sqrt{x}}$,

$D = [0, \infty)$. $(g \circ f)(x) = g(f(x)) = g(\sqrt[3]{x}) = 1 - x^{1/6}$,

$D = [0, \infty)$.

$(f \circ f)(x) = f(f(x)) = f(\sqrt[3]{x}) = x^{1/9}$, $D = \mathbb{R}$.

$(g \circ g)(x) = g(g(x)) = g(1 - \sqrt{x}) = 1 - \sqrt{1 - \sqrt{x}}$,

$D = \{x \geq 0 \mid 1 - \sqrt{x} \geq 0\} = [0, 1]$.

10. $f(x) = \dfrac{x+2}{2x+1}$, $D = \left\{x \mid x \neq -\dfrac{1}{2}\right\}$; $g(x) = \dfrac{x}{x-2}$,

$D = \{x \mid x \neq 2\}$.

$(f \circ g)(x) = f(g(x))$

$\qquad = f\left(\dfrac{x}{x-2}\right) = \dfrac{x/(x-2) + 2}{2x/(x-2) + 1}$

$\qquad = \dfrac{3x-4}{3x-2}$, $D = \left\{x \mid x \neq 2, \dfrac{2}{3}\right\}$.

$(g \circ f)(x) = g(f(x))$

$\qquad = g\left(\dfrac{x+2}{2x+1}\right) = \dfrac{(x+2)/(2x+1)}{(x+2)/(2x+1) - 2}$

$\qquad = \dfrac{-x-2}{3x}$, $D = \left\{x \mid x \neq 0, -\dfrac{1}{2}\right\}$.

$(f \circ f)(x) = f(f(x))$

$\qquad = f\left(\dfrac{x+2}{2x+1}\right) = \dfrac{(x+2)/(2x+1) + 2}{2(x+2)/(2x+1) + 1}$

$\qquad = \dfrac{5x+4}{4x+5}$, $D = \left\{x \mid x \neq -\dfrac{1}{2}, -\dfrac{5}{4}\right\}$.

$(g \circ g)(x) = g(g(x))$

$\qquad = g\left(\dfrac{x}{x-2}\right) = \dfrac{x/(x-2)}{x/(x-2) - 2}$

$\qquad = \dfrac{x}{4-x}$, $D = \{x \mid x \neq 2, 4\}$.

11. $f(x) = 1/\sqrt{x}$, $D = (0, \infty)$; $g(x) = x^2 - 4x$, $D = \mathbb{R}$.

$(f \circ g)(x) = f(g(x)) = f(x^2 - 4x) = 1/\sqrt{x^2 - 4x}$,

$D = \{x \mid x^2 - 4x > 0\} = (-\infty, 0) \cup (4, \infty)$.

$(g \circ f)(x) = g(f(x)) = g\left(\dfrac{1}{\sqrt{x}}\right) = \dfrac{1}{x} - \dfrac{4}{\sqrt{x}}$,

$D = (0, \infty)$.

$(f \circ f)(x) = f(f(x)) = f\left(\dfrac{1}{\sqrt{x}}\right) = \dfrac{1}{\sqrt{1/\sqrt{x}}} = x^{1/4}$,

$D = (0, \infty)$.

$(g \circ g)(x) = g(g(x)) = g(x^2 - 4x)$

$\qquad = (x^2 - 4x)^2 - 4(x^2 - 4x)$

$\qquad = x^4 - 8x^3 + 12x^2 + 16x$, $D = \mathbb{R}$.

12. $(f \circ g \circ h)(x) = f(g(h(x))) = f(g(x-1))$

$\qquad = f(\sqrt{x-1}) = \sqrt{x-1} - 1$

13. $(f \circ g \circ h)(x) = f(g(h(x))) = f(g(x^2 + 2))$

$= f((x^2 + 2)^3) = 1/(x^2 + 2)^3$

14. $(f \circ g \circ h)(x) = f(g(h(x))) = f(g(\sqrt{x}))$

$= f(\sqrt{x} - 5) = (\sqrt{x} - 5)^4 + 1$

15. $(f \circ g \circ h)(x) = f(g(h(x))) = f(g(\sqrt[3]{x}))$

$= f\left(\dfrac{\sqrt[3]{x}}{\sqrt[3]{x} - 1}\right) = \sqrt{\dfrac{\sqrt[3]{x}}{\sqrt[3]{x} - 1}}$

16. For the curve $y = \sqrt{x}$ and the point $P(4, 2)$:

(a)

	x	Q	m_{PQ}
(i)	5	(5, 2.236068)	0.236068
(ii)	4.5	(4.5, 2.121320)	0.242641
(iii)	4.1	(4.1, 2.024846)	0.248457
(iv)	4.01	(4.01, 2.002498)	0.249844
(v)	4.001	(4.001, 2.000250)	0.249984
(vi)	3	(3, 1.732051)	0.267949
(vii)	3.5	(3.5, 1.870829)	0.258343
(viii)	3.9	(3.9, 1.974842)	0.251582
(ix)	3.99	(3.99, 1.997498)	0.250156
(x)	3.999	(3.999, 1.999750)	0.250016

(b) The slope appears to be $\dfrac{1}{4}$.

(c) $y - 2 = \dfrac{1}{4}(x - 4)$ or $y = \dfrac{1}{4}x + 1$.

17. For the curve $y = 1/x$ and the point $P(0.5, 2)$:

(a)

	x	Q	m_{PQ}
(i)	2	(2, 0.5)	-1
(ii)	1	(1, 1)	-2
(iii)	0.9	(0.9, 1.111111)	-2.222222
(iv)	0.8	(0.8, 1.25)	-2.5
(v)	0.7	(0.7, 1.428571)	-2.857143
(vi)	0.6	(0.6, 1.666667)	-3.333333
(vii)	0.55	(0.55, 1.818182)	-3.636364
(viii)	0.51	(0.51, 1.960784)	-3.921569
(ix)	0.45	(0.45, 2.222222)	-4.444444
(x)	0.49	(0.49, 2.040816)	-4.081633

(b) The slope appears to be -4.

(c) $y - 2 = -4(x - 0.5)$ or $y = -4x + 4$

(d)

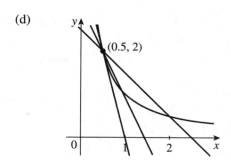

(0.5, 2)

18. For the curve $f(x) = 1 + x + x^2$ and the point $P(1, 3)$:

(a)

	x	Q	m_{PQ}
(i)	2	(2, 7)	4
(ii)	1.5	(1.5, 4.75)	3.5
(iii)	1.1	(1.1, 3.31)	3.1
(iv)	1.01	(1.01, 3.0301)	3.01
(v)	1.001	(1.001, 3.003001)	3.001
(vi)	0	(0, 1)	2
(vii)	0.5	(0.5, 1.75)	2.5
(viii)	0.9	(0.9, 2.71)	2.9
(ix)	0.99	(0.99, 2.9701)	2.99
(x)	0.999	(0.999, 2.997001)	2.999

(b) The slope appears to be 3.

(c) $y - 3 = 3(x - 1)$ or $y = 3x$

19. For the curve $y = 1 - 2x^3$ and the point $P(-1, 3)$:

(a)

	x	Q	m_{PQ}
(i)	-2	$(-2, 17)$	-14
(ii)	-1.5	$(-1.5, 7.75)$	-9.5
(iii)	-1.1	$(-1.1, 3.662)$	-6.62
(iv)	-1.01	$(-1.01, 3.060602)$	-6.0602
(v)	-1.001	$(-1.001, 3.006006)$	-6.006002
(vi)	0	(0, 1)	-2
(vii)	-0.5	$(-0.5, 1.25)$	-3.5
(viii)	-0.9	$(-0.9, 2.458)$	-5.42
(ix)	-0.99	$(-0.99, 2.940598)$	-5.9402
(x)	-0.999	$(-0.999, 2.994006)$	-5.994002

(b) The slope appears to be -6.

(c) $y - 3 = -6(x + 1)$ or $6x + y + 3 = 0$

20. (a) The average velocity between times 0 and h is

$$\frac{s(h) - s(0)}{h} = \frac{h^2 + h - 0}{h} = h + 1.$$

   (i) $[0, 2]$: $2 + 1 = 3\,\text{m/s}$

   (ii) $[0, 1]$: $1 + 1 = 2\,\text{m/s}$

   (iii) $[0, 0.5]$: $0.5 + 1 = 1.5\,\text{m/s}$

   (iv) $[0, 0.1]$: $0.1 + 1 = 1.1\,\text{m/s}$

(b) As h approaches 0, the velocity approaches $1\,\text{m/s}$.

(c), (d)

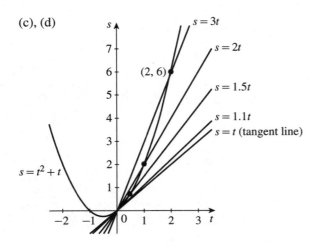

21. (a) Slopes of the secant lines:

x	m_{PQ}
0	$\dfrac{2.6 - 1.3}{0 - 3} \approx -0.43$
1	$\dfrac{2.0 - 1.3}{1 - 3} = -0.35$
2	$\dfrac{1.1 - 1.3}{2 - 3} = 0.2$
4	$\dfrac{2.1 - 1.3}{4 - 3} = 0.8$
5	$\dfrac{3.5 - 1.3}{5 - 3} = 1.1$

(b) We average the slopes of the two closest secant lines from part (a): $\dfrac{1}{2}(0.2 + 0.8) = 0.5$.

(c) Using the points $(0.6, 0)$ and $(5, 2.5)$ from the graph, the slope of the tangent line at P is about $\dfrac{2.5 - 0}{5 - 0.6} \approx 0.57$.

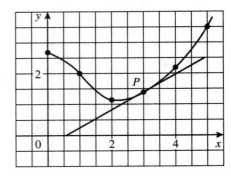

22. (a) $\displaystyle\lim_{x \to 1} f(x) = 3$ (b) $\displaystyle\lim_{x \to 3^-} f(x) = 2$

   (c) $\displaystyle\lim_{x \to 3^+} f(x) = 2$

   (d) $\displaystyle\lim_{x \to 3} f(x)$ doesn't exist because the limits in part (b) and part (c) are not equal.

   (e) $f(3) = 1$ (f) $\displaystyle\lim_{x \to -2^-} f(x) = -1$

   (g) $\displaystyle\lim_{x \to -2^+} f(x) = -1$ (h) $\displaystyle\lim_{x \to -2} f(x) = -1$

   (i) $f(-2) = -3$

23. (a) $\displaystyle\lim_{x \to 3} f(x) = 2$ (b) $\displaystyle\lim_{x \to 1} f(x) = -1$

   (c) $\displaystyle\lim_{x \to -3} f(x) = 1$ (d) $\displaystyle\lim_{x \to 2^-} f(x) = 1$

   (e) $\displaystyle\lim_{x \to 2^+} f(x) = 2$

   (f) $\displaystyle\lim_{x \to 2} f(x)$ doesn't exist because the limits in part (d) and part (e) are not equal.

24. (a) $\displaystyle\lim_{x \to -6} g(x) = 0$ (b) $\displaystyle\lim_{x \to 0^-} g(x) = \infty$

   (c) $\displaystyle\lim_{x \to 0^+} g(x) = -\infty$ (d) $\displaystyle\lim_{x \to 4} g(x) = -\infty$

   (e) The equations of the vertical asymptotes: $x = -5$, $x = 0$, $x = 4$

25. (a) $\displaystyle\lim_{x \to 3} f(x) = \infty$ (b) $\displaystyle\lim_{x \to 7} f(x) = -\infty$

   (c) $\displaystyle\lim_{x \to -4} f(x) = -\infty$ (d) $\displaystyle\lim_{x \to -9^-} f(x) = \infty$

   (e) $\displaystyle\lim_{x \to -9^+} f(x) = -\infty$

   (f) The equations of the vertical asymptotes: $x = -9$, $x = -4$, $x = 3$, $x = 7$

26. (a) $\displaystyle\lim_{x \to 1} g(x) = 0$ (b) $\displaystyle\lim_{x \to 0} g(x)$ does not exist

   (c) $\displaystyle\lim_{x \to 2} g(x) = 1$ (d) $\displaystyle\lim_{x \to -2} g(x) = 0$

   (e) $\displaystyle\lim_{x \to -1^-} g(x) = 1$ (f) $\displaystyle\lim_{x \to -1} g(x)$ does not exist

27. $\displaystyle\lim_{x \to 3} \frac{1}{(x - 3)^8} = \infty$ since $(x - 3) \to 0$ as $x \to 3$ and $\dfrac{1}{(x - 3)^8} > 0$.

28. $\lim\limits_{x\to1^+}\dfrac{x+1}{x\sin\pi x}=-\infty$ since $\dfrac{x+1}{x}\to2$ as $x\to1^+$
and $\sin\pi x\to0$ through negative values as $x\to1^+$.

29. (a) $\lim\limits_{x\to1^-}f(x)=\lim\limits_{x\to1^-}(x^2-2x+2)$
$$=\lim\limits_{x\to1^-}x^2-2\lim\limits_{x\to1^-}x+\lim\limits_{x\to1^-}2$$
$$=1^2-2+2=1$$

$\lim\limits_{x\to1^+}f(x)=\lim\limits_{x\to1^+}(3-x)=\lim\limits_{x\to1^+}3-\lim\limits_{x\to1^+}x$
$$=3-1=2$$

(b) $\lim\limits_{x\to1}f(x)$ does not exist because
$$\lim\limits_{x\to1^-}f(x)\neq\lim\limits_{x\to1^+}f(x).$$

(c)

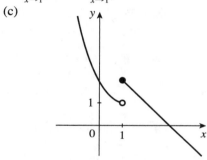

30. (a) $\lim\limits_{x\to-1^-}g(x)=\lim\limits_{x\to-1^-}(-x^3)=-(-1)^3=1,$
$\lim\limits_{x\to-1^+}g(x)=\lim\limits_{x\to-1^+}(x+2)^2=(-1+2)^2=1$

(b) By part (a), $\lim\limits_{x\to-1}g(x)=1.$

(c)

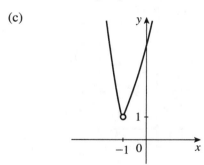

31. (a)

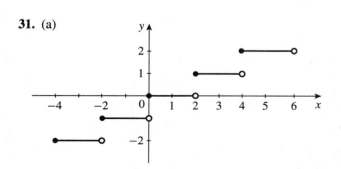

(b) (i) $\lim\limits_{x\to1^+}g(x)=0$ since $[\![x/2]\!]=0$ for $0\leq x<2.$

(ii) $\lim\limits_{x\to1^-}g(x)=0$ since $[\![x/2]\!]=0$ for $0\leq x<2.$

(iii) $\lim\limits_{x\to1}g(x)=0$ since $[\![x/2]\!]=0$ for $0\leq x<2.$

(iv) $\lim\limits_{x\to2^+}g(x)=1$ since $[\![x/2]\!]=1$ for $2\leq x<4.$

(v) $\lim\limits_{x\to2^-}g(x)=0$ since $[\![x/2]\!]=0$ for $0\leq x<2.$

(vi) $\lim\limits_{x\to2}g(x)$ does not exist because
$\lim\limits_{x\to2^+}g(x)\neq\lim\limits_{x\to2^-}g(x).$

(c) $\lim\limits_{x\to a}g(x)$ exists except when a is an even integer.

32. Given $\varepsilon>0$, we need $\delta>0$ such that if $|x-2|<\delta$
then $\left|\dfrac{x}{7}-\dfrac{2}{7}\right|<\varepsilon\Leftrightarrow\dfrac{1}{7}|x-2|<\varepsilon\Leftrightarrow|x-2|<7\varepsilon.$
So take $\delta=7\varepsilon.$ Then $|x-2|<\delta\Rightarrow\left|\dfrac{x}{7}-\dfrac{2}{7}\right|<\varepsilon.$
Thus $\lim\limits_{x\to2}\dfrac{x}{7}=\dfrac{2}{7}$ by the definition of a limit.

33. Given $\varepsilon>0$, we need $\delta>0$ such that if $|x-4|<\delta$
then $\left|\left(\dfrac{x}{3}+1\right)-\dfrac{7}{3}\right|<\varepsilon\Leftrightarrow\dfrac{1}{3}|x-4|<\varepsilon\Leftrightarrow$
$|x-4|<3\varepsilon.$ So take $\delta=3\varepsilon.$ Then $|x-4|<\delta\Rightarrow$
$\left|\left(\dfrac{x}{3}+1\right)-\dfrac{7}{3}\right|<\varepsilon.$ Thus $\lim\limits_{x\to4}\left(\dfrac{x}{3}+1\right)=\dfrac{7}{3}$ by the
definition of a limit.

34. Given $\varepsilon>0$, we need $\delta>0$ such that if $|x-2|<\delta$ then
$\left|\dfrac{x^2+x-6}{x-2}-5\right|<\varepsilon\Leftrightarrow\left|\dfrac{(x-2)(x+3)}{x-2}-5\right|<\varepsilon$
$\Leftrightarrow|x+3-5|<\varepsilon\,(\text{for }x\neq2)\Leftrightarrow|x-2|<\varepsilon.$
So take $\delta=\varepsilon,$ and certainly $|x-2|<\delta\Rightarrow$
$|x-2|<\varepsilon.$ Thus $\lim\limits_{x\to2}\dfrac{x^2+x-6}{x-2}=5,$ by the
definition of a limit.

35. $f(x)=(x+1)(x^3+8x+9)$ is a polynomial, so by
Theorem 5 it is continuous on $\mathbb{R}.$

36. $G(x)=\dfrac{x^4+17}{6x^2+x-1}$ is a rational function, so by
Theorem 5 it is continuous on its domain, which is
$\{x\mid(3x-1)(2x+1)\neq0\}=\left\{x\mid x\neq-\dfrac{1}{2},\dfrac{1}{3}\right\}.$

37. $g(x)=x+1,$ a polynomial, is continuous (by
Theorem 5) and $f(x)=\sqrt{x}$ is continuous on $[0,\infty)$
by Theorem 9, so $f(g(x))=\sqrt{x+1}$ is continuous on $[-1,\infty)$ by Theorem 9. By Theorem 4 #5,
$H(x)=1/\sqrt{x+1}$ is continuous on $(-1,\infty).$

38. $G(t)=25-t^2$ is a polynomial, so it is continuous
(Theorem 5). $F(x)=\sqrt{x}$ is continuous by Theorem 9.

So, by Theorem 9, $F(G(t)) = \sqrt{25 - t^2}$ is continuous on its domain, which is $\{t \mid 25 - t^2 \geq 0\} = \{t \mid |t| \leq 5\} = [-5, 5]$. Also, $2t$ is continuous on $\mathbb{R}$, so by Theorem 4 #1, $f(t) = 2t + \sqrt{25 - t^2}$ is continuous on its domain, which is $[-5, 5]$.

39. $g(x) = x - 1$ and $G(x) = x^2 - 2$ are both polynomials, so by Theorem 5 they are continuous. Also $f(x) = \sqrt[5]{x}$ is continuous by Theorem 9, so $f(g(x)) = \sqrt[5]{x - 1}$ is continuous on $\mathbb{R}$. Thus the product $h(x) = \sqrt[5]{x - 1}\,(x^2 - 2)$ is continuous on $\mathbb{R}$ by Theorem 4 #4.

40. $G(t) = t^2 - 4$ is continuous since it is a polynomial (Theorem 5). $F(x) = \sqrt{x}$ is continuous by Theorem 7. So, by Theorem 9, $F(G(t)) = \sqrt{t^2 - 4}$ is continuous on its domain, which is $D = \{t \mid t^2 - 4 \geq 0\} = \{t \mid |t| \geq 2\}$. Also t is continuous so $t + \sqrt{t^2 - 4}$ is continuous on D by Theorem 4 #1. Thus by Theorem 4 #5, $g(t) = 1/(t + \sqrt{t^2 - 4})$ is continuous on its domain, which is $\{t \in D \mid t + \sqrt{t^2 - 4} \neq 0\}$. But if $t + \sqrt{t^2 - 4} = 0$, then $\sqrt{t^2 - 4} = -t$ $\Rightarrow\ t^2 - 4 = t^2 \Rightarrow -4 = 0$ which is false. So the domain of g is $\{t \in D \mid |t| \geq 2\} = (-\infty, -2] \cup [2, \infty)$.

41. Since the discriminant of $t^2 + t + 1$ is negative, $t^2 + t + 1$ is always positive. So the domain of $F(t)$ is $\mathbb{R}$. By Theorem 5 the polynomial $(t^2 + t + 1)^3$ is continuous. By Theorems 7 and 9 the composition $F(t) = \sqrt{(t^2 + t + 1)^3}$ is continuous on $\mathbb{R}$.

42. $H(x) = \sqrt{(x - 2)/(5 + x)}$. The domain is $\{x \mid (x - 2)/(5 + x) > 0\} = (-\infty, -5) \cup [2, \infty)$ by the methods of Appendix A. By Theorem 5 the rational function $(x - 2)/(5 + x)$ is continuous. Since the square root function is continuous (Theorem 7), the composition $H(x) = \sqrt{(x - 2)/(5 + x)}$ is continuous on its domain by Theorem 9.

43. $g(x) = x^3 - x$ is continuous on $\mathbb{R}$ since it is a polynomial [Theorem 5(a)], and $f(x) = |x|$ is continuous on $\mathbb{R}$. So $L(x) = |x^3 - x|$ is continuous on $\mathbb{R}$ by Theorem 9.

44. $f(x) = x^3 - 3x + 1$ is continuous on $[0, 1]$ and $f(0) = 1$, $f(1) = -1$. Since $-1 < 0 < 1$, there is a number c in $(0, 1)$ such that $f(c) = 0$ by the Intermediate Value Theorem. Thus there is a root of the equation $x^3 - 3x + 1 = 0$ in the interval $(0, 1)$.

45. $f(x) = x^5 - 2x^4 - x - 3$ is continuous on $[2, 3]$ and $f(2) = -5$, $f(3) = 75$. Since $-5 < 0 < 75$, there is a number c in $(2, 3)$ such that $f(c) = 0$ by the Intermediate Value Theorem. Thus there is a root of the equation $x^5 - 2x^4 - x - 3 = 0$ in the interval $(2, 3)$.

46. $f(x) = x^3 + 2x - (x^2 + 1) = x^3 + 2x - x^2 - 1$ is continuous on $[0, 1]$ and $f(0) = -1$, $f(1) = 1$. Since $-1 < 0 < 1$, there is a number c in $(0, 1)$ such that $f(c) = 0$ by the Intermediate Value Theorem. Thus there is a root of the equation $x^3 + 2x - x^2 - 1 = 0$, or, equivalently, $x^3 + 2x = x^2 + 1$, in the interval $(0, 1)$.

47. $f(x) = x^2 - \sqrt{x + 1}$ is continuous on $[1, 2]$ and $f(1) = 1 - \sqrt{2}$, $f(2) = 4 - \sqrt{3}$. Since $1 - \sqrt{2} < 0 < 4 - \sqrt{3}$, there is a number c in $(1, 2)$ such that $f(c) = 0$ by the Intermediate Value Theorem. Thus there is a root of the equation $x^2 - \sqrt{x + 1} = 0$, or $x^2 = \sqrt{x + 1}$, in the interval $(1, 2)$.

48. $|x| + |y| = 1 + |xy| \Leftrightarrow |xy| - |x| - |y| + 1 = 0$
$\Leftrightarrow |x||y| - |x| - |y| + 1 = 0$
$\Leftrightarrow (|x| - 1)(|y| - 1) = 0$
$\Leftrightarrow x = \pm 1$ or $y = \pm 1$.

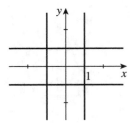

2 DERIVATIVES

1–4 ■ Find an equation of the tangent line to the curve at the given point.

1. $y = 1 - 2x - 3x^2$, $(-2, -7)$

2. $y = 1/\sqrt{x}$, $(1, 1)$

3. $y = 1/x^2$, $\left(-2, \dfrac{1}{4}\right)$

4. $y = x/(1-x)$, $(0, 0)$

5–11 ■ Find $f'(a)$.

5. $f(x) = 1 + x - 2x^2$

6. $f(x) = x^3 + 3x$

7. $f(x) = \dfrac{x}{2x - 1}$

8. $f(x) = \dfrac{x}{x^2 - 1}$

9. $f(x) = \dfrac{2}{\sqrt{3 - x}}$

10. $f(x) = \sqrt{x - 1}$

11. $f(x) = \sqrt{3x + 1}$

12–16 ■ Find the derivative of the function using the definition of derivative. State the domain of the function and the domain of its derivative.

12. $f(x) = 5x + 3$

13. $f(x) = 5 - 4x + 3x^2$

14. $f(x) = x^3 - x^2 + 2x$

15. $f(x) = \dfrac{x + 1}{x - 1}$

16. $G(x) = \dfrac{4 - 3x}{2 + x}$

17–31 ■ Differentiate.

17. $H(x) = (x^3 - x + 1)(x^{-2} + 2x^{-3})$

18. $H(t) = \sqrt[3]{t}(t + 2)$

19. $h(x) = \dfrac{x + 2}{x - 1}$

20. $f(u) = \dfrac{1 - u^2}{1 + u^2}$

21. $y = \dfrac{x^2 + 4x + 3}{\sqrt{x}}$

22. $y = x^4 - \sqrt[4]{x}$

23. $u = x^{\sqrt{2}}$

24. $y = \dfrac{3t - 7}{t^2 + 5t - 4}$

25. $y = \dfrac{4t + 5}{2 - 3t}$

26. $y = x + \sqrt[5]{x^2}$

27. $u = \sqrt[3]{t^2} + 2\sqrt{t^3}$

28. $v = x\sqrt{x} + \dfrac{1}{x^2\sqrt{x}}$

29. $v = \dfrac{6}{\sqrt[3]{t^5}}$

30. $f(x) = \dfrac{x^5}{x^3 - 2}$

31. $s = \sqrt{t}(t^3 - \sqrt{t} + 1)$

32–33 ■ Find an equation of the tangent line to the given curve at the specified point.

32. $y = 2 \sin x$, $(\pi/6, 1)$

33. $y = \sec x - 2 \cos x$, $(\pi/3, 1)$

34–39 ■ Find an equation of the tangent line to the curve at the given point.

34. $y = \dfrac{8}{\sqrt{4 + 3x}}$, $(4, 2)$

35. $y = \sin x + \cos 2x$, $(\pi/6, 1)$

36. $y = (x^3 - x^2 + x - 1)^{10}$, $(1, 0)$

37. $y = \sqrt{x + (1/x)}$, $(1, \sqrt{2})$

38. $y = \dfrac{x}{(3 - x^2)^5}$, $(2, -2)$

39. $y = \cot^2 x$, $(\pi/4, 1)$

40–43 ■ Find an equation of the tangent line to the curve at the given point.

40. $\dfrac{x^2}{16} - \dfrac{y^2}{9} = 1$, $\left(-5, \dfrac{9}{4}\right)$ (hyperbola)

41. $\dfrac{x^2}{9} + \dfrac{y^2}{36} = 1$, $(-1, 4\sqrt{2})$ (ellipse)

42. $y^2 = x^3(2 - x)$, $(1, 1)$ (piriform)

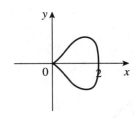

43. $x^2 y^2 = (y + 1)^2(4 - y^2)$, $(0, -2)$ (conchoid of Nicomedes)

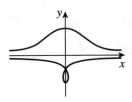

44–47 ■ (a) Find the differential dy and (b) evaluate dy for the given values of x and dx.

44. $y = (x^2 + 5)^3$, $x = 1$, $dx = 0.05$

45. $y = \sqrt{1 - x}$, $x = 0$, $dx = 0.02$

46. $y = \cos x$, $x = \pi/6$, $dx = 0.05$

47. $y = \sin x$, $x = \pi/6$, $dx = -0.1$

2 | ANSWERS TO SELECTED EXERCISES

1. $y = 10x + 13$

2. $y = -\dfrac{1}{2}x + \dfrac{3}{2}$

3. $y = \dfrac{1}{4}x + \dfrac{3}{4}$

4. $y = x$

5. $1 - 4a$

6. $\dfrac{1}{2\sqrt{a-1}}$

7. $\dfrac{-1}{(2a-1)^2}$

8. $-\dfrac{a^2+1}{(a^2-1)^2}$

9. $\dfrac{1}{(3-a)^{3/2}}$

10. $\dfrac{1}{2\sqrt{a-1}}$

11. $\dfrac{3}{2\sqrt{3a+1}}$

12. $f'(x) = 5$, $\mathbb{R}$, $\mathbb{R}$

13. $f'(x) = 6x - 4$, $\mathbb{R}$, $\mathbb{R}$

14. $f'(x) = 3x^2 - 2x + 2$, $\mathbb{R}$, $\mathbb{R}$

15. $f'(x) = \dfrac{-2}{(x-1)^2}$, $\{x \,|\, x \neq 1\}$, $\{x \,|\, x \neq 1\}$

16. $G'(x) = -10/(2+x)^2$, $\{x \,|\, x \neq -2\}$, $\{x \,|\, x \neq -2\}$

17. $H'(x) = 1 + x^{-2} + 2x^{-3} - 6x^{-4}$

18. $H'(t) = \dfrac{4}{3}t^{1/3} + \dfrac{2}{3}t^{-2/3}$

19. $h'(x) = -\dfrac{3}{(x-1)^2}$

20. $f'(u) = -\dfrac{4u}{(1+u^2)^2}$

21. $y' = \dfrac{3}{2}\sqrt{x} + \dfrac{2}{\sqrt{x}} - \dfrac{3}{2x\sqrt{x}}$

22. $y' = 4x^3 - \dfrac{1}{4}x^{-3/4}$

23. $u' = \sqrt{2}x^{\sqrt{2}-1}$

24. $y' = \dfrac{-3t^2 + 14t + 23}{(t^2 + 5t - 4)^2}$

25. $y' = \dfrac{23}{(2-3t)^2}$

26. $y' = 1 + \dfrac{2}{5\sqrt[5]{x^3}}$

27. $u' = \dfrac{2}{3\sqrt[3]{t}} + 3\sqrt{t}$

28. $v' = \dfrac{3}{2}\sqrt{x} - \dfrac{5}{2x^3\sqrt{x}}$

29. $v' = -\dfrac{10}{\sqrt[3]{t^8}}$

30. $f'(x) = \dfrac{2x^4(x^3 - 5)}{(x^3 - 2)^2}$

31. $s' = \dfrac{7}{2}t^{5/2} - 1 + \dfrac{1}{2\sqrt{t}}$

32. $y = \sqrt{3}x + 1 - \dfrac{1}{6}\sqrt{3}\pi$

33. $y = 3\sqrt{3}x + 1 - \pi\sqrt{3}$

34. $y = -\dfrac{3}{16}x + \dfrac{11}{4}$

35. $y = -\dfrac{\sqrt{3}}{2}x + 1 + \dfrac{\sqrt{3}\pi}{12}$

36. $y = 0$

37. $y = \sqrt{2}$

38. $y = 39x - 80$

39. $4x + y = \pi + 1$

40. $y = -\dfrac{5}{4}x - 4$

41. $y = \dfrac{1}{\sqrt{2}}(x + 9)$

42. $y = x$

43. $y = -2$

44. (a) $dy = 6x(x^2 + 5)^2 \, dx$

(b) 10.8

45. (a) $dy = -\dfrac{1}{2\sqrt{1 - x}} \, dx$

(b) -0.01

46. (a) $dy = -\sin x \, dx$

(b) -0.025

47. (a) $dy = \cos x \, dx$

(b) $-\dfrac{\sqrt{3}}{20}$

2 | SOLUTIONS TO SELECTED EXERCISES

1. Using (1),

$$m = \lim_{x \to a} \frac{f(x) - f(a)}{x - a}$$

$$= \lim_{x \to -2} \frac{(1 - 2x - 3x^2) - (-7)}{x - (-2)}$$

$$= \lim_{x \to -2} \frac{-3x^2 - 2x + 8}{x + 2}$$

$$= \lim_{x \to -2} \frac{(-3x + 4)(x + 2)}{x + 2}$$

$$= \lim_{x \to -2} (-3x + 4) = 10$$

Thus, an equation of the tangent is
$y + 7 = 10(x + 2)$, or $y = 10x + 13$.

Alternate Solution: Using (2),

$$m = \lim_{h \to 0} \frac{f(a + h) - f(a)}{h}$$

$$= \lim_{h \to 0} \frac{f(-2 + h) - f(-2)}{h}$$

$$= \lim_{h \to 0} \frac{\left[1 - 2(-2 + h) - 3(-2 + h)^2\right] - (-7)}{h}$$

$$= \lim_{h \to 0} \frac{(-3h^2 + 10h - 7) + 7}{h}$$

$$= \lim_{h \to 0} \frac{h(-3h + 10)}{h}$$

$$= \lim_{h \to 0} (-3h + 10) = 10$$

2. Using (1),

$$m = \lim_{x \to 1} \frac{1/\sqrt{x} - 1}{x - 1} = \lim_{x \to 1} \frac{-(\sqrt{x} - 1)}{\sqrt{x}(\sqrt{x} - 1)(\sqrt{x} + 1)}$$

$$= \lim_{x \to 1} \frac{-1}{\sqrt{x}(\sqrt{x} + 1)} = -\frac{1}{2}$$

Thus, an equation of the tangent line is
$y - 1 = -\dfrac{1}{2}(x - 1)$ or $y = -\dfrac{1}{2}x + \dfrac{3}{2}$.

3. Using (1),

$$m = \lim_{x \to -2} \frac{1/x^2 - \dfrac{1}{4}}{x - (-2)} = \lim_{x \to -2} \frac{4 - x^2}{4x^2(x + 2)}$$

$$= \lim_{x \to -2} \frac{(2 - x)(2 + x)}{4x^2(x + 2)} = \lim_{x \to -2} \frac{2 - x}{4x^2} = \frac{1}{4}$$

Thus, an equation of the tangent line is
$$y - \frac{1}{4} = \frac{1}{4}(x + 2) \implies y = \frac{1}{4}x + \frac{3}{4}.$$

4. Using (1),

$$m = \lim_{x \to 0} \frac{x/(1 - x) - 0}{x - 0} = \lim_{x \to 0} \frac{x}{x(1 - x)}$$

$$= \lim_{x \to 0} \frac{1}{1 - x} = 1$$

Thus, an equation of the tangent line is
$y - 0 = 1(x - 0) \implies y = x$.

5. $f'(a) = \lim_{h \to 0} \dfrac{f(a + h) - f(a)}{h}$

$$= \lim_{h \to 0} \frac{1 + (a + h) - 2(a + h)^2 - (1 + a - 2a^2)}{h}$$

$$= \lim_{h \to 0} \frac{h - 4ah - 2h^2}{h} = \lim_{h \to 0} (1 - 4a - 2h)$$

$$= 1 - 4a$$

6. $f'(a) = \lim_{h \to 0} \dfrac{f(a + h) - f(a)}{h}$

$$= \lim_{h \to 0} \frac{(a + h)^3 + 3(a + h) - (a^3 + 3a)}{h}$$

$$= \lim_{h \to 0} \frac{3a^2h + 3ah^2 + h^3 + 3h}{h}$$

$$= \lim_{h \to 0} (3a^2 + 3ah + h^2 + 3)$$

$$= 3a^2 + 3$$

7. $f'(a) = \lim_{h \to 0} \dfrac{f(a + h) - f(a)}{h}$

$$= \lim_{h \to 0} \frac{\dfrac{a + h}{2(a + h) - 1} - \dfrac{a}{2a - 1}}{h}$$

$$= \lim_{h \to 0} \frac{(a + h)(2a - 1) - a(2a + 2h - 1)}{h(2a + 2h - 1)(2a - 1)}$$

$$= \lim_{h \to 0} \frac{-h}{h\,(2a + 2h - 1)\,(2a - 1)}$$

$$= \lim_{h \to 0} \frac{-1}{(2a + 2h - 1)\,(2a - 1)}$$

$$= -\frac{1}{(2a - 1)^2}$$

8. $f'(a) = \lim_{h \to 0} \dfrac{f(a + h) - f(a)}{h}$

$$= \lim_{h \to 0} \frac{\dfrac{a + h}{(a + h)^2 - 1} - \dfrac{a}{a^2 - 1}}{h}$$

$$= \lim_{h \to 0} \frac{(a + h)\,(a^2 - 1) - a\,(a^2 + 2ah + h^2 - 1)}{h(a^2 - 1)\,(a^2 + 2ah + h^2 - 1)}$$

$$= \lim_{h \to 0} \frac{h(-a^2 - 1 - ah)}{h(a^2 - 1)\,(a^2 + 2ah + h^2 - 1)}$$

$$= \lim_{h \to 0} \frac{-a^2 - 1 - ah}{(a^2 - 1)\,(a^2 + 2ah + h^2 - 1)}$$

$$= \frac{-a^2 - 1}{(a^2 - 1)\,(a^2 - 1)} = -\frac{a^2 + 1}{(a^2 - 1)^2}$$

9. $f'(a) = \lim_{h \to 0} \dfrac{f(a + h) - f(a)}{h}$

$$= \lim_{h \to 0} \frac{\dfrac{2}{\sqrt{3 - (a + h)}} - \dfrac{2}{\sqrt{3 - a}}}{h}$$

$$= \lim_{h \to 0} \frac{2\,(\sqrt{3 - a} - \sqrt{3 - a - h})}{h\sqrt{3 - a} - h\sqrt{3 - a}}$$

$$= \lim_{h \to 0} \frac{2\,(\sqrt{3 - a} - \sqrt{3 - a - h})}{h\sqrt{3 - a} - h\sqrt{3 - a}} \cdot \frac{\sqrt{3 - a} + \sqrt{3 - a - h}}{\sqrt{3 - a} + \sqrt{3 - a - h}}$$

$$= \lim_{h \to 0} \frac{2[3 - a - (3 - a - h)]}{h\sqrt{3 - a} - h\sqrt{3 - a}\,(\sqrt{3 - a} + \sqrt{3 - a - h})}$$

$$= \lim_{h \to 0} \frac{2}{\sqrt{3 - a} - h\sqrt{3 - a}\,(\sqrt{3 - a} + \sqrt{3 - a - h})}$$

$$= \frac{2}{\sqrt{3 - a}\sqrt{3 - a}\,(2\sqrt{3 - a})} = \frac{1}{(3 - a)^{3/2}}$$

10. $f'(a) = \lim_{h \to 0} \dfrac{f(a + h) - f(a)}{h}$

$$= \lim_{h \to 0} \frac{\sqrt{a + h - 1} - \sqrt{a - 1}}{h}$$

$$= \lim_{h \to 0} \frac{\sqrt{a + h - 1} - \sqrt{a - 1}}{h} \cdot \frac{\sqrt{a + h - 1} + \sqrt{a - 1}}{\sqrt{a + h - 1} + \sqrt{a - 1}}$$

$$= \lim_{h \to 0} \frac{(a + h - 1) - (a - 1)}{h(\sqrt{a + h - 1} + \sqrt{a - 1})}$$

$$= \lim_{h \to 0} \frac{1}{\sqrt{a + h - 1} + \sqrt{a - 1}}$$

$$= \frac{1}{\sqrt{a - 1} + \sqrt{a - 1}} = \frac{1}{2\sqrt{a - 1}}$$

11. $f'(a) = \lim_{h \to 0} \dfrac{f(a + h) - f(a)}{h}$

$$= \lim_{h \to 0} \frac{\sqrt{3(a + h) + 1} - \sqrt{3a + 1}}{h}$$

$$= \lim_{h \to 0} \frac{(\sqrt{3a + 3h + 1} - \sqrt{3a + 1})\,(\sqrt{3a + 3h + 1} + \sqrt{3a + 1})}{h(\sqrt{3a + 3h + 1} + \sqrt{3a + 1})}$$

$$= \lim_{h \to 0} \frac{(3a + 3h + 1) - (3a + 1)}{h(\sqrt{3a + 3h + 1} + \sqrt{3a + 1})}$$

$$= \lim_{h \to 0} \frac{3}{\sqrt{3a + 3h + 1} + \sqrt{3a + 1}} = \frac{3}{2\sqrt{3a + 1}}$$

12. $f'(x) = \lim_{h \to 0} \dfrac{f(x + h) - f(x)}{h}$

$$= \lim_{h \to 0} \frac{[5(x + h) + 3] - (5x + 3)}{h}$$

$$= \lim_{h \to 0} \frac{5h}{h} = \lim_{h \to 0} 5 = 5$$

Domain of f = domain of f' = $\mathbb{R}$.

13. $f'(x) = \lim_{h \to 0} \dfrac{f(x + h) - f(x)}{h}$

$$= \lim_{h \to 0} \frac{[5 - 4(x + h) + 3(x + h)^2] - [5 - 4x + 3x^2]}{h}$$

$$= \lim_{h \to 0} \frac{[5 - 4x - 4h + 3x^2 + 6xh + 3h^2] - [5 - 4x + 3x^2]}{h}$$

$$= \lim_{h \to 0} \frac{-4h + 6xh + 3h^2}{h}$$

$$= \lim_{h \to 0} (-4 + 6x + 3h) = -4 + 6x$$

Domain of f = domain of f' = $\mathbb{R}$.

14. $f'(x) = \lim\limits_{h \to 0} \dfrac{f(x+h) - f(x)}{h}$

$= \lim\limits_{h \to 0} \dfrac{\left[(x+h)^3 - (x+h)^2 + 2(x+h)\right] - (x^3 - x^2 + 2x)}{h}$

$= \lim\limits_{h \to 0} \dfrac{3x^2h + 3xh^2 + h^3 - 2xh - h^2 + 2h}{h}$

$= \lim\limits_{h \to 0} (3x^2 + 3xh + h^2 - 2x - h + 2)$

$= 3x^2 - 2x + 2$

Domain of f = domain of f' = $\mathbb{R}$.

15. $f'(x) = \lim\limits_{h \to 0} \dfrac{f(x+h) - f(x)}{h}$

$= \lim\limits_{h \to 0} \dfrac{\dfrac{x+h+1}{x+h-1} - \dfrac{x+1}{x-1}}{h}$

$= \lim\limits_{h \to 0} \dfrac{(x+h+1)(x-1) - (x+1)(x+h-1)}{h(x+h-1)(x-1)}$

$= \lim\limits_{h \to 0} \dfrac{-2h}{h(x+h-1)(x-1)}$

$= \lim\limits_{h \to 0} \dfrac{-2}{(x+h-1)(x-1)} = \dfrac{-2}{(x-1)^2}$

Domain of f = domain of f' = $\{x \,|\, x \neq 1\}$.

16. $G'(x) = \lim\limits_{h \to 0} \dfrac{G(x+h) - G(x)}{h}$

$= \lim\limits_{h \to 0} \dfrac{\dfrac{4 - 3(x+h)}{2 + (x+h)} - \dfrac{4 - 3x}{2 + x}}{h}$

$= \lim\limits_{h \to 0} \dfrac{(4 - 3x - 3h)(2 + x) - (4 - 3x)(2 + x + h)}{h(2 + x + h)(2 + x)}$

$= \lim\limits_{h \to 0} \dfrac{-10h}{h(2 + x + h)(2 + x)}$

$= \lim\limits_{h \to 0} \dfrac{-10}{(2 + x + h)(2 + x)} = -\dfrac{10}{(2 + x)^2}$

Domain of G = domain of G' = $\{x \,|\, x \neq -2\}$.

17. $H(x) = (x^3 - x + 1)(x^{-2} + 2x^{-3})$

$= (x^3 - x + 1)(x^{-2}) + (x^3 - x + 1)(2x^{-3})$

$= x - x^{-1} + x^{-2} + 2 - 2x^{-2} + 2x^{-3}$

$= 2 + x - x^{-1} - x^{-2} + 2x^{-3} \implies$

$H'(x) = 1 + x^{-2} + 2x^{-3} - 6x^{-4}$

Another Method: Use the Product Rule.

18. $H(t) = \sqrt[3]{t}\,(t + 2) = t^{4/3} + 2t^{1/3} \implies$

$H'(t) = \dfrac{4}{3}t^{1/3} + \dfrac{2}{3}t^{-2/3}$

Another Method: Use the Product Rule.

19. $h(x) = \dfrac{x+2}{x-1} \implies$

$h'(x) = \dfrac{(x-1)(1) - (x+2)(1)}{(x-1)^2} = \dfrac{x-1-x-2}{(x-1)^2}$

$= -\dfrac{3}{(x-1)^2}$

20. $f(u) = \dfrac{1-u}{1+u^2} \implies$

$f'(u) = \dfrac{(1+u^2)(-2u) - (1-u^2)(2u)}{(1+u^2)^2}$

$= \dfrac{-2u - 2u^3 - 2u + 2u^3}{(1+u^2)^2} = -\dfrac{4u}{(1+u^2)^2}$

21. $y = \dfrac{x^2 + 4x + 3}{\sqrt{x}} = x^{3/2} + 4x^{1/2} + 3x^{-1/2} \implies$

$y' = \dfrac{3}{2}x^{1/2} + 4\left(\dfrac{1}{2}\right)x^{-1/2} + 3\left(-\dfrac{1}{2}\right)x^{-3/2}$

$= \dfrac{3}{2}\sqrt{x} + \dfrac{2}{\sqrt{x}} - \dfrac{3}{2x\sqrt{x}}$

Another Method: Use the Quotient Rule.

22. $y = x^4 - \sqrt[4]{x} = x^4 - x^{1/4} \implies y' = 4x^3 - \dfrac{1}{4}x^{-3/4}$

23. $u = x^{\sqrt{2}} \implies u' = \sqrt{2}x^{\sqrt{2}-1}$

24. $y = \dfrac{3t - 7}{t^2 + 5t - 4} \implies$

$y' = \dfrac{(t^2 + 5t - 4)(3) - (3t - 7)(2t + 5)}{(t^2 + 5t - 4)^2}$

$= \dfrac{-3t^2 + 14t + 23}{(t^2 + 5t - 4)^2}$

25. $y = \dfrac{4t + 5}{2 - 3t} \implies$

$y' = \dfrac{(2 - 3t)(4) - (4t + 5)(-3)}{(2 - 3t)^2} = \dfrac{23}{(2 - 3t)^2}$

26. $y = x + \sqrt[5]{x^2} = x + x^{2/5} \implies$

$y' = 1 + \dfrac{2}{5}x^{-3/5} = 1 + \dfrac{2}{5\sqrt[5]{x^3}}$

27. $u = \sqrt[3]{t^2} + 2\sqrt{t^3} = t^{2/3} + 2t^{3/2} \implies$

$$u' = \frac{2}{3}t^{-1/3} + 2\left(\frac{3}{2}\right)t^{1/2} = \frac{2}{3\sqrt[3]{t}} + 3\sqrt{t}$$

28. $v = x\sqrt{x} + \dfrac{1}{x^2\sqrt{x}} = x^{3/2} + x^{-5/2} \implies$

$$v' = \frac{3}{2}x^{1/2} - \frac{5}{2}x^{-7/2} = \frac{3}{2}\sqrt{x} - \frac{5}{2x^3\sqrt{x}}$$

29. $v = \dfrac{6}{\sqrt[3]{t^5}} = 6t^{-5/3} \implies$

$$v' = 6\left(-\frac{5}{3}\right)t^{-8/3} = -\frac{10}{\sqrt[3]{t^8}}$$

30. $f(x) = \dfrac{x^5}{x^3 - 2} \implies$

$$f'(x) = \frac{(x^3 - 2)(5x^4) - x^5(3x^2)}{(x^3 - 2)^2} = \frac{2x^4(x^3 - 5)}{(x^3 - 2)^2}$$

31. $s = \sqrt{t}(t^3 - \sqrt{t} + 1) = t^{7/2} - t + t^{1/2} \implies$

$$s' = \frac{7}{2}t^{5/2} - 1 + \frac{1}{2\sqrt{t}}.$$

Another Method: Use the Product Rule.

32. $y = 2\sin x \implies y' = 2\cos x \implies$ the slope of the tangent line at $\left(\dfrac{\pi}{6}, 1\right)$ is $2\cos\dfrac{\pi}{6} = 2\cdot\dfrac{\sqrt{3}}{2} = \sqrt{3}$ and an equation is $y - 1 = \sqrt{3}\left(x - \dfrac{\pi}{6}\right)$ or $y = \sqrt{3}x + 1 - \dfrac{\sqrt{3}\pi}{6}.$

33. $y = \sec x - 2\cos x \implies y' = \sec x\tan x + 2\sin x \implies$ the slope of the tangent line at $\left(\dfrac{\pi}{3}, 1\right)$ is $\sec\dfrac{\pi}{3}\tan\dfrac{\pi}{3} + 2\sin\dfrac{\pi}{3} = 2\sqrt{3} + 2\cdot\dfrac{\sqrt{3}}{2} = 3\sqrt{3}$ and an equation is $y - 1 = 3\sqrt{3}\left(x - \dfrac{\pi}{3}\right)$ or $y = 3\sqrt{3}x + 1 - \pi\sqrt{3}.$

34. $y = f(x) = \dfrac{8}{\sqrt{4 + 3x}} = 8(4 + 3x)^{-1/2} \implies$

$f'(x) = 8\left(-\dfrac{1}{2}\right)(4 + 3x)^{-3/2}(3) =$ $-12(4 + 3x)^{-3/2}.$ The slope of the tangent at $(4, 2)$ is $f'(4) = -\dfrac{12}{64} = -\dfrac{3}{16}$ and its equation is $y - 2 = -\dfrac{3}{16}(x - 4)$ or $y = -\dfrac{3}{16}x + \dfrac{11}{4}.$

35. $y = f(x) = \sin x + \cos 2x \implies$
$f'(x) = \cos x - 2\sin 2x.$ The slope of the tangent at $\left(\dfrac{\pi}{6}, 1\right)$ is $f'\left(\dfrac{\pi}{6}\right) = \dfrac{\sqrt{3}}{2} - 2\left(\dfrac{\sqrt{3}}{2}\right) = -\dfrac{\sqrt{3}}{2}$
and its equation is $y - 1 = -\dfrac{\sqrt{3}}{2}\left(x - \dfrac{\pi}{6}\right)$ or $\sqrt{3}x + 2y = 2 + \dfrac{\sqrt{3}}{6}\pi.$

36. $y = f(x) = (x^3 - x^2 + x - 1)^{10} \implies$
$f'(x) = 10(x^3 - x^2 + x - 1)^9(3x^2 - 2x + 1).$ The slope of the tangent at $(1, 0)$ is $f'(1) = 0$ and its equation is $y - 0 = 0(x - 1)$ or $y = 0.$

37. $y = f(x) = \sqrt{x + 1/x} \implies$
$f'(x) = \dfrac{1}{2}\left(x + \dfrac{1}{x}\right)^{-1/2}\left(1 - \dfrac{1}{x^2}\right).$ The slope of the tangent at $(1, \sqrt{2})$ is $f'(1) = 0$ and its equation is $y - \sqrt{2} = 0(x - 1)$ or $y = \sqrt{2}.$

38. $y = f(x) = \dfrac{x}{(3 - x^2)^5} \implies$

$$f'(x) = \frac{(3 - x^2)^5(1) - x(5)(3 - x^2)^4(-2x)}{(3 - x^2)^{10}}$$

$$= \frac{9x^2 + 3}{(3 - x^2)^6}$$

The slope of the tangent at $(2, -2)$ is $f'(2) = 39$ and its equation is $y + 2 = 39(x - 2)$ or $y = 39x - 80.$

39. $y = f(x) = \cot^2 x \implies$
$y' = 2\cot x(-\csc^2 x) = -2\cot x\csc^2 x.$
The slope of the tangent at $\left(\dfrac{\pi}{4}, 1\right)$ is $f'\left(\dfrac{\pi}{4}\right) = -2(1)(\sqrt{2})^2 = -4$ and its equation is $y - 1 = -4\left(x - \dfrac{\pi}{4}\right)$ or $4x + y = \pi + 1.$

40. $\dfrac{x^2}{16} - \dfrac{y^2}{9} = 1 \implies \dfrac{x}{8} - \dfrac{2yy'}{9} = 0 \implies y' = \dfrac{9x}{16y}.$
When $x = -5$ and $y = \dfrac{9}{4}$, we have $y' = \dfrac{9(-5)}{16(9/4)} = -\dfrac{5}{4}$, so an equation of the tangent is $y - \dfrac{9}{4} = -\dfrac{5}{4}(x + 5)$ or $y = -\dfrac{5}{4}x - 4.$

41. $\dfrac{x^2}{9} + \dfrac{y^2}{36} = 1 \;\Rightarrow\; \dfrac{2x}{9} + \dfrac{yy'}{18} = 0 \;\Rightarrow\; y' = -\dfrac{4x}{y}.$

When $x = -1$ and $y = 4\sqrt{2}$, we have

$y' = -\dfrac{4\,(-1)}{4\sqrt{2}} = \dfrac{1}{\sqrt{2}}$, so an equation of the tangent

line is $y - 4\sqrt{2} = \dfrac{1}{\sqrt{2}}\,(x + 1)$ or $y = \dfrac{1}{\sqrt{2}}\,(x + 9).$

42. $y^2 = x^3\,(2 - x) = 2x^3 - x^4 \;\Rightarrow\; 2yy' = 6x^2 - 4x^3$

$\Rightarrow\; y' = \dfrac{3x^2 - 2x^3}{y}.$ When $x = y = 1$,

$y' = \dfrac{3\,(1)^2 - 2\,(1)^3}{1} = 1$, so an equation of the

tangent line is $y - 1 = 1(x - 1)$ or $y = x.$

43. $x^2 y^2 = (y + 1)^2\,(4 - y^2) \;\Rightarrow\; 2xy^2 + 2x^2 yy'$

$= 2\,(y + 1)y'(4 - y^2) + (y + 1)^2\,(-2yy')$

$\Rightarrow\; y' = \dfrac{xy^2}{(y + 1)\,(4 - y^2) - y\,(y + 1)^2 - x^2 y} = 0$

when $x = 0$. So an equation of the tangent line at
$(0, -2)$ is $y + 2 = 0\,(x - 0)$ or $y = -2.$

44. (a) $y = (x^2 + 5)^3 \;\Rightarrow$
$dy = 3\,(x^2 + 5)^2\,2x\,dx = 6x\,(x^2 + 5)^2\,dx$

(b) When $x = 1$ and $dx = 0.05$,
$dy = 6\,(1)\,(1^2 + 5)^2\,(0.05) = 10.8.$

45. (a) $y = \sqrt{1 - x} \;\Rightarrow$

$dy = \dfrac{1}{2}\,(1 - x)^{-1/2}\,(-1)\,dx = -\dfrac{1}{2\sqrt{1 - x}}\,dx$

(b) When $x = 0$ and $dx = 0.02$,

$dy = -\dfrac{1}{2}\,(0.02) = -0.01.$

46. (a) $y = \cos x \;\Rightarrow\; dy = -\sin x\,dx$

(b) When $x = \dfrac{\pi}{6}$ and $dx = 0.05$,

$dy = -\dfrac{1}{2}\,(0.05) = -0.025.$

47. (a) $y = \sin x \;\Rightarrow\; dy = \cos x\,dx$

(b) When $x = \dfrac{\pi}{6}$ and $dx = -0.1$,

$dy = \dfrac{\sqrt{3}}{2}\,(-0.1) = -\dfrac{\sqrt{3}}{20}.$

$$\frac{7}{3} = \sqrt[3]{31 - 11^2}$$

3 | DIFFERENTIATION RULES AND APPLICATIONS OF DIFFERENTIATION

1–16 ■ Find the critical numbers of the function.

1. $f(x) = 2x - 3x^2$ **2.** $f(x) = 5 + 8x$

3. $f(x) = x^3 - 3x + 1$ **4.** $f(t) = t^3 + 6t^2 + 3t - 1$

5. $g(x) = \sqrt[9]{x}$ **6.** $g(x) = |x + 1|$

7. $f(x) = 5 + 6x - 2x^3$ **8.** $f(t) = 2t^3 + 3t^2 + 6t + 4$

9. $f(x) = 4x^3 - 9x^2 - 12x + 3$

10. $s(t) = 2t^3 + 3t^2 - 6t + 4$

11. $s(t) = t^4 + 4t^3 + 2t^2$

12. $f(r) = \dfrac{r}{r^2 + 1}$ **13.** $f(\theta) = \sin^2(2\theta)$

14. $g(\theta) = \theta + \sin \theta$ **15.** $V(x) = x\sqrt{x - 2}$

16. $T(x) = x^2(2x - 1)^{2/3}$

17–23 ■ Verify that the function satisfies the hypotheses of the Mean Value Theorem on the given interval. Then find all numbers c that satisfy the conclusion of the Mean Value Theorem.

17. $f(x) = x^2 - 4x + 5, \ [1, 5]$

18. $f(x) = x^3 - 2x + 1, \ [-2, 3]$

19. $f(x) = 1 - x^2, \ [0, 3]$

20. $f(x) = 2x^3 + x^2 - x - 1, \ [0, 2]$

21. $f(x) = 1/x, \ [1, 2]$

22. $f(x) = \sqrt{x}; \ [1, 4]$

23. $f(x) = 1 + \sqrt[3]{x - 1}; \ [2, 9]$

24. Suppose f is continuous on $[2, 5]$ and $1 \le f'(x) \le 4$ for all x in $(2, 5)$. Show that $3 \le f(5) - f(2) \le 12$.

25–27 ■ Find the intervals on which the function is increasing or decreasing.

25. $f(x) = x^3 + 2x^2 - x + 1$

26. $f(x) = x^5 + 4x^3 - 6$

27. $f(x) = 2 \tan x - \tan^2 x$

28–31 ■ Find the intervals on which the curve is concave upward.

28. $y = 6x^2 - 2x^3 - x^4$ **29.** $y = \dfrac{x^2}{\sqrt{1 + x}}$

30. $y = \dfrac{x}{(1 + x)^2}$ **31.** $y = \dfrac{x^3}{x^2 - 3}$

32–39 ■ Use the guidelines of this section to sketch the curve.

32. $y = \dfrac{1 + x^2}{1 - x^2}$ **33.** $y = \dfrac{4}{(x - 5)^2}$

34. $y = \dfrac{x - 3}{x + 3}$ **35.** $y = \dfrac{1}{4x^3 - 9x}$

36. $y = \dfrac{x^3 - 1}{x}$ **37.** $y = \sqrt{x} - \sqrt{x - 1}$

38. $y = \sqrt[4]{x^2 - 25}$ **39.** $y = x\sqrt{x^2 - 9}$

40. Find the points on the hyperbola $y^2 - x^2 = 4$ that are closest to the point $(2, 0)$.

41. Find the point on the parabola $x + y^2 = 0$ that is closest to the point $(0, -3)$.

42–46 ■ Use Newton's method to approximate the indicated root of the equation correct to six decimal places.

42. The root of $x^3 - 2x - 1 = 0$ in the interval $[1, 2]$

43. The root of $x^3 + x^2 + x - 2 = 0$ in the interval $[0, 1]$

44. The root of $x^4 + x^3 - 22x^2 - 2x + 41 = 0$ in the interval $[3, 4]$

45. The positive root of $2 \sin x = x$

46. The root of $\tan x = x$ in the interval $(\pi/2, 3\pi/2)$

47–52 ■ Find $f(x)$.

47. $f''(x) = x^2 + x^3$ **48.** $f''(x) = 60x^4 - 45x^2$

49. $f''(x) = 1$ **50.** $f''(x) = \sin x$

51. $f'''(x) = 24x$ **52.** $f'''(x) = \sqrt{x}$

53. A triangle with sides a, b, and c varies with time t, but its area never changes. Let θ be the angle opposite the side of length a and suppose θ always remains acute.

(a) Express $d\theta/dt$ in terms of b, c, θ, db/dt, and dc/dt.

(b) Express da/dt in terms of the quantities in part (a).

54. Let a and b be positive numbers. Show that not both of the numbers $a(1 - b)$ and $b(1 - a)$ can be greater than $\dfrac{1}{4}$.

3 | ANSWERS TO SELECTED EXERCISES

1. $\dfrac{1}{3}$ **2.** None

3. ± 1 **4.** $-2 \pm \sqrt{3}$

5. 0   **6.** -1

7. ± 1 **8.** None

9. $-\dfrac{1}{2}, 2$ **10.** $\dfrac{1}{2}(-1 \pm \sqrt{5})$

11. $0, \dfrac{1}{2}(-3 \pm \sqrt{5})$ **12.** ± 1

13. $n\pi/4$, n an integer   **14.** $(2n+1)\pi$, n an integer

15. 2   **16.** $0, \dfrac{1}{2}, \dfrac{3}{8}$

17. $\dfrac{3}{2}$ **18.** $\pm \sqrt{7/3}$

19. $\dfrac{3}{2}$ **20.** $\dfrac{1}{6}(-1 + \sqrt{61})$

21. $\sqrt{2}$ **22.** $\dfrac{9}{4}$

23. $1 + (7/3)^{3/2}$

25. Inc. on $\left(-\infty, \dfrac{-2-\sqrt{7}}{3}\right), \left(\dfrac{-2+\sqrt{7}}{3}, \infty\right)$; dec. on $\left(\dfrac{-2-\sqrt{7}}{3}, \dfrac{-2+\sqrt{7}}{3}\right)$

26. Inc. on $\mathbb{R}$

27. Inc. on $\left(n\pi - \dfrac{\pi}{2}, n\pi + \dfrac{\pi}{4}\right)$, dec. on $\left(n\pi + \dfrac{\pi}{4}, n\pi + \dfrac{\pi}{2}\right)$, n an integer

28. $\left(\dfrac{-1-\sqrt{5}}{2}, \dfrac{-1+\sqrt{5}}{2}\right)$

29. $(-1, \infty)$

30. $(2, \infty)$

31. $(-\sqrt{3}, 0), (\sqrt{3}, \infty)$

32. A. $\{x \mid x \neq \pm 1\}$ **B.** y-int. 1
C. About y-axis   **D.** HA $y = -1$, VA $x = \pm 1$
E. Inc. on $(0, 1), (1, \infty)$; dec. on $(-\infty, -1)$, $(-1, 0)$

F. Loc. min. $f(0) = 1$
G. CU on $(-1, 1)$; CD on $(-\infty, -1), (1, \infty)$
H.
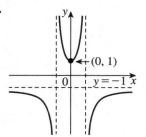

33. A. $\{x \mid x \neq 5\}$ **B.** y-int. $\dfrac{4}{25}$
C. None   **D.** HA $y = 0$, VA $x = 5$
E. Inc. on $(-\infty, 5)$, dec. on $(5, \infty)$
F. None   **G.** CU on $(-\infty, 5), (5, \infty)$
H.
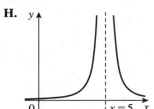

34. A. $\{x \mid x \neq -3\}$ **B.** x-int. 3, y-int. -1
C. None   **D.** HA $y = 1$, VA $x = -3$
E. Inc. on $(-\infty, -3), (3, \infty)$
F. None
G. CU on $(-\infty, -3)$, CD on $(-3, \infty)$
H.
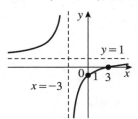

35. A. $\left\{x \mid x \neq 0, \pm \dfrac{3}{2}\right\}$
B. None
C. About the origin
D. HA $y = 0$, VA $x = 0$, $x = \pm \dfrac{3}{2}$

E. Inc. on $\left(-\dfrac{\sqrt{3}}{2}, 0\right), \left(0, \dfrac{\sqrt{3}}{2}\right)$; dec. on

$\left(-\infty, -\dfrac{3}{2}\right), \left(-\dfrac{3}{2}, -\dfrac{\sqrt{3}}{2}\right), \left(\dfrac{\sqrt{3}}{2}, \dfrac{3}{2}\right), \left(\dfrac{3}{2}, \infty\right)$

F. Loc. min. $f\left(-\dfrac{\sqrt{3}}{2}\right) = \dfrac{1}{3\sqrt{3}}$, loc. max.

$f\left(\dfrac{\sqrt{3}}{2}\right) = -\dfrac{1}{3\sqrt{3}}$

G. CU on $\left(-\dfrac{3}{2}, 0\right), \left(\dfrac{3}{2}, \infty\right)$; CD on $\left(-\infty, -\dfrac{3}{2}\right)$,
$\left(0, \dfrac{3}{2}\right)$

H.

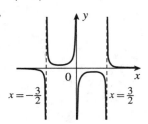

36. A. $\{x \mid x \neq 0\}$ **B.** x-int. 1

    C. None   **D.** VA $x = 0$

    E. Inc. on $\left(-\dfrac{1}{\sqrt[3]{2}}, 0\right)$, $(0, \infty)$; dec. on

    $\left(-\infty, -\dfrac{1}{\sqrt[3]{2}}\right)$

    F. Loc. min. $f\left(-\dfrac{1}{\sqrt[3]{2}}\right) = \dfrac{3\sqrt[3]{2}}{2}$

    G. CU on $(-\infty, 0)$, $(1, \infty)$; CD on $(0, 1)$. IP $(1, 0)$

    H.

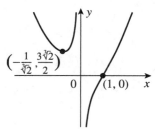

37. A. $[1, \infty)$ **B.** None

    C. None   **D.** HA $y = 0$

    E. Dec. on $(1, \infty)$ **F.** None

    G. CU on $(1, \infty)$

    H.

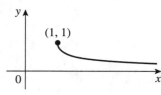

38. A. $(-\infty, -5) \cup (5, \infty)$ **B.** x-int. ± 5

    C. About the y-axis   **D.** None

    E. Inc. on $(5, \infty)$, dec. on $(-\infty, -5)$

    F. None   **G.** CD on $(-\infty, -5)$, $(5, \infty)$

    H.

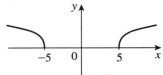

39. A. $(-\infty, -3] \cup [3, \infty)$ **B.** x-int. ± 3

    C. About the origin   **D.** None

    E. Inc. on $(-\infty, -3)$, $(3, \infty)$ **F.** None

    G. CU on $\left(3\sqrt{\dfrac{3}{2}}, \infty\right), \left(-3\sqrt{\dfrac{3}{2}}, -3\right)$;

       CD on $\left(-\infty, -3\sqrt{\dfrac{3}{2}}\right), \left(3, 3\sqrt{\dfrac{3}{2}}\right)$. IP

       $\left(\pm 3\sqrt{\dfrac{3}{2}}, \pm\dfrac{9\sqrt{3}}{2}\right)$

    H.

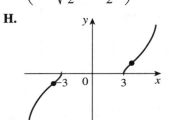

40. $(1, \pm\sqrt{5})$ **41.** $(-1, -1)$

42. 1.618034   **43.** 0.810536

44. 3.992020   **45.** 1.895494

46. 4.493409

47. $\dfrac{1}{12}x^4 + \dfrac{1}{20}x^5 + Cx + D$

48. $2x^6 - \dfrac{15}{4}x^4 + Cx + D$

49. $\dfrac{1}{2}x^2 + Cx + D$ **50.** $-\sin x + Cx + D$

51. $x^4 + \dfrac{1}{2}Cx^2 + Dx + E$

52. $\dfrac{8}{105}x^{7/2} + \dfrac{1}{2}Cx^2 + Dx + E$

53. (a) $\tan\theta\left[\dfrac{1}{c}\dfrac{dc}{dt} + \dfrac{1}{b}\dfrac{db}{dt}\right]$

     (b) $\dfrac{b\dfrac{db}{dt} + c\dfrac{dc}{dt} - \left(b\dfrac{dc}{dt} + c\dfrac{db}{dt}\right)\sec\theta}{\sqrt{b^2 + c^2 - 2bc\cos\theta}}$

3 | SOLUTIONS TO SELECTED EXERCISES

1. $f(x) = 2x - 3x^2 \Rightarrow f'(x) = 2 - 6x = 0 \Leftrightarrow x = \frac{1}{3}$.
So the critical number is $\frac{1}{3}$.

2. $f(x) = 5 + 8x \Rightarrow f'(x) = 8 \neq 0$. No critical number.

3. $f(x) = x^3 - 3x + 1 \Rightarrow$
$f'(x) = 3x^2 - 3 = 3(x^2 - 1) = 3(x + 1)(x - 1)$.
So the critical numbers are ± 1.

4. $f(t) = t^3 + 6t^2 + 3t - 1 \Rightarrow$
$f'(t) = 3t^2 + 12t + 3 = 3(t^2 + 4t + 1)$.
By the quadratic formula, solutions are
$t = \frac{-4 \pm \sqrt{12}}{2} = -2 \pm \sqrt{3}$. Critical numbers are
$t = -2 \pm \sqrt{3}$.

5. $g(x) = \sqrt[9]{x} = x^{1/9} \Rightarrow g'(x) = \frac{1}{9}x^{-8/9} = \frac{1}{9\sqrt[9]{x^8}} \neq 0$,
but $g'(0)$ does not exist, so $x = 0$ is a critical number.

6. $g(x) = |x + 1| \Rightarrow g'(x) = 1$ if $x > -1$, $g'(x) = -1$ if $x < -1$, but $g'(-1)$ does not exist, so $x = -1$ is a critical number.

7. $f(x) = 5 + 6x - 2x^3 \Rightarrow$
$f'(x) = 6 - 6x^2 = 6(1 + x)(1 - x)$.
$f'(x) = 0 \Rightarrow x = \pm 1$, so ± 1 are the critical numbers.

8. $f(t) = 2t^3 + 3t^2 + 6t + 4 \Rightarrow f'(t) = 6t^2 + 6t + 6$.
But $t^2 + t + 1 = 0$ has no real solution since
$b^2 - 4ac = 1 - 4(1)(1) = -3 < 0$. No critical number.

9. $f(x) = 4x^3 - 9x^2 - 12x + 3 \Rightarrow$
$f'(x) = 12x^2 - 18x - 12$
$= 6(2x^2 - 3x - 2) = 6(2x + 1)(x - 2)$
$f'(x) = 0 \Rightarrow x = -\frac{1}{2}, 2$; so the critical numbers are
$x = -\frac{1}{2}, 2$.

10. $s(t) = 2t^3 + 3t^2 - 6t + 4 \Rightarrow$
$s'(t) = 6t^2 + 6t - 6 = 6(t^2 + t - 1)$. By the quadratic formula, the critical numbers are
$t = (-1 \pm \sqrt{5})/2$.

11. $s(t) = t^4 + 4t^3 + 2t^2 \Rightarrow$
$s'(t) = 4t^3 + 12t^2 + 4t = 4t(t^2 + 3t + 1) = 0$ when
$t = 0$ or $t^2 + 3t + 1 = 0$. By the quadratic formula,
the critical numbers are $t = 0, \frac{-3 \pm \sqrt{5}}{2}$.

12. $f(r) = \frac{r}{r^2 + 1} \Rightarrow$
$f'(r) = \frac{(r^2 + 1)1 - r(2r)}{(r^2 + 1)^2} = \frac{-r^2 + 1}{(r^2 + 1)^2} = 0 \Leftrightarrow$
$r^2 = 1 \Leftrightarrow r = \pm 1$, so these are the critical numbers.
Note that $f'(r)$ always exists since $r^2 + 1 \neq 0$.

13. $f(\theta) = \sin^2(2\theta) \Rightarrow$
$f'(\theta) = 2\sin(2\theta)\cos(2\theta)(2)$
$= 2(2\sin 2\theta \cos 2\theta) = 2[\sin(2 \cdot 2\theta)]$
$= 2\sin 4\theta = 0$
$f(\theta) = 0 \Leftrightarrow \sin 4\theta = 0 \Leftrightarrow 4\theta = n\pi$, n an integer. So $\theta = n\pi/4$ are the critical numbers.

14. $g(\theta) = \theta + \sin\theta \Rightarrow g'(\theta) = 1 + \cos\theta = 0$
$\Leftrightarrow \cos\theta = -1$. The critical numbers are
$\theta = \pi + 2n\pi = (2n + 1)\pi$, n an integer.

15. $V(x) = x\sqrt{x - 2} \Rightarrow$
$V'(x) = \sqrt{x - 2} + \frac{x}{2\sqrt{x - 2}} \Rightarrow V'(-2)$ does not
exist. For $x > 2$ [the domain of $V'(x)$], $V'(x) > 0$, so 2 is the only critical number.

16. $T(x) = x^2(2x - 1)^{2/3} \Rightarrow$
$T'(x) = 2x(2x - 1)^{2/3} + x^2\left(\frac{2}{3}\right)(2x - 1)^{-1/3}(2)$. So
$T'\left(\frac{1}{2}\right)$ does not exist.

$T'(x) = 2x(2x - 1)^{-1/3}\left(2x - 1 + \frac{2}{3}x\right)$

$= 2x(2x - 1)^{-1/3}\left(\frac{8}{3}x - 1\right) = 0 \Leftrightarrow$

$x = 0$ or $x = \frac{3}{8}$. So the critical numbers are $x = 0, \frac{3}{8}$, and $\frac{1}{2}$.

17. $f(x) = x^2 - 4x + 5$, $[1, 5]$. f, being a polynomial, is continuous on $[1, 5]$ and differentiable on $(1, 5)$.
$\frac{f(5) - f(1)}{5 - 1} = \frac{10 - 2}{4} = 2$ and
$2 = f'(c) = -2c \Rightarrow c = \frac{3}{2}$.

18. $f(x) = x^3 - 2x + 1$, $[-2, 3]$. f, being a polynomial, is continuous on $[-2, 3]$ and differentiable
on $(-2, 3)$. $\frac{f(3) - f(-2)}{3 - (-2)} = \frac{22 - (-3)}{5} = 5$ and
$5 = f'(c) = 3c^2 - 2 \Rightarrow 3c^2 = 7 \Rightarrow c = \pm\sqrt{\frac{7}{3}}$.

19. $f(x) = 1 - x^2$, $[0, 3]$. f, being a polynomial, is continuous on $[0, 3]$ and differentiable on $(0, 3)$.

$$\frac{f(3) - f(0)}{3 - 0} = \frac{-8 - 1}{3} = -3 \text{ and}$$

$$-3 = f'(c) = -2c \implies c = \frac{3}{2}.$$

20. $f(x) = 2x^3 + x^2 - x - 1$, $[0, 2]$. f, being a polynomial, is continuous on $[0, 2]$ and differentiable on $(0, 2)$. $\dfrac{f(2) - f(0)}{2 - 0} = \dfrac{17 - (-1)}{2} = 9$ and

$9 = f'(c) = 6c^2 + 2c - 1 \implies 0 = 6c^2 + 2c - 10 \implies$

$c = \dfrac{-2 \pm \sqrt{244}}{2} = \dfrac{-1 \pm \sqrt{61}}{6}$, but only $\dfrac{-1 + \sqrt{61}}{6}$ lies in $(0, 2)$.

21. $f(x) = 1/x$, $[1, 2]$. f, being a rational function, is continuous on $[1, 2]$ and differentiable on $(1, 2)$.

$$\frac{f(2) - f(1)}{2 - 1} = \frac{\frac{1}{2} - 1}{1} = -\frac{1}{2} \text{ and } -\frac{1}{2} = f'(c) = -\frac{1}{c^2}$$

$\implies c^2 = 2 \implies c = \sqrt{2}$ (since c must lie in $[1, 2]$).

22. $f(x) = \sqrt{x}$, $[1, 4]$. $f(x)$ is continuous on $[1, 4]$ and differentiable on $(1, 4)$.

$$\frac{f(4) - f(1)}{4 - 1} = \frac{2 - 1}{3} = \frac{1}{3} \text{ and } \frac{1}{3} = f'(c) = \frac{1}{2\sqrt{c}}$$

$$\implies \sqrt{c} = \frac{3}{2} \implies c = \left(\frac{3}{2}\right)^2 = \frac{9}{4}.$$

23. 1, $x - 1$, and $\sqrt[3]{x}$ are continuous on $\mathbb{R}$, and therefore $f(x) = 1 + \sqrt[3]{x - 1}$ is continuous on $\mathbb{R}$, and hence continuous on $[2, 9]$. $f'(x) = \dfrac{1}{3}(x - 1)^{-2/3}$, so that f is differentiable for all $x \neq 1$ and so f is differentiable on $(2, 9)$. By the Mean Value Theorem, there exists a number c such that

$$f'(c) = \frac{1}{3}(c - 1)^{-2/3} = \frac{f(9) - f(2)}{9 - 2} = \frac{3 - 2}{7} = \frac{1}{7} \implies$$

$$\frac{1}{3}(c - 1)^{-2/3} = \frac{1}{7} \implies (c - 1)^2 = \left(\frac{7}{3}\right)^3 \implies$$

$$c = \pm\left(\frac{7}{3}\right)^{3/2} + 1 \implies c = \left(\frac{7}{3}\right)^{3/2} + 1 \approx 4.564$$

since $c \in [2, 9]$.

24. By the Mean Value Theorem, $\dfrac{f(5) - f(2)}{5 - 2} = f'(c)$ for some $c \in (2, 5)$. Since $1 \leq f'(x) \leq 4$, we have

$$1 \leq \frac{f(5) - f(2)}{5 - 2} \leq 4 \text{ or } 1 \leq \frac{f(5) - f(2)}{3} \leq 4 \text{ or}$$

$$3 \leq f(5) - f(2) \leq 12.$$

25. $f(x) = x^3 + 2x^2 - x + 1$.
$f'(x) = 3x^2 + 4x - 1 = 0 \implies$

$x = \dfrac{-4 \pm \sqrt{28}}{6} = \dfrac{-2 \pm \sqrt{7}}{3}$. Now $f'(x) > 0$ for

$x < \dfrac{-2 - \sqrt{7}}{3}$ or $x > \dfrac{-2 + \sqrt{7}}{3}$ and $f'(x) < 0$

for $\dfrac{-2 - \sqrt{7}}{3} < x < \dfrac{-2 + \sqrt{7}}{3}$. f is increasing

on $\left(-\infty, \dfrac{-2 - \sqrt{7}}{3}\right)$ and $\left(\dfrac{-2 + \sqrt{7}}{3}, \infty\right)$ and

decreasing on $\left(\dfrac{-2 - \sqrt{7}}{3}, \dfrac{-2 + \sqrt{7}}{3}\right)$.

26. $f(x) = x^5 + 4x^3 - 6$. $f'(x) = 5x^4 + 12x^2 > 0$ for all $x \neq 0$. So f is increasing on $\mathbb{R}$.

27. $f(x) = 2 \tan x - \tan^2 x$.
$f'(x) = 2 \sec^2 x - 2 \tan x \sec^2 x = 2 \sec^2 x (1 - \tan x)$.
So $f'(x) > 0 \iff 1 - \tan x > 0 \iff \tan x < 1 \iff$

$x \in \left(n\pi - \dfrac{\pi}{2}, n\pi + \dfrac{\pi}{4}\right)$, n an integer. So f is

increasing on $\left(n\pi - \dfrac{\pi}{2}, n\pi + \dfrac{\pi}{4}\right)$, n an integer, and

decreasing on $\left(n\pi + \dfrac{\pi}{4}, n\pi + \dfrac{\pi}{2}\right)$, n an integer.

28. $f(x) = 6x^2 - 2x^3 - x^4 \implies$
$f'(x) = 12x - 6x^2 - 4x^3 \implies$
$f''(x) = 12 - 12x - 12x^2 = 0 \iff x^2 + x - 1 = 0$

$\implies x = \dfrac{-1 \pm \sqrt{5}}{2}$. For $x < \dfrac{-1 - \sqrt{5}}{2}$, $f''(x) < 0$.

For $\dfrac{-1 - \sqrt{5}}{2} < x < \dfrac{-1 + \sqrt{5}}{2}$, $f''(x) > 0$, and if

$x > \dfrac{-1 + \sqrt{5}}{2}$ then $f''(x) < 0$. Therefore f is CU on

$\left(\dfrac{-1 - \sqrt{5}}{2}, \dfrac{-1 + \sqrt{5}}{2}\right)$.

29. $y = \dfrac{x^2}{\sqrt{1 + x}}$, $D = \{x | x > -1\} \implies$

$$y' = \frac{2x\sqrt{1 + x} - \frac{1}{2}(1 + x)^{-1/2} \cdot x^2}{1 + x} = \frac{4x + 3x^2}{2(1 + x)^{3/2}} \implies$$

$$y'' = \frac{(4 + 6x)2(1 + x)^{3/2} - 3(1 + x)^{1/2}(4x + 3x^2)}{4(1 + x)^3}$$

$$= \frac{3x^2 + 8x + 8}{4(1 + x)^{5/2}} > 0 \iff$$

$3x^2 + 8x + 8 > 0$, which is true for all x since the discriminant is negative, so the function is CU on its domain, which is $(-1, \infty)$.

30. $f(x) = x(1 + x)^{-2}$ $\Rightarrow$
$f'(x) = (1 + x)^{-2} - 2x(1 + x)^{-3}$
$= (1 + x)^{-3}(1 - x)$ $\Rightarrow$
$f''(x) = -3(1 + x)^{-4}(1 - x) - (1 + x)^{-3}$
$= (1 + x)^{-4}(2x - 4) > 0$ $\Leftrightarrow$

$(2x - 4) > 0$ $\Leftrightarrow$ $x > 2$. Therefore f is CU on $(2, \infty)$.

31. $y = \dfrac{x^3}{x^2 - 3}$ $\Rightarrow$ $y' = \dfrac{x^4 - 9x^2}{(x^2 - 3)^2}$ $\Rightarrow$

$y'' = \dfrac{(4x^3 - 18x)(x^2 - 3)^2 - 4x(x^2 - 3)(x^4 - 9x^2)}{(x^2 - 3)^4}$

$= \dfrac{6x(x^2 + 9)}{(x^2 - 3)^3}$

Now since $x^2 + 9 > 0$, the quotient is positive $\Leftrightarrow$

$$\frac{x}{x^2 - 3} = \frac{x}{(x - \sqrt{3})(x + \sqrt{3})} > 0.$$

Interval	x	$x + \sqrt{3}$	$x - \sqrt{3}$	$\dfrac{x}{x^2 - 3}$
$x < -\sqrt{3}$	$-$	$-$	$-$	$-$
$-\sqrt{3} < x < 0$	$-$	$+$	$-$	$-$
$0 < x < \sqrt{3}$	$+$	$+$	$-$	$-$
$x > \sqrt{3}$	$+$	$+$	$+$	$+$

So y is concave upward on $(-\sqrt{3}, 0)$ and $(\sqrt{3}, \infty)$.

32. $y = f(x) = \dfrac{1 + x^2}{1 - x^2} = -1 + \dfrac{2}{1 - x^2}$

A. $D = \{x \mid x \neq \pm 1\}$

B. No x-intercept, y-intercept $= f(0) = 1$

C. $f(-x) = f(x)$, so f is even and the curve is symmetric about the y-axis.

D. $\displaystyle\lim_{x \to \pm\infty} \frac{1 + x^2}{1 - x^2} = \lim_{x \to \pm\infty} \frac{(1/x^2) + 1}{(1/x^2) - 1} = -1$,

so $y = -1$ is a HA. $\displaystyle\lim_{x \to 1^-} \frac{1 + x^2}{1 - x^2} = \infty$,

$\displaystyle\lim_{x \to 1^+} \frac{1 + x^2}{1 - x^2} = -\infty$, $\displaystyle\lim_{x \to -1^-} \frac{1 + x^2}{1 - x^2} = -\infty$,

$\displaystyle\lim_{x \to -1^+} \frac{1 + x^2}{1 - x^2} = \infty$. So $x = 1$ and $x = -1$ are VA.

E. $f'(x) = \dfrac{4x}{(1 - x^2)^2} > 0$ $\Leftrightarrow$ $x > 0$ $(x \neq 1)$, so f increases on $(0, 1)$ and $(1, \infty)$, and decreases on $(-\infty, -1)$ and $(-1, 0)$.

F. $f(0) = 1$ is a local minimum.

G. $y'' = \dfrac{4(1 - x^2)^2 - 4x \cdot 2(1 - x^2)(-2x)}{(1 - x^2)^4}$

$= \dfrac{4(1 + 3x^2)}{(1 - x^2)^3} > 0$ $\Leftrightarrow$

$x^2 < 1$ $\Leftrightarrow$ $-1 < x < 1$, so f is CU on $(-1, 1)$ and CD on $(-\infty, -1)$ and $(1, \infty)$. No IP

H.

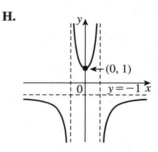

33. $y = f(x) = 4/(x - 5)^2$

A. $D = \{x \mid x \neq 5\} = (-\infty, 5) \cup (5, \infty)$

B. y-intercept $= f(0) = \dfrac{4}{25}$, no x-intercept

C. No symmetry

D. $\displaystyle\lim_{x \to \pm\infty} \frac{4}{(x - 5)^2} = 0$, so $y = 0$ is a HA.

$\displaystyle\lim_{x \to 5} \frac{4}{(x - 5)^2} = \infty$, so $x = 5$ is a VA.

E. $f'(x) = -8/(x - 5)^3 > 0$ $\Leftrightarrow$ $x < 5$ and $f'(x) < 0$ $\Leftrightarrow$ $x > 5$. So f is increasing on $(-\infty, 5)$ and decreasing on $(5, \infty)$.

F. No maximum or minimum

G. $f''(x) = 24/(x - 5)^4 > 0$ for $x \neq 5$, so f is CU on $(-\infty, 5)$ and $(5, \infty)$.

H.

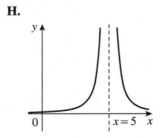

34. $y = f(x) = (x - 3)/(x + 3)$

A. $D = \{x \mid x \neq -3\} = (-\infty, -3) \cup (3, \infty)$

B. x-intercept is 3, y-intercept $= f(0) = -1$

C. No symmetry

D. $\lim\limits_{x\to\pm\infty}\dfrac{x-3}{x+3}=\lim\limits_{x\to\pm\infty}\dfrac{1-3/x}{1+3/x}=1$,

so $y=1$ is a HA. $\lim\limits_{x\to-3^-}\dfrac{x-3}{x+3}=\infty$ and

$\lim\limits_{x\to-3^+}\dfrac{x-3}{x+3}=-\infty$, so $x=-3$ is a VA.

E. $f'(x)=\dfrac{(x+3)-(x-3)}{(x+3)^2}=\dfrac{6}{(x+3)^2}\ \Rightarrow$
$f'(x)>0\ (x\neq-3)$ so f is increasing on
$(-\infty,-3)$ and $(3,\infty)$.

F. No maximum or minimum

G. $f''(x)=-\dfrac{12}{(x+3)^3}>0\ \Leftrightarrow\ x<-3$, so f is
CU on $(-\infty,-3)$ and CD on $(-3,\infty)$. No IP

H.

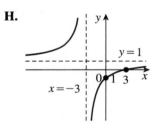

35. $y=f(x)=1/\left[x(4x^2-9)\right]$

A. $D=\left\{x\mid x\neq 0,\pm\frac{3}{2}\right\}$

B. No intercept

C. $f(-x)=-f(x)$, so the curve is symmetric about the origin.

D. $\lim\limits_{x\to\pm\infty}\dfrac{1}{x(4x^2-9)}=0$, so $y=0$ is a HA.

$\lim\limits_{x\to0^+}\dfrac{1}{x(4x^2-9)}=-\infty,\ \lim\limits_{x\to0^-}\dfrac{1}{x(4x^2-9)}=\infty$,

$\lim\limits_{x\to3/2^+}\dfrac{1}{x(4x^2-9)}=\infty,\ \lim\limits_{x\to3/2^-}\dfrac{1}{x(4x^2-9)}=-\infty$,

$\lim\limits_{x\to-3/2^+}\dfrac{1}{x(4x^2-9)}=\infty$, and

$\lim\limits_{x\to-3/2^-}\dfrac{1}{x(4x^2-9)}=-\infty$, so $x=0$ and $x=\pm\dfrac{3}{2}$

are VA.

E. $f'(x)=-\dfrac{12x^2-9}{(4x^3-9x)^2}>0\ \Leftrightarrow\ x^2<\dfrac{3}{4}$

$\Leftrightarrow\ |x|<\dfrac{\sqrt{3}}{2}\ \Leftrightarrow\ -\dfrac{\sqrt{3}}{2}<x<\dfrac{\sqrt{3}}{2}$ and

$f'(x)<0\ \Leftrightarrow\ x>\dfrac{\sqrt{3}}{2}$ or $x<-\dfrac{\sqrt{3}}{2}$, so f

is increasing on $\left(-\dfrac{\sqrt{3}}{2},0\right)$ and $\left(0,\dfrac{\sqrt{3}}{2}\right)$,

and decreasing on $\left(-\infty,-\dfrac{3}{2}\right),\ \left(-\dfrac{3}{2},-\dfrac{\sqrt{3}}{2}\right)$,
$\left(\dfrac{\sqrt{3}}{2},\dfrac{3}{2}\right)$, and $\left(\dfrac{3}{2},\infty\right)$.

F. $f\left(-\dfrac{\sqrt{3}}{2}\right)=\dfrac{1}{3\sqrt{3}}$ is a local minimum,

$f\left(\dfrac{\sqrt{3}}{2}\right)=-\dfrac{1}{3\sqrt{3}}$ is a local maximum.

G. $f''(x)$
$=\dfrac{-24x(4x^3-9x)^2+(12x^2-9)^2 2(4x^3-9x)}{(4x^3-9x)^4}$
$=\dfrac{6(32x^4-36x^2+27)}{x^3(4x^2-9)^3}$

Since $32x^4-36x^2+27>0$ for all x,

$f''(x)>0\ \Leftrightarrow\ -\dfrac{3}{2}<x<0$ or $x>\dfrac{3}{2}$, so f

is CU on $\left(-\dfrac{3}{2},0\right)$ and $\left(\dfrac{3}{2},\infty\right)$ and CD on

$\left(-\infty,-\dfrac{3}{2}\right)$ and $\left(0,\dfrac{3}{2}\right)$.

H.

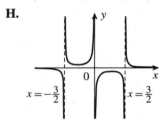

36. $y=f(x)=\dfrac{x^3-1}{x}=x^2-\dfrac{1}{x}$

A. $D=\{x\mid x\neq 0\}$

B. x-intercept 1, no y-intercept

C. No symmetry

D. $\lim\limits_{x\to\pm\infty}=\infty$, so no HA. $\lim\limits_{x\to0^+}\dfrac{x^3-1}{x}=-\infty$ and

$\lim\limits_{x\to0^-}\dfrac{x^3-1}{x}=\infty$, so $x=0$ is a VA.

E. $f'(x)=2x+\dfrac{1}{x^2}=\dfrac{2x^3+1}{x^2}>0\ \Leftrightarrow$

$2x^3+1>0\ \Leftrightarrow\ x>-\dfrac{1}{\sqrt[3]{2}}\ (x\neq0)$, so f is

increasing on $\left(-\dfrac{1}{\sqrt[3]{2}},0\right)$ and $(0,\infty)$ and

decreasing on $\left(-\infty,-\dfrac{1}{\sqrt[3]{2}}\right)$.

F. $f\left(-\dfrac{1}{\sqrt[3]{2}}\right)=\dfrac{3\sqrt[3]{2}}{2}$ is a local minimum.

G. $f''(x) = 2 - \dfrac{2}{x^3} = \dfrac{2(x^3 - 1)}{x^3} \implies$
$f''(x) > 0 \iff x > 1$ or $x < 0$, so f is CU on $(-\infty, 0)$ and $(1, \infty)$ and CD on $(0, 1)$. IP is $(1, 0)$.

H.

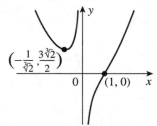

37. $y = f(x) = \sqrt{x} - \sqrt{x - 1}$

A. $D = \{x \mid x \geq 0 \text{ and } x \geq 1\}$
$= \{x \mid x \geq 1\} = [1, \infty)$

B. No intercept

C. No symmetry

D. $\displaystyle\lim_{x \to \infty} (\sqrt{x} - \sqrt{x - 1}) =$
$\displaystyle\lim_{x \to \infty} (\sqrt{x} - \sqrt{x - 1}) \dfrac{\sqrt{x} + \sqrt{x - 1}}{\sqrt{x} + \sqrt{x - 1}} =$
$\displaystyle\lim_{x \to \infty} \dfrac{1}{\sqrt{x} + \sqrt{x - 1}} = 0$, so $y = 0$ is a HA.

E. $f'(x) = \dfrac{1}{2\sqrt{x}} - \dfrac{1}{2\sqrt{x - 1}} < 0$ for all $x > 1$,
since $x - 1 < x \implies \sqrt{x - 1} < \sqrt{x}$, so f is decreasing on $(1, \infty)$.

F. No local maximum or minimum

G. $f''(x) = -\dfrac{1}{4}\left[\dfrac{1}{x^{3/2}} - \dfrac{1}{(x - 1)^{3/2}}\right] \implies f''(x) > 0$ for $x > 1$, so f is CU on $(1, \infty)$.

H.

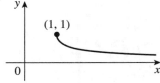

38. $y = f(x) = \sqrt[4]{x^2 - 25}$

A. $D = \{x \mid x^2 \geq 25\} = (-\infty, -5] \cup [5, \infty)$

B. x-intercepts are ± 5, no y-intercept

C. $f(-x) = f(x)$, so the curve is symmetric about the y-axis.

D. $\displaystyle\lim_{x \to \pm\infty} \sqrt[4]{x^2 - 25} = \infty$, no asymptote

E. $f'(x) = \dfrac{1}{4}(x^2 - 25)^{-3/4}(2x) = \dfrac{x}{2(x^2 - 25)^{3/4}} > 0$
if $x > 5$, so f is increasing on $(5, \infty)$ and decreasing on $(-\infty, -5)$.

F. No local maximum or minimum

G. $y'' = \dfrac{2(x^2 - 25)^{3/4} - 3x^2(x^2 - 25)^{-1/4}}{4(x^2 - 25)^{3/2}}$
$= -\dfrac{x^2 + 50}{4(x^2 - 25)^{7/4}} < 0$
so f is CD on $(-\infty, -5)$ and $(5, \infty)$. No IP

H.

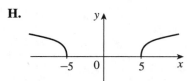

39. $y = f(x) = x\sqrt{x^2 - 9}$

A. $D = \{x \mid x^2 \geq 9\} = (-\infty, -3] \cup [3, \infty)$

B. x-intercepts are ± 3, no y-intercept.

C. $f(-x) = -f(x)$, so the curve is symmetric about the origin.

D. $\displaystyle\lim_{x \to \infty} x\sqrt{x^2 - 9} = \infty$, $\displaystyle\lim_{x \to -\infty} x\sqrt{x^2 - 9} = -\infty$, no asymptote

E. $f'(x) = \sqrt{x^2 - 9} + \dfrac{x^2}{\sqrt{x^2 - 9}} > 0$ for $x \in D$, so f is increasing on $(-\infty, -3)$ and $(3, \infty)$.

F. No maximum or minimum

G. $f''(x) = \dfrac{x}{\sqrt{x^2 - 9}} + \dfrac{2x\sqrt{x^2 - 9} - x^2(x/\sqrt{x^2 - 9})}{x^2 - 9}$
$= \dfrac{x(2x^2 - 27)}{(x^2 - 9)^{3/2}} > 0 \iff x > 3\sqrt{\dfrac{3}{2}}$ or
$-3\sqrt{\dfrac{3}{2}} < x < 0$, so f is CU on $\left(3\sqrt{\dfrac{3}{2}}, \infty\right)$ and
$\left(-3\sqrt{\dfrac{3}{2}}, -3\right)$ and CD on $\left(-\infty, -3\sqrt{\dfrac{3}{2}}\right)$ and
$\left(3, 3\sqrt{\dfrac{3}{2}}\right)$. IP $\left(\pm 3\sqrt{\dfrac{3}{2}}, \pm \dfrac{9\sqrt{3}}{2}\right)$

H.

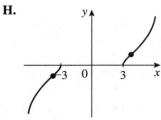

40. By symmetry, the points are (x, y) and $(x, -y)$, where $y > 0$. The square of the distance is

$$D(x) = (x - 2)^2 + y^2$$
$$= (x - 2)^2 + (4 + x^2)$$
$$= 2x^2 - 4x + 8$$

So $D'(x) = 4x - 4 = 0 \Rightarrow x = 1$ and $y = \pm\sqrt{4 + 1} = \pm\sqrt{5}$. The points are $(1, \pm\sqrt{5})$.

41. The square of the distance from a point (x, y) on the parabola $x = -y^2$ is $x^2 + (y + 3)^2 = y^4 + y^2 + 6y + 9 = D(y)$.

Now

$$D'(y) = 4y^3 + 2y + 6$$
$$= 2(y + 1)(2y^2 - 2y + 3)$$

Since $2y^2 - 2y + 3 = 0$ has no real roots, $y = -1$ is the only critical number. Then $x = -(-1)^2 = -1$, so the point is $(-1, -1)$.

42. $f(x) = x^3 - 2x - 1 \Rightarrow f'(x) = 3x^2 - 2$, so

$$x_{n+1} = x_n - \frac{x_n^3 - 2x_n - 1}{3x_n^2 - 2}. \text{ Taking } x_1 = 1.5, \text{ we get}$$

$x_2 \approx 1.631579$, $x_3 \approx 1.618184$, $x_4 \approx 1.618034$, and $x_5 \approx 1.618034$. So the root is 1.618034 to six decimal places.

43. $f(x) = x^3 + x^2 + x - 2 \Rightarrow f'(x) = 3x^2 + 2x + 1$,

$$\text{so } x_{n+1} = x_n - \frac{x_n^3 + x_n^2 + x_n - 2}{3x_n^2 + 2x_n - 1}. \text{ Taking } x_1 = 1,$$

we get $x_2 \approx 0.833333$, $x_3 \approx 0.810916$, $x_4 \approx 0.810536$, and $x_5 \approx 0.810536$. So the root is 0.810536 to six decimal places.

44. $f(x) = x^4 + x^3 - 22x^2 - 2x + 41 \Rightarrow$
$f'(x) = 4x^3 + 3x^2 - 44x - 2$, so

$$x_{n+1} = x_n - \frac{x_n^4 + x_n^3 - 22x_n^2 + 41}{4x_n^3 + 3x_n^2 - 44x_n - 2}. \text{ Taking } x_1 = 4,$$

we get $x_2 \approx 3.992063$, $x_3 \approx 3.992020$, and $x_4 \approx 3.992020$. So the root in the interval $[3, 4]$ is 3.992020 to six decimal places.

45.

From the graph it appears that there is a root near 2, so we take $x_1 = 2$. Write the equation as $f(x) = 2 \sin x - x = 0$. Then $f'(x) = 2 \cos x - 1$,

$$\text{so } x_{n+1} = x_n - \frac{2 \sin x_n - x_n}{2 \cos x_n - 1} \Rightarrow x_1 = 2,$$

$x_2 \approx 1.900996$, $x_3 \approx 1.895512$, $x_4 \approx 1.895494 \approx x_5$. So the root is 1.895494, to six decimal places.

46.

From the graph, it appears that there is a root near 4.5. So we take $x_1 = 4.5$. Write the equation as $f(x) = \tan x - x = 0$. Then $f'(x) = \sec^2 x - 1$, so

$$x_{n+1} = x_n - \frac{\tan x_n - x_n}{\sec^2 x_n - 1}. \quad x_1 = 4.5, \ x_2 \approx 4.493614,$$

$x_3 \approx 4.493410$, $x_4 \approx 4.493409 \approx x_5$. To six decimal places, the root is 4.493409.

47. $f''(x) = x^2 + x^3 \Rightarrow$

$$f'(x) = \frac{1}{3}x^3 + \frac{1}{4}x^4 + C \Rightarrow$$

$$f(x) = \frac{1}{12}x^4 + \frac{1}{20}x^5 + Cx + D$$

48. $f''(x) = 60x^4 - 45x^2 \Rightarrow$

$$f'(x) = 60\left(\frac{1}{5}x^5\right) - 45\left(\frac{1}{3}x^3\right) + C$$
$$= 12x^5 - 15x^3 + C \Rightarrow$$

$$f(x) = 12\left(\frac{1}{6}x^6\right) - 15\left(\frac{1}{4}x^4\right) + Cx + D$$
$$= 2x^6 - \frac{15}{4}x^4 + Cx + D$$

49. $f''(x) = 1 \Rightarrow f'(x) = x + C \Rightarrow$

$$f(x) = \frac{1}{2}x^2 + Cx + D$$

50. $f''(x) = \sin x \Rightarrow f'(x) = -\cos x + C \Rightarrow$
$f(x) = -\sin x + Cx + D$

51. $f'''(x) = 24x \Rightarrow f''(x) = 12x^2 + C \Rightarrow$

$f'(x) = 4x^3 + Cx + D \Rightarrow$

$$f(x) = x^4 + \frac{1}{2}Cx^2 + Dx + E$$

52. $f'''(x) = x^{1/2} \Rightarrow f''(x) = \frac{2}{3}x^{3/2} + C \Rightarrow$

$$f'(x) = \frac{2}{3} \cdot \frac{2}{5}x^{5/2} + Cx + D = \frac{4}{15}x^{5/2} + Cx + D \Rightarrow$$

$$f(x) = \frac{4}{15} \cdot \frac{2}{7}x^{7/2} + C\left(\frac{1}{2}x^2\right) + Dx + E$$
$$= \frac{8}{105}x^{7/2} + \frac{1}{2}Cx^2 + Dx + E$$

53. (a) $A = \dfrac{1}{2}bh$ with

$\sin\theta = h/c$,

$A = \dfrac{1}{2}bc\sin\theta$. But A is a

constant, so differentiating this equation with respect to t, we get

$$\dfrac{dA}{dt} = 0 = \dfrac{1}{2}\left[bc\cos\theta\,\dfrac{d\theta}{dt} + b\,\dfrac{dc}{dt}\sin\theta \right.$$
$$\left. + \dfrac{db}{dt}c\sin\theta \right] \;\Rightarrow$$

$$bc\cos\theta\,\dfrac{d\theta}{dt} = -\sin\theta\left[b\,\dfrac{dc}{dt} + c\,\dfrac{db}{dt} \right] \;\Rightarrow$$

$$\dfrac{d\theta}{dt} = -\tan\theta\left[\dfrac{1}{c}\dfrac{dc}{dt} + \dfrac{1}{b}\dfrac{db}{dt} \right].$$

(b) We use the Law of Cosines to get the length of side a in terms of those of b and c, and then we differentiate implicitly with respect to t: $a^2 = b^2 + c^2 - 2bc\cos\theta \;\Rightarrow$

$$2a\,\dfrac{da}{dt} = 2b\,\dfrac{db}{dt} + 2c\,\dfrac{dc}{dt} - 2\left[bc(-\sin\theta)\dfrac{d\theta}{dt} \right.$$
$$+ b\,\dfrac{dc}{dt}\cos\theta + \dfrac{db}{dt}c\cos\theta \Bigg] \;\Rightarrow$$

$$\dfrac{da}{dt} = \dfrac{1}{a}\bigg(b\,\dfrac{db}{dt} + c\,\dfrac{dc}{dt} + bc\sin\theta\,\dfrac{d\theta}{dt}$$
$$- b\,\dfrac{dc}{dt}\cos\theta - c\,\dfrac{db}{dt}\cos\theta \bigg).$$

Now we substitute our value of a from the Law of Cosines and the value of $d\theta/dt$ from part (a), and simplify (primes signify differentiation by t):

$$\dfrac{da}{dt} = \dfrac{bb' + cc' + bc\sin\theta\big[-\tan\theta(c'/c + b'/b) \big] - (bc' + cb')(\cos\theta)}{\sqrt{b^2 + c^2 - 2bc\cos\theta}}$$

$$= \dfrac{bb' + cc' - \big[\sin^2\theta(bc' + cb') + \cos^2\theta(bc' + cb') \big]/\cos\theta}{\sqrt{b^2 + c^2 - 2bc\cos\theta}}$$

$$= \dfrac{bb' + cc' - (bc' + cb')\sec\theta}{\sqrt{b^2 + c^2 - 2bc\cos\theta}}$$

54. First we show that $x(1-x) \le \dfrac{1}{4}$ for all x. Let $f(x) = x(1-x) = x - x^2$. Then $f'(x) = 1 - 2x$. This is 0 when $x = \dfrac{1}{2}$ and $f'(x) > 0$ for $x < \dfrac{1}{2}$, $f'(x) < 0$ for $x > \dfrac{1}{2}$, so the absolute maximum of f is $f\left(\dfrac{1}{2}\right) = \dfrac{1}{4}$. Thus, $x(1-x) \le \dfrac{1}{4}$ for all x.

Now suppose that the given assertion is false, that is, $a(1-b) > \dfrac{1}{4}$ and $b(1-a) > \dfrac{1}{4}$. Multiply these inequalities: $a(1-b)b(1-a) > \dfrac{1}{16} \;\Rightarrow$ $\big[a(1-a) \big]\big[b(1-b) \big] > \dfrac{1}{16}$. But we know that $a(1-a) \le \dfrac{1}{4}$ and $b(1-b) \le \dfrac{1}{4} \;\Rightarrow$ $\big[a(1-a) \big]\big[b(1-b) \big] \le \dfrac{1}{16}$. Thus, we have a contradiction, so the given assertion is proved.

4 INTEGRALS

1–4 ■ Write the given sum or difference as a single integral in the form $\int_a^b f(x)\,dx$.

1. $\int_1^3 f(x)\,dx + \int_3^6 f(x)\,dx + \int_6^{12} f(x)\,dx$

2. $\int_5^8 f(x)\,dx + \int_0^5 f(x)\,dx$

3. $\int_2^{10} f(x)\,dx - \int_2^7 f(x)\,dx$

4. $\int_{-3}^5 f(x)\,dx - \int_{-3}^0 f(x)\,dx + \int_5^6 f(x)\,dx$

5. If $\int_2^8 f(x)\,dx = 1.7$ and $\int_5^8 f(x)\,dx = 2.5$, find $\int_2^5 f(x)\,dx$.

6. If $\int_0^1 f(t)\,dt = 2$, $\int_0^4 f(t)\,dt = -6$, and $\int_3^4 f(t)\,dt = 1$, find $\int_1^3 f(t)\,dt$.

7–12 ■ Use Part 1 of the Fundamental Theorem of Calculus to find the derivative of the function.

7. $g(x) = \int_1^x (t^2 - 1)^{20}\,dt$

8. $g(x) = \int_{-1}^x \sqrt{t^3 + 1}\,dt$

9. $g(u) = \int_\pi^u \dfrac{1}{1 + t^4}\,dt$

10. $g(t) = \int_0^t \sin(x^2)\,dx$

11. $F(x) = \int_x^4 (2 + \sqrt{u})^8\,du$

12. $h(x) = \int_2^{1/x} \sin^4 t\,dt$

13–20 ■ Use Part 2 of the Fundamental Theorem of Calculus to evaluate the integral, or explain why it does not exist.

13. $\int_{-2}^4 (3x - 5)\,dx$

14. $\int_1^2 x^{-2}\,dx$

15. $\int_0^4 \sqrt{x}\,dx$

16. $\int_0^1 x^{3/7}\,dx$

17. $\int_{-1}^4 \pi\,dx$

18. $\int_{-4}^{-1} \sqrt{3}\,dx$

19. $\int_3^6 (4 - 7x)\,dx$

20. $\int_1^4 (2x^2 - 3x + 1)\,dx$

21–22 ■ Find the general indefinite integral.

21. $\int \sqrt{x}(x^2 - 1/x)\,dx$

22. $\int (2x + \sec x \tan x)\,dx$

23–32 ■ Evaluate the indefinite integral.

23. $\int (2x + 1)(x^2 + x + 1)^3\,dx$

24. $\int x^3(1 - x^4)^5\,dx$

25. $\int \sqrt{x - 1}\,dx$

26. $\int \sqrt[3]{1 - x}\,dx$

27. $\int x^3\sqrt{2 + x^4}\,dx$

28. $\int x(x^2 + 1)^{3/2}\,dx$

29. $\int \dfrac{2}{(t + 1)^6}\,dt$

30. $\int \dfrac{1}{(1 - 3t)^4}\,dt$

31. $\int (1 - 2y)^{1.3}\,dy$

32. $\int \sqrt[5]{3 - 5y}\,dy$

33. Show that the area under the graph of $y = \sin\sqrt{x}$ from 0 to 4 is the same as the area under the graph of $y = 2x\sin x$ from 0 to 2.

CHALLENGE

34. In Sections 4.1 and 4.2, we used the formulas for the sums of the kth powers of the first n integers when $k = 1$, 2, and 3. (These formulas are proved in Appendix E.) In this problem we derive formulas for any k. These formulas were first published in 1713 by the Swiss mathematician James Bernoulli in his book *Ars Conjectandi*.

(a) The **Bernoulli polynomials** B_n are defined by

$$B_0(x) = 1, \quad B_n'(x) = B_{n-1}(x), \quad \text{and} \quad \int_0^1 B_n(x)\,dx = 0$$

for $n = 1, 2, 3, \ldots$.

Find $B_n(x)$ for $n = 1$, 2, 3, and 4.

(b) Use the Fundamental Theorem of Calculus to show that $B_n(0) = B_n(1)$ for $n \geq 2$.

(c) If we introduce the **Bernoulli numbers** $b_n = n!\,B_n(0)$, then we can write

$$B_0(x) = b_0$$

$$B_1(x) = \frac{x}{1!} + \frac{b_1}{1!}$$

$$B_2(x) = \frac{x^2}{2!} + \frac{b_1\,x}{1!\,1!} + \frac{b_2}{2!}$$

$$B_3(x) = \frac{x^3}{3!} + \frac{b_1\,x^2}{1!\,2!} + \frac{b_2\,x}{2!\,1!} + \frac{b_3}{3!}$$

and, in general,

$$B_n(x) = \frac{1}{n!}\sum_{k=0}^{n}\binom{n}{k}b_k x^{n-k}$$

where

$$\binom{n}{k} = \frac{n!}{k!\,(n-k)!}$$

[The numbers $\binom{n}{k}$ are the binomial coefficients.] Use part (b) to show that, for $n \geq 2$,

$$b_n = \sum_{k=0}^{n}\binom{n}{k}b_k$$

and therefore

$$b_{n-1} = -\frac{1}{n}\left[\binom{n}{0}b_0 + \binom{n}{1}b_1 + \binom{n}{2}b_2 + \cdots + \binom{n}{n-2}b_{n-2}\right]$$

This gives an efficient way of computing the Bernoulli numbers and therefore the Bernoulli polynomials.

(d) Show that $B_n(1 - x) = (-1)^n B_n(x)$ and deduce that $b_{2n+1} = 0$ for $n > 0$.

(e) Use parts (c) and (d) to calculate b_6 and b_8. Then calculate the polynomials B_5, B_6, B_7, B_8, and B_9.

(f) Graph the Bernoulli polynomials B_1, B_2, $\ldots$, B_9 for $0 \leq x \leq 1$. What pattern do you notice in the graphs?

(g) Use mathematical induction to prove that $B_{k+1}(x + 1) - B_{k+1}(x) = x^k/k!$.

(h) By putting $x = 0, 1, 2, \ldots, n$ in part (g), prove that

$$1^k + 2^k + 3^k + \cdots + n^k$$
$$= k!\left[B_{k+1}(n + 1) - B_{k+1}(0)\right]$$
$$= k!\int_0^{n+1} B_k(x)\,dx$$

(i) Use part (h) with $k = 3$ and the formula for B_4 in part (a) to confirm the formula for the sum of the first n cubes in Section 4.2.

(j) Show that the formula in part (h) can be written symbolically as

$$1^k + 2^k + 3^k + \cdots + n^k$$
$$= \frac{1}{k+1}\left[(n + 1 + b)^{k+1} - b^{k+1}\right]$$

where the expression $(n + 1 + b)^{k+1}$ is to be expanded formally using the Binomial Theorem and each power b^i is to be replaced by the Bernoulli number b_i.

(k) Use part (j) to find a formula for $1^5 + 2^5 + 3^5 + \cdots + n^5$.

4 | ANSWERS TO SELECTED EXERCISES

1. $\displaystyle\int_1^{12} f(x)\,dx$

2. $\displaystyle\int_0^8 f(x)\,dx$

3. $\displaystyle\int_7^{10} f(x)\,dx$

4. $\displaystyle\int_0^6 f(x)\,dx$

5. -0.8

6. -9

7. $g'(x) = (x^2 - 1)^{20}$

8. $g'(x) = \sqrt{x^3 + 1}$

9. $g'(u) = \dfrac{1}{1 + u^4}$

10. $g'(t) = \sin(t^2)$

11. $F'(x) = -(2 + \sqrt{x})^8$

12. $h'(x) = \dfrac{-\sin^4(1/x)}{x^2}$

13. -12

14. $\dfrac{1}{2}$

15. $\dfrac{16}{3}$

16. $\dfrac{7}{10}$

17. 5π

18. $3\sqrt{3}$

19. $-\dfrac{165}{2}$

20. $\dfrac{45}{2}$

21. $\dfrac{2}{7}x^{7/2} - 2x^{1/2} + C$

22. $x^2 + \sec x + C$

23. $\dfrac{1}{4}(x^2 + x + 1)^4 + C$

24. $-\dfrac{1}{24}(1 - x^4)^6 + C$

25. $\dfrac{2}{3}(x - 1)^{3/2} + C$

26. $-\dfrac{3}{4}(1 - x)^{4/3} + C$

27. $\dfrac{1}{6}(2 + x^4)^{3/2} + C$

28. $\dfrac{1}{5}(x^2 + 1)^{5/2} + C$

29. $-\dfrac{2}{5(t + 1)^5} + C$

30. $\dfrac{1}{9(1 - 3t)^3} + C$

31. $-\dfrac{(1 - 2y)^{2.3}}{4.6} + C$

32. $-\dfrac{1}{6}(3 - 5y)^{6/5} + C$

34. (a) $B_1(x) = x - \dfrac{1}{2}$, $B_2(x) = \dfrac{1}{2}x^2 - \dfrac{1}{2}x + \dfrac{1}{12}$,

$$B_3(x) = \frac{1}{6}x^3 - \frac{1}{4}x^2 + \frac{1}{12}x,$$

$$B_4(x) = \frac{1}{24}x^4 - \frac{1}{12}x^3 + \frac{1}{24}x^2 - \frac{1}{720}$$

(e) $b_6 = \dfrac{1}{42}$, $b_8 = -\dfrac{1}{30}$;

$$B_5(x) = \frac{1}{120}\left(x^5 - \frac{5}{2}x^4 + \frac{5}{3}x^3 - \frac{1}{6}x\right),$$

$$B_6(x) = \frac{1}{720}\left(x^6 - 3x^5 + \frac{5}{2}x^4 - \frac{1}{2}x^2 + \frac{1}{42}\right),$$

$$B_7(x) = \frac{1}{5040}\left(x^7 - \frac{7}{2}x^6 + \frac{7}{2}x^5 - \frac{7}{6}x^3 + \frac{1}{6}x\right),$$

$$B_8(x) = \frac{1}{40{,}320}\left(x^8 - 4x^7 + \frac{14}{3}x^6 - \frac{7}{3}x^4 + \frac{2}{3}x^2 - \frac{1}{30}\right),$$

$$B_9(x) = \frac{1}{362{,}880}\left(x^9 - \frac{9}{2}x^8 + 6x^7 - \frac{21}{5}x^5 + 2x^3 - \frac{3}{10}x\right)$$

(f) There are four basic shapes for the graphs of B_n (excluding B_1), and as n increases, they repeat in a cycle of four. For $n = 4m$, the shape resembles that of the graph of $-\cos 2\pi x$; for $n = 4m + 1$, that of $-\sin 2\pi x$; for $n = 4m + 2$, that of $\cos 2\pi x$; and for $n = 4m + 3$, that of $\sin 2\pi x$.

(k) $\dfrac{1}{12}n^2(n + 1)^2(2n^2 + 2n - 1)$

4 | SOLUTIONS TO SELECTED EXERCISES

1. $\displaystyle\int_1^3 f(x)\,dx + \int_3^6 f(x)\,dx + \int_6^{12} f(x)\,dx$

$\displaystyle = \int_1^6 f(x)\,dx + \int_6^{12} f(x)\,dx = \int_1^{12} f(x)\,dx$

2. $\displaystyle\int_5^8 f(x)\,dx + \int_0^5 f(x)\,dx$

$\displaystyle = \int_0^5 f(x)\,dx + \int_5^8 f(x)\,dx = \int_0^8 f(x)\,dx$

3. $\displaystyle\int_2^{10} f(x)\,dx - \int_2^7 f(x)\,dx$

$\displaystyle = \int_2^7 f(x)\,dx + \int_7^{10} f(x)\,dx - \int_2^7 f(x)\,dx$

$\displaystyle = \int_7^{10} f(x)\,dx$

4. $\displaystyle\int_{-3}^5 f(x)\,dx - \int_{-3}^0 f(x)\,dx + \int_5^6 f(x)\,dx$

$\displaystyle = \int_{-3}^0 f(x)\,dx + \int_0^5 f(x)\,dx - \int_{-3}^0 f(x)\,dx$

$\displaystyle \quad + \int_5^6 f(x)\,dx = \int_0^6 f(x)\,dx$

5. $\displaystyle\int_2^5 f(x)\,dx + \int_5^8 f(x)\,dx = \int_2^8 f(x)\,dx \;\Rightarrow$

$\displaystyle\int_2^5 f(x)\,dx + 2.5 = 1.7 \;\Rightarrow\; \int_2^5 f(x)\,dx = -0.8$

6. $\displaystyle\int_0^1 f(t)\,dt + \int_1^3 f(t)\,dt + \int_3^4 f(t)\,dt = \int_0^4 f(t)\,dt$

$\displaystyle \Rightarrow\; 2 + \int_1^3 f(t)\,dt + 1 = -6 \;\Rightarrow$

$\displaystyle\int_1^3 f(t)\,dt = -6 - 2 - 1 = -9$

7. $\displaystyle g(x) = \int_1^x (t^2 - 1)^{20}\,dt \;\Rightarrow\; g'(x) = (x^2 - 1)^{20}$

8. $\displaystyle g(x) = \int_{-1}^x \sqrt{t^3 + 1}\,dt \;\Rightarrow\; g'(x) = \sqrt{x^3 + 1}$

9. $\displaystyle g(u) = \int_\pi^u \frac{1}{1 + t^4}\,dt \;\Rightarrow\; g'(u) = \frac{1}{1 + u^4}$

10. $\displaystyle g(t) = \int_0^t \sin(x^2)\,dx \;\Rightarrow\; g'(t) = \sin(t^2)$

11. $\displaystyle F(x) = \int_x^4 (2 + \sqrt{u})^8\,du$

$\displaystyle = -\int_4^x (2 + \sqrt{u})^8\,du \;\Rightarrow$

$F'(x) = -(2 + \sqrt{x})^8$

12. Let $u = \dfrac{1}{x}$. Then $\dfrac{du}{dx} = -\dfrac{1}{x^2}$, so

$\displaystyle \frac{d}{dx}\int_2^{1/x} \sin^4 t\,dt = \frac{d}{du}\int_2^u \sin^4 t\,dt \cdot \frac{du}{dx}$

$\displaystyle = \sin^4 u\,\frac{du}{dx} = \frac{-\sin^4(1/x)}{x^2}$

13. $\displaystyle\int_{-2}^4 (3x - 5)\,dx = \left(3 \cdot \frac{1}{2}x^2 - 5x\right)\Big|_{-2}^4$

$= (3 \cdot 8 - 5 \cdot 4) - [3 \cdot 2 - (-10)] = -12$

14. $\displaystyle\int_1^2 x^{-2}\,dx = \left[-x^{-1}\right]_1^2 = \left[-1/x\right]_1^2 = -\frac{1}{2} + 1 = \frac{1}{2}$

15. $\displaystyle\int_0^4 \sqrt{x}\,dx = \int_0^4 x^{1/2}\,dx = \left[\frac{x^{3/2}}{3/2}\right]_0^4 = \left[\frac{2x^{3/2}}{3}\right]_0^4$

$\displaystyle = \frac{2(4)^{3/2}}{3} - 0 = \frac{16}{3}$

16. $\displaystyle\int_0^1 x^{3/7}\,dx = \left[\frac{x^{10/7}}{10/7}\right]_0^1 = \left[\frac{7}{10}x^{10/7}\right]_0^1 = \frac{7}{10} - 0 = \frac{7}{10}$

17. $\displaystyle\int_{-1}^4 \pi\,dx = \pi[4 - (-1)] = 5\pi$

18. $\displaystyle\int_{-4}^{-1} \sqrt{3}\,dx = \sqrt{3}(-1 + 4) = 3\sqrt{3}$

19. $\displaystyle\int_3^6 (4 - 7x)\,dx = \int_3^6 4\,dx - \int_3^6 7x\,dx$

$\displaystyle = 4(6 - 3) - 7\int_3^6 x\,dx$

$\displaystyle = 12 - 7 \cdot \frac{1}{2}(6^2 - 3^2)$

$\displaystyle = 12 - \frac{7}{2}(27) = -\frac{165}{2}$

20. $\displaystyle\int_1^4 (2x^2 - 3x + 1)\, dx$

$$= 2\int_1^4 x^2\, dx - 3\int_1^4 x\, dx + \int_1^4 1\, dx$$

$$= 2\cdot\frac{1}{3}(4^3 - 1^3) - 3\cdot\frac{1}{2}(4^2 - 1^2) + 1(4 - 1)$$

$$= \frac{45}{2} = 22.5$$

21. $\displaystyle\int \sqrt{x}(x^2 - 1/x)\, dx = \int (x^{5/2} - x^{-1/2})\, dx$

$$= \frac{2}{7}x^{7/2} - 2x^{1/2} + C$$

22. $\displaystyle\int (2x + \sec x \tan x)\, dx = x^2 + \sec x + C$

23. Let $u = x^2 + x + 1$. Then $du = (2x + 1)\, dx$, so

$$\int (2x + 1)(x^2 + x + 1)^3\, dx = \int u^3\, du$$

$$= \frac{1}{4}u^4 + C$$

$$= \frac{1}{4}(x^2 + x + 1)^4 + C$$

24. Let $u = 1 - x^4$. Then $du = -4x^3\, dx$, so

$$\int x^3(1 - x^4)^5\, dx = \int u^5\left(-\frac{1}{4}\, du\right)$$

$$= -\frac{1}{4}\left(\frac{1}{6}u^6\right) + C$$

$$= -\frac{1}{24}(1 - x^4)^6 + C$$

25. Let $u = x - 1$. Then $du = dx$, so

$$\int \sqrt{x - 1}\, dx = \int u^{1/2}\, du = \frac{2}{3}u^{3/2} + C$$

$$= \frac{2}{3}(x - 1)^{3/2} + C$$

26. Let $u = 1 - x$. Then $du = -dx$, so

$$\int \sqrt[3]{x - 1}\, dx = -\int u^{1/3}\, du = -\frac{3}{4}u^{4/3} + C$$

$$= -\frac{3}{4}(1 - x)^{4/3} + C$$

27. Let $u = 2 + x^4$. Then $du = 4x^3\, dx$, so

$$\int x^3\sqrt{2 + x^4}\, dx = \int u^{1/2}\left(\frac{1}{4}\, du\right)$$

$$= \frac{1}{4}\frac{u^{3/2}}{3/2} + C$$

$$= \frac{1}{6}(2 + x^4)^{3/2} + C$$

28. Let $u = x^2 + 1$. Then $du = 2x\, dx$, so

$$\int x(x^2 + 1)^{3/2}\, dx = \int u^{3/2}\left(\frac{1}{2}\, du\right)$$

$$= \frac{1}{2}\frac{u^{5/2}}{5/2} + C = \frac{1}{5}u^{5/2} + C$$

$$= \frac{1}{5}(x^2 + 1)^{5/2} + C$$

29. Let $u = t + 1$. Then $du = dt$, so

$$\int \frac{2}{(t + 1)^6}\, dt = 2\int u^{-6}\, du = -\frac{2}{5}u^{-5} + C$$

$$= -\frac{2}{5(t + 1)^5} + C$$

30. Let $u = 1 - 3t$. Then $du = -3\, dt$, so

$$\int \frac{1}{(1 - 3t)^4}\, dt = \int u^{-4}\left(-\frac{1}{3}\, du\right)$$

$$= -\frac{1}{3}\left(\frac{u^{-3}}{-3}\right) + C = \frac{1}{9u^3} + C$$

$$= \frac{1}{9(1 - 3t)^3} + C$$

31. Let $u = 1 - 2y$. Then $du = -2\, dy$, so

$$\int (1 - 2y)^{1.3}\, dy = \int u^{1.3}\left(-\frac{1}{2}\, du\right)$$

$$= -\frac{1}{2}\left(\frac{u^{2.3}}{2.3}\right) + C$$

$$= -\frac{(1 - 2y)^{2.3}}{4.6} + C$$

32. Let $u = 3 - 5y$. Then $du = -5\, dy$, so

$$\int \sqrt[5]{3 - 5y}\, dy = \int u^{1/5}\left(-\frac{1}{5}\, du\right)$$

$$= -\frac{1}{5}\cdot\frac{5}{6}u^{6/5} + C$$

$$= -\frac{1}{6}(3 - 5y)^{6/5} + C$$

33. The area under the graph of $y = \sin\sqrt{x}$ from 0 to 4 is $A_1 = \displaystyle\int_0^4 \sin\sqrt{x}\, dx$. The area under the graph of $y = 2x \sin x$ from 0 to 2 is

$$A_2 = \int_0^2 2x \sin x\, dx \begin{bmatrix} u = x^2,\ du = 2x\, dx, \\ \sqrt{u} = x \text{ for } 0 \le x \le 2 \end{bmatrix}$$

$$= \int_0^4 \sin\sqrt{u}\, du$$

Since the integration variable is immaterial, $A_1 = A_2$.

34. (a) To find $B_1(x)$, we use the fact that

$$B_1'(x) = B_0(x) \implies B_1(x) = \int B_0(x)\,dx =$$

$$\int 1\,dx = x + C. \text{ Now we impose the}$$

condition that $\int_0^1 B_1(x)\,dx = 0 \implies$

$$0 = \int_0^1 (x + C)\,dx$$

$$= \left[\frac{1}{2}x^2\right]_0^1 + \left[Cx\right]_0^1 = \frac{1}{2} + C \implies C = -\frac{1}{2}.$$

So $B_1(x) = x - \frac{1}{2}$. Similarly $B_2(x) =$

$$\int B_1(x)\,dx = \int \left(x - \frac{1}{2}\right) dx = \frac{1}{2}x^2 - \frac{1}{2}x + D.$$

But $\int_0^1 B_2(x)\,dx = 0 \implies$

$$0 = \int_0^1 \left(\frac{1}{2}x^2 - \frac{1}{2}x + D\right) dx = \frac{1}{6} - \frac{1}{4} + D \implies$$

$D = \frac{1}{12}$, so $B_2(x) = \frac{1}{2}x^2 - \frac{1}{2}x + \frac{1}{12}$.

$$B_3(x) = \int B_2(x)\,dx = \int \left(\frac{1}{2}x^2 - \frac{1}{2}x + \frac{1}{12}\right) dx$$

$$= \frac{1}{6}x^3 - \frac{1}{4}x^2 + \frac{1}{12}x + E. \text{ But } \int_0^1 B_3(x)\,dx = 0$$

$$\implies \quad 0 = \int_0^1 \left(\frac{1}{6}x^3 - \frac{1}{4}x^2 + \frac{1}{12}x + E\right) dx$$

$$= \frac{1}{24} - \frac{1}{12} + \frac{1}{24} + E \implies E = 0.$$

So $B_3(x) = \frac{1}{6}x^3 - \frac{1}{4}x^2 + \frac{1}{12}x$.

$$B_4(x) = \int B_3(x)\,dx$$

$$= \int \left(\frac{1}{6}x^3 - \frac{1}{4}x^2 + \frac{1}{12}x\right) dx$$

$$= \frac{1}{24}x^4 - \frac{1}{12}x^3 + \frac{1}{24}x^2 + F.$$

But $\int_0^1 B_4(x)\,dx = 0 \implies$

$$0 = \int_0^1 \left(\frac{1}{24}x^4 - \frac{1}{12}x^3 + \frac{1}{24}x^2 + F\right) dx$$

$$= \frac{1}{120} - \frac{1}{48} + \frac{1}{72} + F \implies F = -\frac{1}{720}.$$

So $B_4(x) = \frac{1}{24}x^4 - \frac{1}{12}x^3 + \frac{1}{24}x^2 - \frac{1}{720}$.

(b) By FTC2, $B_n(1) - B_n(0) = \int_0^1 B_n'(x)\,dx$

$$= \int_0^1 B_{n-1}(x)\,dx = 0 \text{ for } n - 1 \geq 1, \text{ by}$$

definition. Thus, $B_n(0) = B_n(1)$ for $n \geq 2$.

(c) We know that $B_n(x) = \frac{1}{n!}\sum_{k=0}^n \binom{n}{k} b_k x^{n-k}$.

If we set $x = 1$ in this expression, and

use the fact that $B_n(1) = B_n(0) = \frac{b_n}{n!}$ for

$n \geq 2$, we get $b_n = \sum_{k=0}^n \binom{n}{k} b_k$. Now if

we expand the right-hand side, we get

$$b_n = \binom{n}{0} b_0 + \binom{n}{1} b_1 + \cdots + \binom{n}{n-2} b_{n-2} +$$

$\binom{n}{n-1} b_{n-1} + \binom{n}{n} b_n$. We cancel the b_n terms,

move the b_{n-1} term to the LHS, and divide

by $-\binom{n}{n-1} = -n$: $b_{n-1} = -\frac{1}{n}\left[\binom{n}{0} b_0 + \right.$

$\left. \binom{n}{1} b_1 + \cdots + \binom{n}{n-2} b_{n-2}\right] \text{ for } n \geq 2,$

as required.

(d) We use mathematical induction. For $n = 0$:
$B_0(1 - x) = 1$ and $(-1)^0 B_0(x) = 1$, so the equation holds for $n = 0$ since $b_0 = 1$.
Now if $B_k(1 - x) = (-1)^k B_k(x)$, then since

$$\frac{d}{dx} B_{k+1}(1 - x) = B_{k+1}'(1 - x)\frac{d}{dx}(1 - x)$$

$= -B_k(1 - x)$, we have $\frac{d}{dx} B_{k+1}(1 - x)$

$= (-1)(-1)^k B_k(x) = (-1)^{k+1} B_k(x)$.
Integrating, we get
$B_{k+1}(1 - x) = (-1)^{k+1} B_{k+1}(x) + C$.
But the constant of integration must be 0, since if we sustitute $x = 0$ in the equation, we get $B_{k+1}(1) = (-1)^{k+1} B_{k+1}(0) + C$, and if we substitute $x = 1$, we get
$B_{k+1}(0) = (-1)^{k+1} B_{k+1}(1) + C$, and these two equations together imply that
$B_{k+1}(0) = (-1)^{k+1}\left[(-1)^{k+1} B_{k+1}(0) + C\right] +$
$C = B_{k+1}(0) + 2C \iff C = 0$. So the equation holds for all n, by induction. Now if the power of -1 is odd, then we have
$B_{2n+1}(1 - x) = -B_{2n+1}(x)$. In particular,
$B_{2n+1}(1) = -B_{2n+1}(0)$. But from part (b), we know that $B_k(1) = B_k(0)$ for $k > 1$. The only possibility is that $B_{2n+1}(0) = B_{2n+1}(1) = 0$ for all $n > 0$, and this implies that
$b_{2n+1} = (2n + 1!) B_{2n+1}(0) = 0$ for $n > 0$.

(e) From part (a), we know that $b_0 = 0!B_0(0) = 1$, and similarly $b_1 = -\dfrac{1}{2}$, $b_2 = \dfrac{1}{6}$, $b_3 = 0$ and $b_4 = -\dfrac{1}{30}$. We use the formula to find

$$b_6 = b_{7-1} = -\frac{1}{7}\left[\binom{7}{0}b_0 + \binom{7}{1}b_1 + \binom{7}{2}b_2 \right.$$
$$\left. + \binom{7}{3}b_3 + \binom{7}{4}b_4 + \binom{7}{5}b_5 \right]$$

The b_3 and b_5 terms are 0, so this is equal to

$$-\frac{1}{7}\left[1 + 7\left(-\frac{1}{2}\right) + \frac{7 \cdot 6}{2 \cdot 1}\left(\frac{1}{6}\right) + \frac{7 \cdot 6 \cdot 5}{3 \cdot 2 \cdot 1}\left(-\frac{1}{30}\right)\right]$$
$$= -\frac{1}{7}\left(1 - \frac{7}{2} + \frac{7}{2} - \frac{7}{6}\right) = \frac{1}{42}$$

Similarly,

$$b_8 = -\frac{1}{9}\left[\binom{9}{0}b_0 + \binom{9}{1}b_1 + \binom{9}{2}b_2 + \binom{9}{4}b_4 + \binom{9}{6}b_6\right]$$
$$= -\frac{1}{9}\left[1 + 9\left(-\frac{1}{2}\right) + \frac{9 \cdot 8}{2 \cdot 1}\left(\frac{1}{6}\right)\right.$$
$$\left. + \frac{9 \cdot 8 \cdot 7 \cdot 6}{4 \cdot 3 \cdot 2 \cdot 1}\left(-\frac{1}{30}\right) + \frac{9 \cdot 8 \cdot 7}{3 \cdot 2 \cdot 1}\left(\frac{1}{42}\right)\right]$$
$$= -\frac{1}{9}\left(1 - \frac{9}{2} + 6 - \frac{21}{5} + 2\right) = -\frac{1}{30}$$

Now we can calculate

$$B_5(x) = \frac{1}{5!}\sum_{k=0}^{5}\binom{5}{k}b_k x^{5-k}$$
$$= \frac{1}{120}\left[x^5 + 5\left(-\frac{1}{2}\right)x^4 + \frac{5 \cdot 4}{2 \cdot 1}\left(\frac{1}{6}\right)x^3 + 5\left(-\frac{1}{30}\right)x\right]$$
$$= \frac{1}{120}\left(x^5 - \frac{5}{2}x^4 + \frac{5}{3}x^3 - \frac{1}{6}x\right)$$

$$B_6(x) = \frac{1}{720}\left[x^6 + 6\left(-\frac{1}{2}\right)x^5 + \frac{6 \cdot 5}{2 \cdot 1}\left(\frac{1}{6}\right)x^4 \right.$$
$$\left. + \frac{6 \cdot 5}{2 \cdot 1}\left(-\frac{1}{30}\right)x^2 + \frac{1}{42}\right]$$
$$= \frac{1}{720}\left(x^6 - 3x^5 + \frac{5}{2}x^4 - \frac{1}{2}x^2 + \frac{1}{42}\right)$$

$$B_7(x) = \frac{1}{5040}\left[x^7 + 7\left(-\frac{1}{2}\right)x^6 + \frac{7 \cdot 6}{2 \cdot 1}\left(\frac{1}{6}\right)x^5 \right.$$
$$\left. + \frac{7 \cdot 6 \cdot 5}{3 \cdot 2 \cdot 1}\left(-\frac{1}{30}\right)x^3 + 7\left(\frac{1}{42}\right)x\right]$$
$$= \frac{1}{5040}\left(x^7 - \frac{7}{2}x^6 + \frac{7}{2}x^5 - \frac{7}{6}x^3 + \frac{1}{6}x\right)$$

$$B_8(x) = \frac{1}{40{,}320}\left[x^8 + 8\left(-\frac{1}{2}\right)x^7 + \frac{8 \cdot 7}{2 \cdot 1}\left(\frac{1}{6}\right)x^6 \right.$$
$$\left. + \frac{8 \cdot 7 \cdot 6 \cdot 5}{4 \cdot 3 \cdot 2 \cdot 1}\left(-\frac{1}{30}\right)x^4 + \frac{8 \cdot 7}{2 \cdot 1}\left(\frac{1}{42}\right)x^2 + \left(-\frac{1}{30}\right)\right]$$
$$= \frac{1}{40{,}320}\left(x^8 - 4x^7 + \frac{14}{3}x^6 - \frac{7}{3}x^4 + \frac{2}{3}x^2 - \frac{1}{30}\right)$$

$$B_9(x) = \frac{1}{362{,}880}\left[x^9 + 9\left(-\frac{1}{2}\right)x^8 + \frac{9 \cdot 8}{2 \cdot 1}\left(\frac{1}{6}\right)x^7 \right.$$
$$\left. + \frac{9 \cdot 8 \cdot 7 \cdot 6}{4 \cdot 3 \cdot 2 \cdot 1}\left(-\frac{1}{30}\right)x^5 + \frac{9 \cdot 8 \cdot 7}{3 \cdot 2 \cdot 1}\left(\frac{1}{42}\right)x^3 + 9\left(-\frac{1}{30}\right)x\right]$$
$$= \frac{1}{362{,}880}\left(x^9 - \frac{9}{2}x^8 + 6x^7 - \frac{21}{5}x^5 + 2x^3 - \frac{3}{10}x\right)$$

(f)

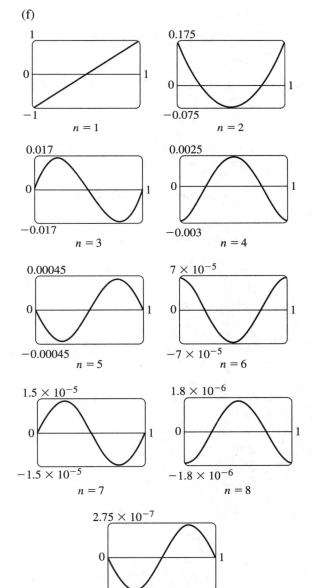

There are four basic shapes for the graphs of B_n (excluding B_1), and as n increases, they repeat in a cycle of four.

For $n = 4m$, the shape resembles that of the graph of $-\cos 2\pi x$; for $n = 4m + 1$, that of $-\sin 2\pi x$; for $n = 4m + 2$, that of $\cos 2\pi x$; and for $n = 4m + 3$, that of $\sin 2\pi x$.

(g) For $k = 0$: $B_1(x + 1) - B_1(x)$

$$= x + 1 - \frac{1}{2} - \left(x - \frac{1}{2}\right) = 1, \text{ and } \frac{x^0}{0!} = 1,$$

so the equation holds for $k = 0$. We now assume that $B_n(x + 1) - B_n(x) = \dfrac{x^{n-1}}{(n-1)!}$.

We integrate this equation with respect to x:

$$\int \left[B_n(x + 1) - B_n(x)\right] dx = \int \frac{x^{n-1}}{(n-1)!} dx.$$

But we can evaluate the LHS using the definition $B_{n+1}(x) = \displaystyle\int B_n(x)\, dx$, and the RHS is a simple integral. The equation becomes

$$B_{n+1}(x + 1) - B_{n+1}(x) = \frac{1}{(n-1)!}\left(\frac{1}{n}x^n\right) = \frac{1}{n!}x^n,$$

since by part (b) $B_{n+1}(1) - B_{n+1}(0) = 0$, and so the constant of integration must vanish. So the equation holds for all k, by induction.

(h) The result from part (g) implies that $p^k = k!\left[B_{k+1}(p + 1) - B_{k+1}(p)\right]$. If we sum both sides of this equation from $p = 0$ to $p = n$ (note that k is fixed in this process), we get

$$\sum_{p=0}^{n} p^k = k! \sum_{p=0}^{n} [B_{k+1}(p + 1) - B_{k+1}(p)].$$

But the RHS is just a telescoping sum, so the equation becomes $1^k + 2^k + 3^k + \cdots + n^k = k!\left[B_{k+1}(n + 1) - B_{k+1}(0)\right]$. But from the definition of Bernoulli polynomials (and using the Fundamental Theorem of Calculus), the RHS is equal to $k!\displaystyle\int_0^{n+1} B_k(x)\, dx$.

(i) If we let $k = 3$ and then substitute from part (a), the formula in part (h) becomes

$$1^3 + 2^3 + \cdots + n^3 = 3!\left[B_4(n + 1) - B_4(0)\right]$$

$$= 6\left[\frac{1}{24}(n + 1)^4 - \frac{1}{12}(n + 1)^3 + \frac{1}{24}(n + 1)^2\right.$$

$$\left. - \frac{1}{720} - \left(\frac{1}{24} - \frac{1}{12} + \frac{1}{24} - \frac{1}{720}\right)\right]$$

$$= \frac{(n + 1)^2\left[1 + (n + 1)^2 - 2(n + 1)\right]}{4}$$

$$= \frac{(n + 1)^2\left[1 - (n + 1)\right]^2}{4}$$

$$= \left[\frac{n(n + 1)}{2}\right]^2$$

(j) $1^k + 2^k + 3^k + \cdots + n^k$

$$= k!\int_0^{n+1} B_k(x)\, dx \quad [\text{by part (h)}]$$

$$= k!\int_0^{n+1} \frac{1}{k!}\sum_{j=0}^{k}\binom{k}{j}b_j x^{k-j}\, dx$$

$$= \int_0^{n+1} \sum_{j=0}^{k}\binom{k}{j}b_j x^{k-j}\, dx$$

Now view $\displaystyle\sum_{j=0}^{k}\binom{k}{j}b_j x^{k-j}$ as $(x + b)^k$, as explained in the problem. Then

$$1^k + 2^k + 3^k + \cdots + n^k = \int_0^{n+1} (x + b)^k\, dx$$

$$= \left[\frac{(x + b)^{k+1}}{k + 1}\right]_0^{n+1} = \frac{(n + 1 + b)^{k+1} - b^{k+1}}{k + 1}$$

(k) We expand the RHS of the formula in (j), turning the b^i into b_i and remembering that $b_{2i+1} = 0$ for $i > 0$:

$$1^5 + 2^5 + \cdots + n^5 = \frac{1}{6}\left[(n + 1)^6 - b^6\right]$$

$$= \frac{1}{6}\left[(n + 1)^6 + 6(n + 1)^5 b_1\right.$$

$$\left. + \frac{6 \cdot 5}{2 \cdot 1}(n + 1)^4 b_2 + \frac{6 \cdot 5}{2 \cdot 1}(n + 1)^2 b_4\right]$$

$$= \frac{1}{6}\left[(n + 1)^6 - 3(n + 1)^5 + \frac{5}{2}(n + 1)^4\right.$$

$$\left. - \frac{1}{2}(n + 1)^2\right]$$

$$= \frac{1}{12}(n + 1)^2\left[2(n + 1)^4 - 6(n + 1)^3\right.$$

$$\left. + 5(n + 1)^2 - 1\right]$$

$$= \frac{1}{12}(n + 1)^2\left[(n + 1) - 1\right]^2\left[2(n + 1)^2\right.$$

$$\left. - 2(n + 1) - 1\right]$$

$$= \frac{1}{12}n^2(n + 1)^2(2n^2 + 2n - 1)$$

5 | APPLICATIONS OF INTEGRATION

1–7 ◾ Sketch the region bounded by the given curves and find the area of the region.

1. $y = x$, $\quad y = x^3$

2. $y = \sqrt{x}$, $\quad y = x/2$

3. $y = \sqrt{x-1}$, $\quad x - 3y + 1 = 0$

4. $y = x^4 - x^2$, $\quad y = 1 - x^2$

5. $y = x^2 + 2$, $\quad y = 2x + 5$, $\quad x = 0$, $\quad x = 6$

6. $x + y^2 = 2$, $\quad x + y = 0$

7. $y = x^2 + 3$, $\quad y = x$, $\quad x = -1$, $\quad x = 1$

8–13 ◾ Find the volume of the solid obtained by rotating the region bounded by the given curves about the x-axis.

8. $y = x^2 - 1$, $\quad y = 0$, $\quad x = 0$, $\quad x = 2$

9. $y = -1/x$, $\quad y = 0$, $\quad x = 1$, $\quad x = 3$

10. $y = \sec x$, $\quad y = 1$, $\quad x = -1$, $\quad x = 1$

11. $y = \cos x$, $\quad y = \sin x$, $\quad x = 0$, $\quad x = \pi/4$

12. $y = |x + 2|$, $\quad y = 0$, $\quad x = -3$, $\quad x = 0$

13. $y = [[x]]$, $\quad x = 1$, $\quad x = 6$, $\quad y = 0$

14–19 ◾ Use the method of cylindrical shells to find the volume of the solid obtained by rotating the region bounded by the given curves about the x-axis.

14. $x = \sqrt[4]{y}$, $\quad x = 0$, $\quad y = 16$

15. $x = y^2$, $\quad x = 0$, $\quad y = 2$, $\quad y = 5$

16. $y = x$, $\quad x = 0$, $\quad x + y = 2$

17. $y = x^2$, $\quad y = 9$

18. $y^2 - 6y + x = 0$, $\quad x = 0$

19. $y = \sqrt{x}$, $\quad y = 0$, $\quad x + y = 2$

20–27 ◾ Find the average value of the function on the given interval.

20. $f(x) = 1 - 2x$, $\quad [0, 3]$

21. $f(x) = x^2 + 2x - 5$, $\quad [-2, 2]$

22. $f(x) = x^3 - x$, $\quad [1, 3]$

23. $f(x) = x^2 - 2x$, $\quad [0, 3]$

24. $f(x) = \sin x$, $\quad [0, \pi]$

25. $f(x) = x^4$, $\quad [-1, 1]$

26. $f(x) = \sin^2 x \cos x$, $\quad [-\pi/2, \pi/4]$

27. $g(x) = \sqrt{x}$, $\quad [1, 4]$

CHALLENGE

28. If n is a positive integer, prove that

$$\int_0^1 (\ln x)^n \, dx = (-1)^n n!$$

29. (a) Evaluate $\int_0^n [[x]] \, dx$, where n is a positive integer.

(b) Evaluate $\int_a^b [[x]] \, dx$, where a and b are real numbers with $0 \le a < b$.

5 | ANSWERS TO SELECTED EXERCISES

1. $\dfrac{1}{2}$ **2.** $\dfrac{4}{3}$ **3.** $\dfrac{1}{6}$ **4.** $\dfrac{8}{5}$ **21.** $-\dfrac{11}{3}$ **22.** 8 **23.** 0

5. 36 **6.** $\dfrac{9}{2}$ **7.** $\dfrac{20}{3}$ **24.** $\dfrac{2}{\pi}$ **25.** $\dfrac{1}{5}$ **26.** $\dfrac{\sqrt{2}+4}{9\pi}$

8. $\dfrac{46}{15}\pi$ **9.** $\dfrac{2}{3}\pi$ **10.** $2\pi(\tan 1 - 1)$ **27.** $\dfrac{14}{9}$

11. $\dfrac{\pi}{2}$ **12.** 3π **13.** 55π **29.** (a) $(n-1)n/2$

14. $\dfrac{4096}{9}\pi$ **15.** $\dfrac{609}{2}\pi$ **16.** $\dfrac{2}{3}\pi$ (b) $\dfrac{1}{2}[[b]](2b - [[b]] - 1) - \dfrac{1}{2}[[a]](2a - [[a]] - 1)$

17. $\dfrac{1944}{5}\pi$ **18.** 216π **19.** $\dfrac{5}{6}\pi$ **20.** -2

5 | SOLUTIONS TO SELECTED EXERCISES

1. $A = \int_{-1}^{0} (x^3 - x)\, dx + \int_{0}^{1} (x - x^3)\, dx$

$\quad = 2\int_{0}^{1} (x - x^3)\, dx = 2\left[\dfrac{1}{2}x^2 - \dfrac{1}{4}x^4\right]_{0}^{1}$

$\quad = 2\left(\dfrac{1}{2} - \dfrac{1}{4}\right) = \dfrac{1}{2}$

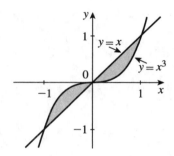

2. $A = \int_{0}^{4}\left(\sqrt{x} - \dfrac{1}{2}x\right)dx = \left[\dfrac{2}{3}x^{3/2} - \dfrac{1}{4}x^2\right]_{0}^{4}$

$\quad = \left(\dfrac{16}{3} - 4\right) - 0 = \dfrac{4}{3}$

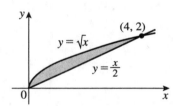

3. $A = \int_{2}^{5}\left(\sqrt{x-1} - \dfrac{1}{3}x - \dfrac{1}{3}\right)dx$

$\quad = \left[\dfrac{2}{3}(x-1)^{3/2} - \dfrac{1}{6}x^2 - \dfrac{1}{3}x\right]_{2}^{5}$

$\quad = \left(\dfrac{16}{3} - \dfrac{25}{6} - \dfrac{5}{3}\right) - \left(\dfrac{2}{3} - \dfrac{4}{6} - \dfrac{2}{3}\right) = \dfrac{1}{6}$

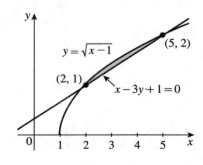

4. $A = \int_{-1}^{1}\left[(1 - x^2) - (x^4 - x^2)\right]dx$

$\quad = 2\int_{0}^{1} (1 - x^4)\, dx = 2\left[x - \dfrac{1}{5}x^5\right]_{0}^{1}$

$\quad = 2\left(1 - \dfrac{1}{5}\right) = \dfrac{8}{5}$

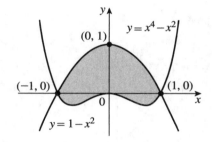

5. $A = \int_{0}^{3}\left[(2x + 5) - (x^2 + 2)\right]dx$

$\quad + \int_{3}^{6}\left[(x^2 + 2) - (2x + 5)\right]dx$

$\quad = \int_{0}^{3} (-x^2 + 2x + 3)\, dx + \int_{3}^{6} (x^2 - 2x - 3)\, dx$

$\quad = \left[-\dfrac{1}{3}x^3 + x^2 + 3x\right]_{0}^{3} + \left[\dfrac{1}{3}x^3 - x^2 - 3x\right]_{3}^{6}$

$\quad = (-9 + 9 + 9) - 0 + (72 - 36 - 18) - (9 - 9 - 9)$

$\quad = 36$

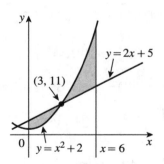

6. $A = \int_{-1}^{2}\left[2 - y^2 - (-y)\right]dy = \int_{-1}^{2} (-y^2 + y + 2)\, dy$

$\quad = \left[-\dfrac{1}{3}y^3 + \dfrac{1}{2}y^2 + 2y\right]_{-1}^{2}$

$\quad = \left(-\dfrac{8}{3} + 2 + 4\right) - \left(\dfrac{1}{3} + \dfrac{1}{2} - 2\right) = \dfrac{9}{2}$

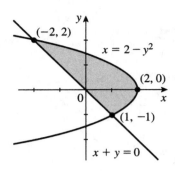

7. $A = \displaystyle\int_{-1}^{1} \left[(x^2 + 3) - x\right] dx = \int_{-1}^{1} (x^2 - x + 3)\, dx$

$= \left[\dfrac{1}{3}x^3 - \dfrac{1}{2}x^2 + 3x\right]_{-1}^{1}$

$= \left(\dfrac{1}{3} - \dfrac{1}{2} + 3\right) - \left(-\dfrac{1}{3} - \dfrac{1}{2} - 3\right) = \dfrac{20}{3}$

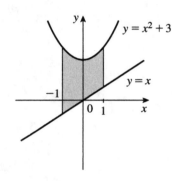

8. $V = \pi \displaystyle\int_{0}^{2} (x^2 - 1)^2\, dx = \pi \int_{0}^{2} (x^4 - 2x^2 + 1)\, dx$

$= \pi \left[\dfrac{1}{5}x^5 - \dfrac{2}{3}x^3 + x\right]_{0}^{2} = \pi \left(\dfrac{32}{5} - \dfrac{16}{3} + 2\right) = \dfrac{46}{15}\pi$

9. $V = \pi \displaystyle\int_{1}^{3} (1/x)^2\, dx = \pi \left[-1/x\right]_{1}^{3} = \pi \left(-\dfrac{1}{3} + 1\right) = \dfrac{2}{3}\pi$

10. $V = \pi \displaystyle\int_{-1}^{1} (\sec^2 x - 1^2)\, dx = \pi \left[\tan x - x\right]_{-1}^{1}$

$= \pi \left[(\tan 1 - 1) - (-\tan 1 + 1)\right] = 2\pi(\tan 1 - 1)$

11. $V = \pi \displaystyle\int_{0}^{\pi/4} (\cos^2 x - \sin^2 x)\, dx$

$= \dfrac{\pi}{2} \displaystyle\int_{0}^{\pi/4} \cos 2x\, (2\, dx) = \dfrac{\pi}{2} \left[\sin 2x\right]_{0}^{\pi/4}$

$= \dfrac{\pi}{2}(1 - 0) = \dfrac{\pi}{2}$

12. $V = \pi \displaystyle\int_{-3}^{-2} (-x - 2)^2\, dx + \pi \int_{-2}^{0} (x + 2)^2\, dx$

$= \pi \displaystyle\int_{-3}^{0} (x + 2)^2\, dx = \left[\dfrac{\pi}{3}(x + 2)^3\right]_{-3}^{0}$

$= \dfrac{\pi}{3}\left[8 - (-1)\right] = 3\pi$

13. $V = \pi \displaystyle\int_{1}^{2} 1^2\, dx + \pi \int_{2}^{3} 2^2\, dx + \pi \int_{3}^{4} 3^2\, dx$

$\qquad + \pi \displaystyle\int_{4}^{5} 4^2\, dx + \pi \int_{5}^{6} 5^2\, dx$

$= \pi \cdot 1 + \pi \cdot 4 + \pi \cdot 9 + \pi \cdot 16 + \pi \cdot 25 = 55\pi$

14. $V = \displaystyle\int_{0}^{16} 2\pi y \sqrt[4]{y}\, dy = 2\pi \int_{0}^{16} y^{5/4}\, dy$

$= 2\pi \left[\dfrac{4}{9}y^{9/4}\right]_{0}^{16} = \dfrac{8}{9}\pi(512 - 0) = \dfrac{4096}{9}\pi$

15. $V = \displaystyle\int_{2}^{5} 2\pi y \cdot y^2\, dy = 2\pi \left[\dfrac{1}{4}y^4\right]_{2}^{5} = \dfrac{\pi}{2}(625 - 16) = \dfrac{609}{2}\pi$

16. $V = \displaystyle\int_{0}^{1} 2\pi y \left[(2 - y) - y\right] dy = 4\pi \int_{0}^{1} y(1 - y)\, dy$

$= 4\pi \left[\dfrac{1}{2}y^2 - \dfrac{1}{3}y^3\right]_{0}^{1} = 4\pi \left(\dfrac{1}{6}\right) = \dfrac{2}{3}\pi$

17. $V = \displaystyle\int_{0}^{9} 2\pi y \cdot 2\sqrt{y}\, dy = 4\pi \int_{0}^{9} y^{3/2}\, dy = 4\pi \left[\dfrac{2}{5}y^{5/2}\right]_{0}^{9}$

$= \dfrac{8}{5}\pi(243 - 0) = \dfrac{1944}{5}\pi$

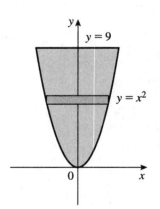
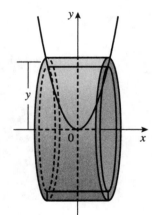

18. The two curves intersect at $(0, 0)$ and $(0, 6)$, so

$$V = \int_0^6 2\pi y \,(-y^2 + 6y)\, dy = 2\pi \left[-\frac{1}{4}y^4 + 2y^3 \right]_0^6$$

$$= 2\pi (-324 + 432) = 216\pi$$

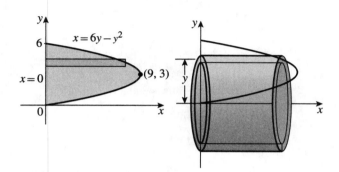

19. $V = \int_0^1 2\pi y \left[(2-y) - y^2 \right] dy = 2\pi \left[y^2 - \frac{1}{3}y^3 - \frac{1}{4}y^4 \right]_0^1$

$$= 2\pi \left(1 - \frac{1}{3} - \frac{1}{4} \right) = \frac{5}{6}\pi$$

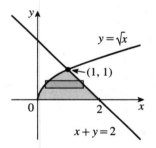

20. $f_{\text{ave}} = \dfrac{1}{3-0} \int_0^3 (1 - 2x)dx = \dfrac{1}{3}(x - x^2)\Big|_0^3$

$$= \frac{1}{3}(3 - 9) = -2$$

21. $f_{\text{ave}} = \dfrac{1}{2-(-2)} \int_{-2}^2 (x^2 + 2x - 5)\, dx$

$$= \frac{1}{4}\left[\frac{1}{3}x^3 + x^2 - 5x \right]_{-2}^2$$

$$= \frac{1}{4}\left[\left(\frac{8}{3} + 4 - 10 \right) - \left(-\frac{8}{3} + 4 + 10 \right) \right] = -\frac{11}{3}$$

22. $f_{\text{ave}} = \dfrac{1}{3-1} \int_1^3 (x^3 - x)\, dx = \dfrac{1}{2}\left[\frac{1}{4}x^4 - \frac{1}{2}x^2 \right]_1^3$

$$= \frac{1}{2}\left[\left(\frac{81}{4} - \frac{9}{2} \right) - \left(\frac{1}{4} - \frac{1}{2} \right) \right] = \frac{1}{2}(16) = 8$$

23. $f_{\text{ave}} = \dfrac{1}{3-0} \int_0^3 (x^2 - 2x)dx = \dfrac{1}{3}\left[\frac{1}{3}x^3 - x^2 \right]_0^3$

$$= \frac{1}{3}(9 - 9) = 0$$

24. $f_{\text{ave}} = \dfrac{1}{\pi - 0} \int_0^\pi \sin x\, dx = \dfrac{1}{\pi}(-\cos x)\Big|_0^\pi$

$$= \frac{1}{\pi}(1 + 1) = \frac{2}{\pi}$$

25. $f_{\text{ave}} = \dfrac{1}{1-(-1)} \int_{-1}^1 x^4\, dx = \dfrac{1}{2} \cdot 2 \int_0^1 x^4\, dx$

$$= \left[\frac{1}{5}x^5 \right]_0^1 = \frac{1}{5}$$

26. $f_{\text{ave}} = \dfrac{1}{\dfrac{\pi}{4} - \left(-\dfrac{\pi}{2} \right)} \int_{-\pi/2}^{\pi/4} \sin^2 x \cos x\, dx$

$$= \frac{4}{3\pi} \int_{-\pi/2}^{\pi/4} \sin^2 x \cos x\, dx$$

$$= \frac{4}{3\pi} \int_{-1}^{1/\sqrt{2}} u^2\, du \ [u = \sin x \Rightarrow du = \cos x\, dx]$$

$$= \frac{4}{3\pi} \left[\frac{1}{3}u^3 \right]_{-1}^{1/\sqrt{2}} = \frac{4}{9\pi}\left(\frac{1}{2\sqrt{2}} + 1 \right)$$

$$= \frac{4}{9\pi}\left(\frac{\sqrt{2}}{4} + 1 \right)$$

$$= \frac{\sqrt{2} + 4}{9\pi}$$

27. $g_{\text{ave}} = \dfrac{1}{4-1} \int_1^4 \sqrt{x}\, dx = \dfrac{1}{3}\left[\frac{2}{3}x^{3/2} \right]_1^4$

$$= \frac{2}{9}\left[x^{3/2} \right]_1^4 = \frac{2}{9}(8 - 1) = \frac{14}{9}$$

28. n is a positive integer, so

$$\int (\ln x)^n\, dx = x(\ln x)^n - \int x \cdot n(\ln x)^{n-1}(dx/x) \text{ [by parts]}$$

$$= x(\ln x)^n - n \int (\ln x)^{n-1} dx$$

Thus,

$$\int_0^1 (\ln x)^n\, dx = \lim_{t \to 0^+} \int_t^1 (\ln x)^n\, dx$$

$$= \lim_{t \to 0^+} \left[x(\ln x)^n \right]_t^1 - n \lim_{t \to 0^+} \int_t^1 (\ln x)^{n-1} dx$$

$$= -\lim_{t \to 0^+} \frac{(\ln t)^n}{1/t} - n \int_0^1 (\ln x)^{n-1}\, dx = -n \int_0^1 (\ln x)^{n-1} dx$$

by repeated application of l'Hospital's Rule. We want to prove that $\int_0^1 (\ln x)^n \, dx = (-1)^n n!$ for every positive integer n. For $n = 1$, we have

$$\int_0^1 (\ln x)^1 \, dx = (-1) \int_0^1 (\ln x)^0 \, dx = -\int_0^1 dx = -1$$

$$\left[\text{or } \int_0^1 \ln x \, dx = \lim_{t \to 0^+} \left[x \ln x - x\right]_t^1 = -1\right]$$

Assuming that the formula holds for n, we find that

$$\int_0^1 (\ln x)^{n+1} \, dx = -(n+1) \int_0^1 (\ln x)^n \, dx$$

$$= -(n+1)(-1)^n n! = (-1)^{n+1}(n+1)!$$

This is the formula for $n + 1$. Thus, the formula holds for all positive integers n by induction.

29. (a) We can split the integral $\int_0^n [\![x]\!] \, dx$ into the sum $\sum_{i=1}^n \left[\int_{i-1}^i [\![x]\!] \, dx\right]$. But on each of the intervals $[i-1, i)$ of integration, $[\![x]\!]$ is a constant function, namely $i-1$. So the ith integral in the sum is equal to $(i-1)\left[i - (i-1)\right] = (i-1)$. So the original integral is equal to $\sum_{i=1}^n (i - 1) = \sum_{i=1}^{n-1} i = \dfrac{(n-1)n}{2}$.

(b) We can write

$$\int_a^b [\![x]\!] \, dx = \int_0^b [\![x]\!] \, dx - \int_0^a [\![x]\!] \, dx.$$

Now $\int_0^b [\![x]\!] \, dx = \int_0^{[\![b]\!]} [\![x]\!] \, dx + \int_{[\![b]\!]}^b [\![x]\!] \, dx$. The first of these integrals is equal to $\dfrac{1}{2}([\![b]\!]-1)[\![b]\!]$, by part (a), and since $[\![x]\!] = [\![b]\!]$ on $\left[[\![b]\!], b\right]$, the second integral is just $[\![b]\!](b - [\![b]\!])$. So

$$\int_0^b [\![x]\!] \, dx = \frac{1}{2}([\![b]\!] - 1)[\![b]\!] + [\![b]\!](b - [\![b]\!])$$

$$= \frac{1}{2}[\![b]\!](2b - [\![b]\!] - 1) \text{ and similarly } \int_0^a [\![x]\!] \, dx$$

$$= \frac{1}{2}[\![a]\!](2a - [\![a]\!] - 1). \text{ Therefore, } \int_a^b [\![x]\!] \, dx$$

$$= \frac{1}{2}[\![b]\!](2b - [\![b]\!] - 1) - \frac{1}{2}[\![a]\!](2a - [\![a]\!] - 1).$$

6

INVERSE FUNCTIONS: EXPONENTIAL, LOGARITHMIC, AND INVERSE TRIGONOMETRIC FUNCTIONS

1–16 ■ Differentiate the function.

1. $y = e^{-mx}$

2. $g(x) = e^{-5x} \cos 3x$

3. $f(x) = e^{\sqrt{x}}$

4. $h(t) = \sqrt{1 - e^t}$

5. $h(\theta) = e^{\sin 5\theta}$

6. $y = e^{x \cos x}$

7. $y = \dfrac{e^{3x}}{1 + e^x}$

8. $f(x) = xe^{-x^2}$

9. $y = xe^{2x}$

10. $y = \dfrac{e^{-x^2}}{x}$

11. $y = e^{-1/x}$

12. $y = e^{x + e^x}$

13. $y = \tan(e^{3x-2})$

14. $y = \sqrt[3]{2x + e^{3x}}$

15. $y = x^e$

16. $y = \sec(e^{\tan x^2})$

17–19 ■ Find an equation of the tangent line to the curve at the given point.

17. $y = \ln \ln x$, $(e, 0)$

18. $y = \ln(x^2 + 1)$, $(1, \ln 2)$

19. $y = \sin(\ln x)$, $(1, 0)$

20–25 ■ Solve the equation for x.

20. $e^x = 16$

21. $\ln x = -1$

22. $\ln(2x - 1) = 3$

23. $e^{3x-4} = 2$

24. $\log_2 x = 3$

25. $2^{x-5} = 3$

26–29 ■ Find the limit.

26. $\lim\limits_{x \to 5^+} \ln(x - 5)$

27. $\lim\limits_{x \to 0^+} \log_{10}(4x)$

28. $\lim\limits_{x \to \infty} \log_2(x^2 - x)$

29. $\lim\limits_{x \to \infty} \ln(1 + x^2)$

30. For what values of r does the function $y = e^{rx}$ satisfy the equation $y'' + 5y' - 6y = 0$?

31. On what interval is the curve $y = e^x - 2e^{-x}$ concave upward?

32. On what interval is the function $f(x) = e^x + e^{-2x}$ increasing?

33–40 ■ Differentiate the function.

33. $y = \dfrac{\ln x}{1 + x^2}$

34. $y = \ln(x\sqrt{1 - x^2} \sin x)$

35. $y = \ln|\tan 2x|$

36. $G(x) = 5^{\tan x}$

37. $f(t) = \pi^{-t}$

38. $g(x) = 1.6^x + x^{1.6}$

39. $g(t) = \sin(\ln t)$

40. $k(r) = r \sin r \ln r$

41–46 ■ Find the derivative of the function. Simplify where possible.

41. $f(x) = \sin^{-1}(2x - 1)$

42. $g(x) = \tan^{-1}(x^3)$

43. $h(x) = (\arcsin x) \ln x$

44. $f(t) = (\cos^{-1} t)/t$

45. $F(t) = \sqrt{1 - t^2} + \sin^{-1} t$

46. $G(t) = \cos^{-1}\sqrt{2t - 1}$

47–48 Prove the identity.

47. $\sinh \dfrac{x}{2} = \pm\sqrt{\dfrac{\cosh x - 1}{2}}$

48. $\cosh \dfrac{x}{2} = \sqrt{\dfrac{\cosh x + 1}{2}}$

49–53 ■ Find the limit. Use l'Hospital's Rule where appropriate. If there is a more elementary method, use it. If l'Hospital's Rule doesn't apply, explain why.

49. $\lim\limits_{x \to 0^+} (\sin x)^{\tan x}$

50. $\lim\limits_{x \to \infty} \left(1 + \dfrac{1}{x^2}\right)^x$

51. $\lim\limits_{x \to 0^+} (\cot x)^{\sin x}$

52. $\lim\limits_{x \to \infty} \left(1 + \dfrac{1}{x}\right)^{x^2}$

53. $\lim\limits_{x \to 0^-} (-\ln x)^x$

54. The **Chebyshev polynomials** T_n are defined by
$T_n(x) = \cos(n \arccos x)$, $n = 0, 1, 2, 3, \ldots$.

(a) What are the domain and range of these functions?

(b) We know that $T_0(x) = 1$ and $T_1(x) = x$. Express T_2 explicitly as a quadratic polynomial and T_3 as a cubic polynomial.

(c) Show that, for $n \geq 1$, $T_{n+1}(x) = 2xT_n(x) - T_{n-1}(x)$.

(d) Use part (c) to show that T_n is a polynomial of degree n.

(e) Use parts (b) and (c) to express T_4, T_5, T_6, and T_7 explicitly as polynomials.

(f) What are the zeros of T_n? At what numbers does T_n have local maximum and minimum values?

(g) Graph T_2, T_3, T_4, and T_5 on a common screen.

(h) Graph T_5, T_6, and T_7 on a common screen.

(i) Based on your observations from parts (g) and (h), how are the zeros of T_n related to the zeros of T_{n+1}? What about the x-coordinates of the maximum and minimum values?

(j) Based on your graphs in parts (g) and (h), what can you say about $\int_{-1}^{1} T_n(x)\,dx$ when n is odd and when n is even?

(k) Use the substitution $u = \arccos x$ to evaluate the integral in part (j).

(l) The family of functions $f(x) = \cos(c \arccos x)$ are defined even when c is not an integer (but then f is not a polynomial). Describe how the graph of f changes as c increases.

6 | ANSWERS TO SELECTED EXERCISES

1. $y' = -me^{-mx}$

2. $g'(x) = -5e^{-5x}\cos 3x - 3e^{-5x}\sin 3x$

3. $f'(x) = e^{\sqrt{x}}/(2\sqrt{x})$

4. $h'(t) = -e^t/(2\sqrt{1-e^t})$

5. $h'(\theta) = 5\cos(5\theta)\,e^{\sin 5\theta}$

6. $y' = e^{x\cos x}(\cos x - x\sin x)$

7. $y' = \dfrac{3e^{3x} + 2e^{4x}}{(1+e^x)^2}$

8. $f'(x) = e^{-x^2}(1-2x^2)$

9. $y' = e^{2x}(1+2x)$

10. $y' = \dfrac{e^{-x^2}(-2x^2-1)}{x^2}$

11. $y' = e^{-1/x}/x^2$

12. $y' = e^{x+e^x}(1+e^x)$

13. $y' = 3e^{3x-2}\sec^2(e^{3x-2})$

14. $y' = \frac{1}{3}(2+3e^{3x})(2x+e^{3x})^{-2/3}$

15. $y' = ex^{e-1}$

16. $y' = 2xe^{\tan x^2}\sec^2(x^2)\sec(e^{\tan x^2})\tan(e^{\tan x^2})$

17. $y = \dfrac{1}{e}x - 1$ **18.** $y = x + \ln 2 - 1$

19. $y = x - 1$ **20.** $x = 4\ln 2$

21. $x = 1/e$ **22.** $x = \frac{1}{2}(e^3+1)$

23. $x = \frac{1}{3}(\ln 2 + 4)$ **24.** $x = 8$

25. $x = 5 + \dfrac{\ln 3}{\ln 2}$ **26.** $-\infty$

27. $-\infty$ **28.** ∞

29. ∞ **30.** $1, -6$

31. $\left(\frac{1}{2}\ln 2, \infty\right)$ **32.** $\left(\frac{1}{3}\ln 2, \infty\right)$

33. $y' = \dfrac{1 + x^2 - 2x^2\ln x}{x(1+x^2)^2}$

34. $y' = \dfrac{1}{x} - \dfrac{x}{1-x^2} + \cot x$

35. $y' = \dfrac{2\sec^2 2x}{\tan 2x}$

36. $G'(x) = 5^{\tan x}(\ln 5)\sec^2 x$

37. $f'(t) = -\pi^{-t}\ln \pi$

38. $g'(x) = 1.6^x\ln(1.6) + 1.6x^{0.6}$

39. $g'(t) = \dfrac{\cos(\ln t)}{t}$

40. $k'(r) = \sin r \ln r + r\cos r\ln r + \sin r$

41. $f'(x) = \dfrac{1}{\sqrt{x - x^2}}$

42. $g'(x) = \dfrac{3x^2}{1+x^6}$

43. $h'(x) = \dfrac{\ln x}{\sqrt{1-x^2}} + \dfrac{\arcsin x}{x}$

44. $f'(t) = -\dfrac{\cos^{-1} t}{t^2} - \dfrac{1}{t\sqrt{1-t^2}}$

45. $F'(t) = \dfrac{1-t}{\sqrt{1-t^2}}$

46. $G'(t) = -\dfrac{1}{\sqrt{2(-2t^2 + 3t - 1)}}$

49. 1 **50.** 1 **51.** 1 **52.** ∞ **53.** 1

54. (a) $[-1, 1]$; $[-1, 1]$ for $n > 0$

(b) $T_2(x) = 2x^2 - 1$, $T_3(x) = 4x^3 - 3x$

(e) $T_4(x) = 8x^4 - 8x^2 + 1$, $T_5(x) = 16x^5 - 20x^3 + 5x$,
$T_6(x) = 32x^6 - 48x^4 + 18x^2 - 1$,
$T_7(x) = 64x^7 - 112x^5 + 56x^3 - 7x$

(f) $x = \cos\dfrac{k\pi + \frac{\pi}{2}}{n}$, k an integer with $0 \le k < n$;
$x = \cos(k\pi/n)$, k an integer with $0 < k < n$

(g)

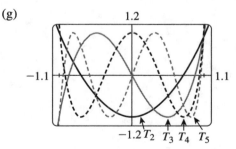

(h)

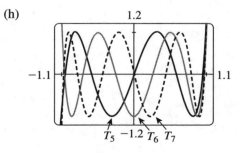

(i) The zeros of T_n and T_{n+1} alternate; the extrema also alternate.

(j) When n is odd, $\int_{-1}^{1} T_n(x)\,dx = 0$; when n is even, the integral is negative but decreases in absolute value as n gets larger.

(k) $\int_0^{\pi} \cos(nu)\sin u\,du = \begin{cases} -\frac{2}{n^2-1} & \text{if } n \text{ is even} \\ 0 & \text{if } n \text{ is odd} \end{cases}$

(l) As c increases through an integer, the graph of f gains a local extremum, which starts at $x = -1$ and moves rightward, compressing the graph of f as c continues to increase.

6 | SOLUTIONS TO SELECTED EXERCISES

1. $y = e^{-mx}$ $\Rightarrow$

$$y' = e^{-mx}\frac{d}{dx}(-mx) = e^{-mx}(-m) = -me^{-mx}$$

2. $g(x) = e^{-5x}\cos 3x$ $\Rightarrow$

$$g'(x) = -5e^{-5x}\cos 3x - 3e^{-5x}\sin 3x$$

3. $f(x) = e^{\sqrt{x}}$ $\Rightarrow$ $f'(x) = e^{\sqrt{x}}/(2\sqrt{x})$

4. $h(t) = \sqrt{1-e^t}$ $\Rightarrow$ $h'(t) = -e^t/(2\sqrt{1-e^t})$

5. $h(\theta) = e^{\sin 5\theta}$ $\Rightarrow$ $h'(\theta) = 5\cos(5\theta)\,e^{\sin 5\theta}$

6. $y = e^{x\cos x}$ $\Rightarrow$ $y' = e^{x\cos x}(\cos x - x\sin x)$

7. $y = \dfrac{e^{3x}}{1+e^x}$ $\Rightarrow$

$$y' = \frac{3e^{3x}(1+e^x) - e^{3x}(e^x)}{(1+e^x)^2}$$

$$= \frac{3e^{3x} + 3e^{4x} - e^{4x}}{(1+e^x)^2} = \frac{3e^{3x} + 2e^{4x}}{(1+e^x)^2}$$

8. $f(x) = xe^{-x^2}$ $\Rightarrow$
$$f'(x) = e^{-x^2} + xe^{-x^2}(-2x) = e^{-x^2}(1-2x^2)$$

9. $y = xe^{2x}$ $\Rightarrow$ $y' = e^{2x} + xe^{2x}(2) = e^{2x}(1+2x)$

10. $y = \dfrac{e^{-x^2}}{x}$ $\Rightarrow$

$$y' = \frac{xe^{-x^2}(-2x) - e^{-x^2}}{x^2} = \frac{e^{-x^2}(-2x^2-1)}{x^2}$$

11. $y = e^{-1/x}$ $\Rightarrow$ $y' = e^{-1/x}/x^2$

12. $y = e^{x+e^x}$ $\Rightarrow$ $y' = e^{x+e^x}(1+e^x)$

13. $y = \tan(e^{3x-2})$ $\Rightarrow$ $y' = 3e^{3x-2}\sec^2(e^{3x-2})$

14. $y = (2x+e^{3x})^{1/3}$ $\Rightarrow$

$$y' = \tfrac{1}{3}(2+3e^{3x})(2x+e^{3x})^{-2/3}$$

15. $y = x^e$ $\Rightarrow$ $y' = ex^{e-1}$

16. $y = \sec\left(e^{\tan x^2}\right)$ $\Rightarrow$

$$y' = \sec\left(e^{\tan x^2}\right)\tan\left(e^{\tan x^2}\right)\left(e^{\tan x^2}\right)\left[\sec^2(x^2)\right](2x)$$

$$= 2xe^{\tan x^2}\sec^2(x^2)\sec\left(e^{\tan x^2}\right)\tan\left(e^{\tan x^2}\right)$$

17. $y = f(x) = \ln\ln x$ $\Rightarrow$ $f'(x) = \dfrac{1}{\ln x}\left(\dfrac{1}{x}\right)$ $\Rightarrow$

$f'(e) = \dfrac{1}{e}$, so an equation of the tangent line at $(e, 0)$

is $y - 0 = \dfrac{1}{e}(x-e)$, or $y = \dfrac{1}{e}x - 1$, or $x - ey = e$.

18. $y = f(x) = \ln(x^2+1)$ $\Rightarrow$

$$f'(x) = \frac{1}{x^2+1}\cdot 2x = \frac{2x}{x^2+1} \quad \Rightarrow \quad f'(1) = 1,$$

so an equation of the tangent line at $(1, \ln 2)$ is
$y - \ln 2 = 1(x-1)$, or $y = x + \ln 2 - 1$.

19. $y = f(x) = \sin(\ln x)$ $\Rightarrow$

$f'(x) = \cos(\ln x)(1/x)$ $\Rightarrow$

$f'(1) = (\cos 0)\left(\tfrac{1}{1}\right) = 1$, so the equation of the tangent

at $(1, 0)$ is $y - 0 = 1(x-1)$ $\Leftrightarrow$ $y = x - 1$.

20. $e^x = 16$ $\Leftrightarrow$ $\ln e^x = \ln 16$ $\Leftrightarrow$
$x = \ln 16 = \ln 2^4 = 4\ln 2$

21. $\ln x = -1$ $\Leftrightarrow$ $e^{\ln x} = e^{-1}$ $\Leftrightarrow$ $x = 1/e$

22. $\ln(2x-1) = 3$ $\Leftrightarrow$ $e^{\ln(2x-1)} = e^3$ $\Leftrightarrow$

$$2x - 1 = e^3 \quad \Leftrightarrow \quad x = \frac{1}{2}(e^3+1)$$

23. $e^{3x-4} = 2$ $\Leftrightarrow$ $\ln(e^{3x-4}) = \ln 2$ $\Leftrightarrow$
$3x - 4 = \ln 2$ $\Leftrightarrow$ $x = \tfrac{1}{3}(\ln 2 + 4)$

24. $\log_2 x = 3$ $\Leftrightarrow$ $x = 2^3 = 8$

25. $2^{x-5} = 3$ $\Leftrightarrow$ $\log_2 3 = x - 5$ $\Leftrightarrow$ $x = 5 + \log_2 3$

Or: $2^{x-5} = 3$ $\Leftrightarrow$ $\ln(2^{x-5}) = \ln 3$ $\Leftrightarrow$

$(x-5)\ln 2 = \ln 3$ $\Leftrightarrow$ $x - 5 = \dfrac{\ln 3}{\ln 2}$ $\Leftrightarrow$

$x = 5 + \dfrac{\ln 3}{\ln 2}$

26. $\lim\limits_{x\to 5^+}\ln(x-5) = -\infty$ since $x - 5 \to 0^+$ as $x \to 5^+$.

27. $\lim\limits_{x\to 0^+}\log_{10}(4x) = -\infty$ since $4x \to 0^+$ as $x \to 0^+$.

28. $\lim\limits_{x\to\infty}\log_2(x^2-x) = \infty$ since $x^2 - x \to \infty$ as $x \to \infty$.

29. Let $t = 1 + x^2$. As $x \to \infty$, $t \to \infty$.

$\lim\limits_{x\to\infty}\ln(1+x^2) = \lim\limits_{t\to\infty}\ln t = \infty$ by (8).

30. $y = e^{rx}$ $\Rightarrow$ $y' = re^{rx}$ $\Rightarrow$ $y'' = r^2e^{rx}$,
so $y'' + 5y' - 6y = r^2e^{rx} + 5re^{rx} - 6e^{rx} =$
$e^{rx}(r^2 + 5r - 6) = e^{rx}(r+6)(r-1) = 0$ $\Rightarrow$
$(r+6)(r-1) = 0$ $\Rightarrow$ $r = 1$ or -6.

31. $y = e^x - 2e^{-x}$, so $y' = e^x + 2e^{-x}$, $y'' = e^x - 2e^{-x}$,
$y'' > 0$ $\Leftrightarrow$ $e^x - 2e^{-x} > 0$ $\Leftrightarrow$
$e^x > 2e^{-x}$ $\Leftrightarrow$ $e^{2x} > 2$ $\Leftrightarrow$
$2x > \ln 2$ $\Leftrightarrow$ $x > \tfrac{1}{2}\ln 2$. Therefore, y is concave
upward on $\left(\tfrac{1}{2}\ln 2, \infty\right)$.

32. $f(x) = e^x + e^{-2x}$, $f'(x) = e^x - 2e^{-2x} > 0$ $\Leftrightarrow$
$e^x > 2e^{-2x}$ $\Leftrightarrow$ $e^{3x} > 2$ $\Leftrightarrow$ $3x > \ln 2$ $\Leftrightarrow$
$x > \tfrac{1}{3}\ln 2$. Thus, f is increasing on $\left(\tfrac{1}{3}\ln 2, \infty\right)$.

33. $y = \dfrac{\ln x}{1+x^2}$ $\Rightarrow$

$$y' = \frac{(1+x^2)(1/x) - 2x\ln x}{(1+x^2)^2} = \frac{1 + x^2 - 2x^2\ln x}{x(1+x^2)^2}$$

34. $y = \ln(x\sqrt{1-x^2}\sin x)$

$\quad = \ln x + \frac{1}{2}\ln(1-x^2) + \ln\sin x \implies$

$y' = \frac{1}{x} + \frac{1}{2}\left(\frac{-2x}{1-x^2}\right) + \frac{\cos x}{\sin x} = \frac{1}{x} - \frac{x}{1-x^2} + \cot x$

35. $y = \ln|\tan 2x| \implies y' = \dfrac{2\sec^2 2x}{\tan 2x}$

36. $G(x) = 5^{\tan x} \implies G'(x) = 5^{\tan x}(\ln 5)\sec^2 x$

37. $f(t) = \pi^{-t} \implies$
$f'(t) = \pi^{-t}(\ln\pi)(-1) = -\pi^{-t}\ln\pi$

38. $g(x) = 1.6^x + x^{1.6} \implies$
$g'(x) = 1.6^x\ln(1.6) + 1.6x^{0.6}$

39. $g(t) = \sin(\ln t) \implies g'(t) = \dfrac{\cos(\ln t)}{t}$

40. $k(r) = r\sin r\ln r \implies$
$k'(r) = \sin r\ln r + r\cos r\ln r + \sin r$

41. $f(x) = \sin^{-1}(2x-1) \implies$
$f'(x) = \dfrac{1}{\sqrt{1-(2x-1)^2}}(2) = \dfrac{1}{\sqrt{x-x^2}}$

42. $g(x) = \tan^{-1}(x^3) \implies$
$g'(x) = \dfrac{1}{1+(x^3)^2}(3x^2) = \dfrac{3x^2}{1+x^6}$

43. $h(x) = (\arcsin x)\ln x \implies$
$h'(x) = \dfrac{\ln x}{\sqrt{1-x^2}} + \dfrac{\arcsin x}{x}$

44. $f(t) = \dfrac{\cos^{-1}t}{t} \implies$

$f'(t) = \dfrac{t(-1/\sqrt{1-t^2}) - \cos^{-1}t}{t^2}$

$\quad = -\dfrac{\cos^{-1}t}{t^2} - \dfrac{1}{t\sqrt{1-t^2}}$

45. $F(t) = \sqrt{1-t^2} + \sin^{-1}t \implies$
$F'(t) = \dfrac{-2t}{2\sqrt{1-t^2}} + \dfrac{1}{\sqrt{1-t^2}} = \dfrac{1-t}{\sqrt{1-t^2}}$

46. $G(t) = \cos^{-1}\sqrt{2t-1} \implies$

$G'(t) = -\dfrac{1}{\sqrt{1-(2t-1)}}\dfrac{2}{2\sqrt{2t-1}}$

$\quad = -\dfrac{1}{\sqrt{2(-2t^2+3t-1)}}$

47. $\cosh 2y = \cosh^2 y + \sinh^2 y = 1 + 2\sinh^2 y \implies$

$\sinh^2 y = \dfrac{\cosh 2y - 1}{2}$. Put $x = 2y$. Then

$\sinh\dfrac{x}{2} = \pm\sqrt{\dfrac{\cosh x - 1}{2}}$.

48. $\cosh 2y = \cosh^2 y + \sinh^2 y = 2\cosh^2 y - 1 \implies$

$\cosh^2 y = \dfrac{\cosh 2y + 1}{2} \implies \cosh y = \sqrt{\dfrac{\cosh 2y + 1}{2}}$

(since $\cosh y > 0$). Put $x = 2y$. Then

$\cosh\dfrac{x}{2} = \sqrt{\dfrac{\cosh x + 1}{2}}$.

49. $y = (\sin x)^{\tan x} \implies \ln y = \tan x\ln(\sin x)$, so

$\lim_{x\to 0^+}\ln y = \lim_{x\to 0^+}\tan x\ln(\sin x) = \lim_{x\to 0^+}\dfrac{\ln(\sin x)}{\cot x}$

$\overset{H}{=}\lim_{x\to 0^+}\dfrac{(\cos x)/\sin x}{-\csc^2 x}$

$= \lim_{x\to 0^+}(-\sin x\cos x) = 0 \implies$

$\lim_{x\to 0^+}(\sin x)^{\tan x} = \lim_{x\to 0^+}e^{\ln y} = e^0 = 1$.

50. Let $y = \left(1 + \dfrac{1}{x^2}\right)^x$. Then $\ln y = x\ln\left(1 + \dfrac{1}{x^2}\right) \implies$

$\lim_{x\to\infty}\ln y = \lim_{x\to\infty}x\ln\left(1 + \dfrac{1}{x^2}\right) = \lim_{x\to\infty}\dfrac{\ln\left(1 + \dfrac{1}{x^2}\right)}{1/x}$

$\overset{H}{=}\lim_{x\to\infty}\dfrac{\left(-\dfrac{2}{x^3}\right)\Big/\left(1 + \dfrac{1}{x^2}\right)}{-1/x^2}$

$= \lim_{x\to\infty}\dfrac{2/x}{1 + 1/x^2} = 0$,

so $\lim_{x\to\infty}(1 + 1/x^2)^x = \lim_{x\to\infty}e^{\ln y} = e^0 = 1$.

51. $y = (\cot x)^{\sin x} \implies \ln y = \sin x\ln(\cot x) \implies$

$\lim_{x\to 0^+}\ln y = \lim_{x\to 0^+}\dfrac{\ln(\cot x)}{\csc x} \overset{H}{=}\lim_{x\to 0^+}\dfrac{(-\csc^2 x)/\cot x}{-\csc x\cot x}$

$= \lim_{x\to 0^+}\dfrac{\csc x}{\cot^2 x} = \lim_{x\to 0^+}\dfrac{\sin x}{\cos^2 x} = 0$,

so $\lim_{x\to 0^+}(\cot x)^{\sin x} = \lim_{x\to 0^+}e^{\ln y} = e^0 = 1$.

52. Let $y = (1 + 1/x)^{x^2}$. Then $\ln y = x^2\ln(1 + 1/x) \implies$

$\lim_{x\to\infty}\ln y = \lim_{x\to\infty}x^2\ln(1 + 1/x) = \lim_{x\to\infty}\dfrac{\ln(1 + 1/x)}{1/x^2}$

$\overset{H}{=}\lim_{x\to\infty}\dfrac{(-1/x^2)/(1 + 1/x)}{-2/x^3}$

$= \lim_{x\to\infty}\dfrac{x}{2(1 + 1/x)} = \infty \implies$

$\lim_{x\to\infty}(1 + 1/x)^{x^2} = \lim_{x\to\infty}e^{\ln y} = \infty$.

53. $y = (-\ln x)^x \implies \ln y = x\ln(-\ln x)$, so

$\lim_{x\to 0^+}\ln y = \lim_{x\to 0^+}x\ln(-\ln x) = \lim_{x\to 0^+}\dfrac{\ln(-\ln x)}{1/x}$

$\overset{H}{=}\lim_{x\to 0^+}\dfrac{(1/-\ln x)(-1/x)}{-1/x^2}$

$= \lim_{x\to 0^+}\dfrac{-x}{\ln x} = 0 \implies$

$\lim_{x\to 0^+}(-\ln x)^x = e^0 = 1$.

54. (a) $T_n(x) = \cos(n\arccos x)$. The domain of arccos is $[-1, 1]$, and the domain of cos is $\mathbb{R}$, so the domain of $T_n(x)$ is $[-1, 1]$. As for the range, $T_0(x) = \cos 0 = 1$, so the range of $T_0(x)$ is $\{1\}$. But since the range of $n\arccos x$ is at least $[0, \pi]$ for $n > 0$, and since $\cos y$ takes on all values in $[-1, 1]$ for $y \in [0, \pi]$, the range of $T_n(x)$ is $[-1, 1]$ for $n > 0$.

(b) Using the usual trigonometric identities, $T_2(x) = \cos(2\arccos x)$
$= 2[\cos(\arccos x)]^2 - 1 = 2x^2 - 1$, and

$$T_3(x) = \cos(3\arccos x)$$
$$= \cos(\arccos x + 2\arccos x)$$
$$= \cos(\arccos x)\cos(2\arccos x)$$
$$\quad - \sin(\arccos x)\sin(2\arccos x)$$
$$= x(2x^2 - 1)$$
$$\quad - \sin(\arccos x)[2\sin(\arccos x)\cos(\arccos x)]$$
$$= 2x^3 - x - 2[\sin^2(\arccos x)]x$$
$$= 2x^3 - x - 2x[1 - \cos^2(\arccos x)]$$
$$= 2x^3 - x - 2x(1 - x^2) = 4x^3 - 3x.$$

(c) Let $y = \arccos x$. Then

$$T_{n+1}(x) = \cos[(n+1)y]$$
$$= \cos(y + ny)$$
$$= \cos y \cos ny - \sin y \sin ny$$
$$= 2\cos y \cos ny - (\cos y \cos ny$$
$$\quad + \sin y \sin ny)$$
$$= 2xT_n(x) - \cos(ny - y)$$
$$= 2xT_n(x) - T_{n-1}(x).$$

(d) Here we use induction. $T_0(x) = 1$, a polynomial of degree 0. Now assume that $T_k(x)$ is a polynomial of degree k. Then $T_{k+1}(x) = 2xT_k(x) - T_{k-1}(x)$. By assumption, the leading term of T_k is $a_k x^k$, say, so the leading term of T_{k+1} is $2xa_k x^k = 2a_k x^{k+1}$, and so T_{k+1} has degree $k + 1$.

(e) $T_4(x) = 2xT_3(x) - T_2(x) = 2x(4x^3 - 3x) - (2x^2 - 1)$
$\quad = 8x^4 - 8x^2 + 1$,

$T_5(x) = 2xT_4(x) - T_3(x)$
$\quad = 2x(8x^4 - 8x^2 + 1) - (4x^3 - 3x)$
$\quad = 16x^5 - 20x^3 + 5x$,

$T_6(x) = 2xT_5(x) - T_4(x)$
$\quad = 2x(16x^5 - 20x^3 + 5x) - (8x^4 - 8x^2 + 1)$
$\quad = 32x^6 - 48x^4 + 18x^2 - 1$,

$T_7(x) = 2xT_6(x) - T_5(x)$
$\quad = 2x(32x^6 - 48x^4 + 18x^2 - 1)$
$\quad\quad - (16x^5 - 20x^3 + 5x)$
$\quad = 64x^7 - 112x^5 + 56x^3 - 7x$.

(f) The zeros of $T_n(x) = \cos(n\arccos x)$ occur when $n\arccos x = k\pi + \frac{\pi}{2}$ for some integer k, since then $\cos(n\arccos x) = \cos(k\pi + \frac{\pi}{2}) = 0$. Note that there will be restrictions on k, since $0 \le \arccos x \le \pi$. We continue:

$n\arccos x = k\pi + \frac{\pi}{2} \iff \arccos x = \dfrac{k\pi + \frac{\pi}{2}}{n}$.

This only has solutions for $0 \le \dfrac{k\pi + \frac{\pi}{2}}{n} \le \pi \iff$

$0 < k\pi + \frac{\pi}{2} < n\pi \iff 0 \le k < n$. [This makes sense, because then $T_n(x)$ has n zeros, and it is a polynomial of degree n.] So, taking cosines of both sides of the last equation, we find that the zeros of $T_n(x)$ occur at $x = \cos\dfrac{k\pi + \frac{\pi}{2}}{n}$, k an integer with $0 \le k < n$. To find the values of x at which $T_n(x)$ has local extrema, we set

$0 = T'_n(x) = -\sin(n\arccos x)\dfrac{-n}{\sqrt{1 - x^2}}$

$\quad = \dfrac{n\sin(n\arccos x)}{\sqrt{1 - x^2}} \iff \sin(n\arccos x) = 0 \iff$

$n\arccos x = k\pi$, k some integer $\iff \arccos x = k\pi/n$. This has solutions for $0 \le k \le n$, but we disallow the cases $k = 0$ and $k = n$, since these give $x = 1$ and $x = -1$, respectively. So the local extrema of $T_n(x)$ occur at $x = \cos(k\pi/n)$, k an integer with $0 < k < n$. [Again, this seems reasonable, since a polynomial of degree n has at most $(n - 1)$ extrema.] By the First Derivative Test, the cases where k is even given maxima of $T_n(x)$, since then $n\arccos[\cos(k\pi/n)] = k\pi$ is an even multiple of π, so $\sin(n\arccos x)$ goes from negative to positive at $x = \cos(k\pi/n)$. Similarly, the cases where k is odd represent minima of $T_n(x)$.

(g)

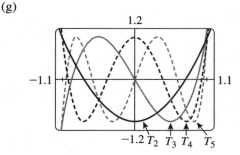

-1.2 T_2 T_3 T_4 T_5

(h)

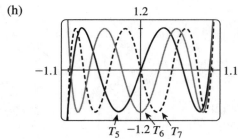

T_5 -1.2 T_6 T_7

(i) From the graph, it seems that the zeros of T_n and T_{n+1} alternate; that is, between two adjacent zeros of T_n, there is a zero of T_{n+1}, and vice versa. The same is true of the x-coordinates of the extrema of T_n and T_{n+1}: between the x-coordinates of any two adjacent extrema of one, there is the x-coordinate of an extremum of the other.

(j) When n is odd, the function $T_n(x)$ is odd, since all of its terms have odd degree, and so $\int_{-1}^{1} T_n(x)\, dx = 0$. When n is even, $T_n(x)$ is even, and it appears that the integral is negative but decreases in absolute value as n gets larger.

(k) $\int_{-1}^{1} T_n(x)\, dx = \int_{-1}^{1} \cos(n \arccos x)\, dx$. We substitute $u = \arccos x \;\Rightarrow\; x = \cos u \;\Rightarrow\; dx = -\sin u\, du$, $x = -1 \;\Rightarrow\; u = \pi$, and $x = 1 \;\Rightarrow\; u = 0$. So the integral becomes

$$\int_{0}^{\pi} \cos(nu)\sin u\, du = \int_{0}^{\pi} \tfrac{1}{2}\big[\sin(u - nu) + \sin(u + nu)\big]\, du$$

$$= \frac{1}{2}\left[\frac{\cos\big[(1-n)u\big]}{n-1} - \frac{\cos\big[(1+n)u\big]}{n+1}\right]_{0}^{\pi}$$

$$= \begin{cases} \dfrac{1}{2}\left[\left(\dfrac{-1}{n-1} - \dfrac{-1}{n+1}\right) - \left(\dfrac{1}{n-1} - \dfrac{1}{n+1}\right)\right] & \text{if } n \text{ is even} \\[3ex] \dfrac{1}{2}\left[\left(\dfrac{1}{n-1} - \dfrac{1}{n+1}\right) - \left(\dfrac{1}{n-1} - \dfrac{1}{n+1}\right)\right] & \text{if } n \text{ is odd} \end{cases}$$

$$= \begin{cases} -\dfrac{2}{n^2 - 1} & \text{if } n \text{ is even; and} \\[2ex] 0 & \text{if } n \text{ is odd.} \end{cases}$$

(l) From the graph, we see that as c increases through an integer, the graph of f gains a local extremum, which starts at $x = -1$ and moves rightward, compressing the graph of f as c continues to increase.

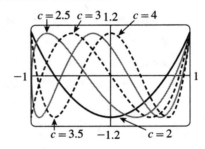

7

TECHNIQUES OF INTEGRATION

1. First make a substitution and then use integration by parts to evaluate $\int x^5 \cos(x^3)\, dx$.

2. Find the area of the region bounded by $y = \sin^{-1} x$, $y = 0$, and $x = 0.5$.

3–8 ■ Evaluate the integral.

3. $\int (1 - \sin 2x)^2\, dx$

4. $\int \sin\left(\theta + \dfrac{\pi}{6}\right) \cos\theta\, d\theta$

5. $\int x \sin^3(x^2)\, dx$

6. $\int \cos^6 x\, dx$

7. $\int \sin^5 2x\, \cos^4 2x\, dx$

8. $\int \sin^5 x\, dx$

9–14 ■ Evaluate the integral.

9. $\displaystyle\int_{1/2}^{\sqrt{3}/2} \dfrac{1}{x^2\sqrt{1 - x^2}}\, dx$

10. $\displaystyle\int_0^2 x^3\sqrt{4 - x^2}\, dx$

11. $\displaystyle\int \dfrac{x}{\sqrt{1 - x^2}}\, dx$

12. $\displaystyle\int x\sqrt{4 - x^2}\, dx$

13. $\displaystyle\int_0^2 \dfrac{x^3}{\sqrt{x^2 + 4}}\, dx$

14. $\displaystyle\int_0^3 \dfrac{dx}{\sqrt{9 + x^2}}$

15–20 ■ Evaluate the integral.

15. $\displaystyle\int_3^7 \dfrac{1}{(x + 1)(x - 2)}\, dx$

16. $\displaystyle\int \dfrac{6x - 5}{2x + 3}\, dx$

17. $\displaystyle\int \dfrac{1}{x(x + 1)(2x + 3)}\, dx$

18. $\displaystyle\int_2^3 \dfrac{6x^2 + 5x - 3}{x^3 + 2x^2 - 3x}\, dx$

19. $\displaystyle\int_0^1 \dfrac{x}{x^2 + 4x + 4}\, dx$

20. $\displaystyle\int \dfrac{18 - 2x - 4x^2}{x^3 + 4x^2 + x - 6}\, dx$

21–24 ■ Use (a) the Trapezoidal Rule, (b) the Midpoint Rule, and (c) Simpson's Rule to approximate the given integral with the specified value of n. (Round your answers to six decimal places.)

21. $\displaystyle\int_0^1 e^{-x^2}\, dx, \quad n = 10$

22. $\displaystyle\int_0^2 \dfrac{1}{\sqrt{1 + x^3}}\, dx, \quad n = 10$

23. $\displaystyle\int_2^3 \dfrac{1}{\ln x}\, dx, \quad n = 10$

24. $\displaystyle\int_0^1 \ln(1 + e^x)\, dx, \quad n = 8$

7 | ANSWERS TO SELECTED EXERCISES

1. $\frac{1}{3}x^3 \sin(x^3) + \frac{1}{3}\cos(x^3) + C$

2. $\frac{1}{12}(\pi + 6\sqrt{3} - 12)$

3. $\frac{3}{2}x + \cos 2x - \frac{1}{8}\sin 4x + C$

4. $-\frac{\sqrt{3}}{8}\cos 2\theta + \frac{1}{4}\theta + \frac{1}{8}\sin 2\theta + C$

5. $-\frac{1}{2}\cos(x^2) + \frac{1}{6}\cos^3(x^2) + C$

6. $\frac{1}{8}\left(\frac{5}{2}x + 2\sin 2x + \frac{3}{8}\sin 4x - \frac{1}{6}\sin^3 2x\right) + C$

7. $-\frac{1}{2}\left(\frac{1}{9}\cos^9 2x - \frac{2}{7}\cos^7 2x + \frac{1}{5}\cos^5 2x\right) + C$

8. $-\frac{1}{5}\cos^5 x + \frac{2}{3}\cos^3 x - \cos x + C$

9. $\frac{2}{\sqrt{3}}$

10. $\frac{64}{15}$

11. $-\sqrt{1 - x^2} + C$

12. $-\frac{1}{3}(4 - x^2)^{3/2} + C$

13. $\frac{8}{3}(2 - \sqrt{2})$

14. $\ln(\sqrt{2} + 1)$

15. $\frac{1}{3}\ln\frac{5}{2}$

16. $3x - 7\ln|2x + 3| + C$

17. $\frac{1}{3}\ln|x| - \ln|x + 1| + \frac{2}{3}\ln|2x + 3| + C$

18. $4\ln 6 - 3\ln 5$

19. $\ln\frac{3}{2} - \frac{1}{3}$

20. $\ln|x - 1| - 2\ln|x + 2| - 3\ln|x + 3| + C$

21. (a) 0.746211   (b) 0.747131   (c) 0.746825

22. (a) 1.401435   (b) 1.402558   (c) 1.402206

23. (a) 1.119061   (b) 1.118107   (c) 1.118428

24. (a) 0.984120   (b) 0.983669   (c) 0.983819

7 | SOLUTIONS TO SELECTED EXERCISES

1. Substitute $t = x^3 \Rightarrow dt = 3x^2\,dx$. Then use parts with $u = t$, $dv = \cos t\,dt$. Thus

$$\int x^5 \cos(x^3)\,dx = \frac{1}{3}\int x^3 \cos(x^3) \cdot 3x^2\,dx$$

$$= \frac{1}{3}\int t \cos t\,dt$$

$$= \frac{1}{3}t \sin t - \frac{1}{3}\int \sin t\,dt$$

$$= \frac{1}{3}t\sin t + \frac{1}{3}\cos t + C$$

$$= \frac{1}{3}x^3 \sin(x^3) + \frac{1}{3}\cos(x^3) + C$$

2. Let $u = \sin^{-1}x$, $dv = dx \Rightarrow du = \dfrac{dx}{\sqrt{1-x^2}}$, $v = x$.

Then

$$\text{area} = \int_0^{1/2} \sin^{-1}x\,dx$$

$$= \left[x\sin^{-1}x\right]_0^{1/2} - \int_0^{1/2} \frac{x}{\sqrt{1-x^2}}\,dx$$

$$= \frac{1}{2}\left(\frac{\pi}{6}\right) + \left[\sqrt{1-x^2}\right]_0^{1/2}$$

$$= \frac{\pi}{12} + \frac{\sqrt{3}}{2} - 1 = \frac{1}{12}(\pi + 6\sqrt{3} - 12)$$

3. $\displaystyle\int (1 - \sin 2x)^2\,dx = \int (1 - 2\sin 2x + \sin^2 2x)\,dx$

$$= \int \left[1 - 2\sin 2x + \frac{1}{2}(1 - \cos 4x)\right]dx$$

$$= \int \left[\frac{3}{2} - 2\sin 2x - \frac{1}{2}\cos 4x\right]dx$$

$$= \frac{3}{2}x + \cos 2x - \frac{1}{8}\sin 4x + C$$

4. $\displaystyle\int \sin\left(\theta + \frac{\pi}{6}\right)\cos\theta\,d\theta$

$$= \int \left(\sin\theta \cdot \frac{\sqrt{3}}{2} + \cos\theta \cdot \frac{1}{2}\right)\cos\theta\,d\theta$$

$$= \frac{\sqrt{3}}{4}\int \sin 2\theta\,d\theta + \frac{1}{4}\int (1 + \cos 2\theta)\,d\theta$$

$$= -\frac{\sqrt{3}}{8}\cos 2\theta + \frac{1}{4}\theta + \frac{1}{8}\sin 2\theta + C$$

5. Let $u = x^2 \Rightarrow du = 2x\,dx$. Then

$$\int x \sin^3(x^2)\,dx = \int \sin^3 u \cdot \frac{1}{2}\,du$$

$$= \frac{1}{2}\left(-\cos u + \frac{1}{3}\cos^3 u\right) + C$$

$$= -\frac{1}{2}\cos(x^2) + \frac{1}{6}\cos^3(x^2) + C$$

6. $\displaystyle\int \cos^6 x\,dx = \int \left[\frac{1}{2}(1 + \cos 2x)\right]^3 dx$

$$= \frac{1}{8}\int (1 + 3\cos 2x + 3\cos^2 2x + \cos^3 2x)\,dx$$

$$= \frac{1}{8}\int \left[1 + 3\cos 2x + \frac{3}{2}(1 + \cos 4x)\right.$$

$$\left. + (1 - \sin^2 2x)\cos x\right]dx$$

$$= \frac{1}{8}\int \left(\frac{5}{2} + 4\cos 2x + \frac{3}{2}\cos 4x - \sin^2 2x \cos 2x\right)dx$$

$$= \frac{1}{8}\left(\frac{5}{2}x + 2\sin 2x + \frac{3}{8}\sin 4x - \frac{1}{6}\sin^3 2x\right) + C$$

7. Let $u = \cos 2x \Rightarrow du = -2\sin 2x\,dx$. Then

$$\int \sin^5 2x \cos^4 2x\,dx = \int \cos^4 2x\,(1 - \cos^2 2x)^2 \sin 2x\,dx$$

$$= \int u^4(1 - u^2)^2\left(-\frac{1}{2}\,du\right) = -\frac{1}{2}\int (u^4 - 2u^6 + u^8)\,du$$

$$= -\frac{1}{2}\left(\frac{1}{9}u^9 - \frac{2}{7}u^7 + \frac{1}{5}u^5\right) + C$$

$$= -\frac{1}{2}\left(\frac{1}{9}\cos^9 2x - \frac{2}{7}\cos^7 2x + \frac{1}{5}\cos^5 2x\right) + C$$

8. Let $u = \cos x \Rightarrow du = -\sin x\,dx$. Then

$$\int \sin^5 x\,dx = \int (1 - \cos^2 x)^2 \sin x\,dx$$

$$= \int (1 - u^2)^2(-du) = \int (-1 + 2u^2 - u^4)\,du$$

$$= -\frac{1}{5}u^5 + \frac{2}{3}u^3 - u + C$$

$$= -\frac{1}{5}\cos^5 x + \frac{2}{3}\cos^3 x - \cos x + C$$

9. Let $x = \sin\theta$, where $-\dfrac{\pi}{2} \le \theta \le \dfrac{\pi}{2}$. Then

$dx = \cos\theta\, d\theta$ and $\sqrt{1-x^2} = |\cos\theta| = \cos\theta$

$\left(\text{since } \cos\theta > 0 \text{ for } \theta \text{ in } \left[-\dfrac{\pi}{2}, \dfrac{\pi}{2}\right]\right)$. Thus

$$\int_{1/2}^{\sqrt{3}/2} \frac{dx}{x^2\sqrt{1-x^2}} = \int_{\pi/6}^{\pi/3} \frac{\cos\theta\, d\theta}{\sin^2\theta \cos\theta}$$

$$= \int_{\pi/6}^{\pi/3} \csc^2\theta\, d\theta = \left[-\cot\theta\right]_{\pi/6}^{\pi/3}$$

$$= -\frac{1}{\sqrt{3}} - (-\sqrt{3})$$

$$= \frac{3}{\sqrt{3}} - \frac{1}{\sqrt{3}} = \frac{2}{\sqrt{3}}$$

10. Let $x = 2\sin\theta$, $-\dfrac{\pi}{2} \le \theta \le \dfrac{\pi}{2}$. Then $dx = 2\cos\theta\, d\theta$

and $\sqrt{4-x^2} = |2\cos\theta| = 2\cos\theta$, so

$$\int_0^2 x^3\sqrt{4-x^2}\, dx = \int_0^{\pi/2} 8\sin^3\theta\,(2\cos\theta)\,(2\cos\theta)\, d\theta$$

$$= 32\int_0^{\pi/2} \cos^2\theta\,(1 - \cos^2\theta)\sin\theta\, d\theta$$

$$= 32\int_1^0 u^2(1-u^2)\,(-du) \quad (\text{where } u = \cos\theta)$$

$$= 32\int_0^1 (u^2 - u^4)\, du = 32\left[\frac{1}{3}u^3 - \frac{1}{5}u^5\right]_0^1$$

$$= 32\left(\frac{1}{3} - \frac{1}{5}\right) = \frac{64}{15}$$

11. Let $u = 1 - x^2$. Then $du = -2x\, dx$, so

$$\int \frac{x}{\sqrt{1-x^2}}\, dx = -\frac{1}{2}\int \frac{du}{\sqrt{u}} = -\sqrt{u} + C$$

$$= -\sqrt{1-x^2} + C$$

12. Let $u = 4 - x^2$. Then $du = -2x\, dx \Rightarrow$

$$\int x\sqrt{4-x^2}\, dx = -\frac{1}{2}\int \sqrt{u}\, du = -\frac{1}{2} \cdot \frac{2}{3} u^{3/2} + C$$

$$= -\frac{1}{3}(4-x^2)^{3/2} + C$$

13. Let $x = 2\tan\theta$, where $-\dfrac{\pi}{2} < \theta < \dfrac{\pi}{2}$. Then

$dx = 2\sec^2\theta\, d\theta$ and $\sqrt{x^2+4} = 2\sec\theta$, so

$$\int_0^2 \frac{x^3}{\sqrt{x^2+4}}\, dx = \int_0^{\pi/4} \frac{8\tan^3\theta}{2\sec\theta}\, 2\sec^2\theta\, d\theta$$

$$= 8\int_0^{\pi/4} (\sec^2\theta - 1)\sec\theta\tan\theta\, d\theta$$

$$= 8\left[\frac{1}{3}\sec^3\theta - \sec\theta\right]_0^{\pi/4}$$

$$= 8\left[\frac{1}{3}\cdot 2\sqrt{2} - \sqrt{2}\right] - 8\left[\frac{1}{3} - 1\right]$$

$$= \frac{8}{3}(2 - \sqrt{2})$$

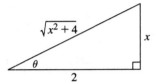

14. Let $x = 3\tan\theta$, where $-\dfrac{\pi}{2} < \theta < \dfrac{\pi}{2}$. Then

$dx = 3\sec^2\theta\, d\theta$ and $\sqrt{9+x^2} = 3\sec\theta$.

$$\int_0^3 \frac{dx}{\sqrt{9+x^2}} = \int_0^{\pi/4} \frac{3\sec^2\theta\, d\theta}{3\sec\theta} = \int_0^{\pi/4} \sec\theta\, d\theta$$

$$= \left[\ln|\sec\theta + \tan\theta|\right]_0^{\pi/4}$$

$$= \ln(\sqrt{2}+1) - \ln 1 = \ln(\sqrt{2}+1)$$

15. $\dfrac{1}{(x+1)(x-2)} = \dfrac{A}{x+1} + \dfrac{B}{x-2} \Rightarrow$

$1 = A(x-2) + B(x+1)$. Taking $x = -1$, then

$x = 2$, gives $A = -\dfrac{1}{3}$, $B = \dfrac{1}{3}$. Hence

$$\int_3^7 \frac{dx}{(x+1)(x-2)} = \frac{1}{3}\int_3^7 \left[\frac{1}{x-2} - \frac{1}{x+1}\right] dx$$

$$= \frac{1}{3}\left[\ln|x-2| - \ln|x+1|\right]_3^7$$

$$= \frac{1}{3}(\ln 5 - \ln 8 - \ln 1 + \ln 4)$$

$$= \frac{1}{3}\ln\frac{5}{2}$$

16. $\displaystyle \int \frac{6x-5}{2x+3}\, dx = \int \left[3 - \frac{14}{2x+3}\right] dx$

$$= 3x - 7\ln|2x+3| + C$$

17. $\dfrac{1}{x(x+1)(2x+3)} = \dfrac{A}{x} + \dfrac{B}{x+1} + \dfrac{C}{2x+3} \Rightarrow$

$1 = A(x+1)(2x+3) + B(x)(2x+3) + C(x)(x+1)$.

Set $x = 0$ to get $A = \dfrac{1}{3}$, take $x = -1$ to get $B = -1$,

and finally set $x = -\dfrac{3}{2}$, giving $C = \dfrac{4}{3}$. Now

$$\int \frac{dx}{x\,(x+1)\,(2x+3)} = \int \left[\frac{1/3}{x} - \frac{1}{x+1} + \frac{4/3}{2x+3} \right] dx$$

$$= \frac{1}{3}\ln|x| - \ln|x+1| + \frac{2}{3}\ln|2x+3| + C$$

18. $\dfrac{6x^2+5x-3}{x^3+2x^2-3x} = \dfrac{A}{x} + \dfrac{B}{x+3} + \dfrac{C}{x-1} \Rightarrow 6x^2+5x-3$

$= A\,(x+3)\,(x-1) + B\,(x)\,(x-1) + C\,(x)\,(x+3)$

Set $x=0$ to get $A=1$, then take $x=-3$ to get $B=3$, then set $x=1$ to get $C=2$:

$$\int_2^3 \frac{6x^2+5x-3}{x^3+2x^2-3x}\,dx = \int_2^3 \left[\frac{1}{x} + \frac{3}{x+3} + \frac{2}{x-1} \right] dx$$

$$= \left[\ln x + 3\ln(x+3) + 2\ln(x-1) \right]_2^3$$

$$= (\ln 3 + 3\ln 6 + 2\ln 2) - (\ln 2 + 3\ln 5)$$

$$= 4\ln 6 - 3\ln 5$$

19. $\dfrac{x}{x^2+4x+4} = \dfrac{A}{x+2} + \dfrac{B}{(x+2)^2} \Rightarrow$

$x = A\,(x+2) + B$. Set $x=-2$ to get $B=-2$ and equate coefficients of x to get $A=1$. Then

$$\int_0^1 \frac{x\,dx}{x^2+4x+4} = \int_0^1 \left[\frac{1}{x+2} - \frac{2}{(x+2)^2} \right] dx$$

$$= \left[\ln(x+2) + \frac{2}{x+2} \right]_0^1$$

$$= \ln 3 + \frac{2}{3} - (\ln 2 + 1) = \ln\frac{3}{2} - \frac{1}{3}$$

20. $\dfrac{18-2x-4x^2}{x^3+4x^2+x-6} = \dfrac{18-2x-4x^2}{(x-1)\,(x+2)\,(x+3)}$

$$= \frac{A}{x-1} + \frac{B}{x+2} + \frac{C}{x+3} \Rightarrow$$

$18 - 2x - 4x^2 = A\,(x+2)\,(x+3) + B\,(x-1)\,(x+3)$
$\qquad\qquad\qquad\quad + C\,(x-1)\,(x+2)$

Set $x=1$ to get $A=1$. Now setting $x=-2$ gives $B=-2$, and setting $x=-3$ gives $C=-3$. Then

$$\int \frac{18-2x-4x^2}{x^3+4x^2+x-6}\,dx$$

$$= \int \left(\frac{1}{x-1} - \frac{2}{x+2} - \frac{3}{x+3} \right) dx$$

$$= \ln|x-1| - 2\ln|x+2| - 3\ln|x+3| + C$$

21. $f(x) = e^{-x^2}$, $\Delta x = \dfrac{1-0}{10} = \dfrac{1}{10}$

(a) $T_{10} = \dfrac{1}{10\cdot 2}\left[f(0) + 2f(0.1) + 2f(0.2) + \right.$

$$\left. \cdots + 2f(0.8) + 2f(0.9) + f(1) \right]$$

$$\approx 0.746211$$

(b) $M_{10} = \dfrac{1}{10}\left[f(0.05) + f(0.15) + f(0.25) + \right.$

$$\left. \cdots + f(0.75) + f(0.85) + f(0.95) \right]$$

$$\approx 0.747131$$

(c) $S_{10} = \dfrac{1}{10\cdot 3}\left[f(0) + 4f(0.1) + 2f(0.2) + 4f(0.3) \right.$

$$+ 2f(0.4) + 4f(0.5) + 2f(0.6) + 4f(0.7)$$

$$\left. + 2f(0.8) + 4f(0.9) + f(1) \right]$$

$$\approx 0.746825$$

22. $f(x) = \dfrac{1}{\sqrt{1+x^3}}$, $\Delta x = \dfrac{2-0}{10} = \dfrac{1}{5}$

(a) $T_{10} = \dfrac{1}{5\cdot 2}\left[f(0) + 2f(0.2) + 2f(0.4) + \right.$

$$\left. \cdots + 2f(1.6) + 2f(1.8) + f(2) \right]$$

$$\approx 1.401435$$

(b) $M_{10} = \dfrac{1}{5}\left[f(0.1) + f(0.3) + f(0.5) + \right.$

$$\left. \cdots + f(1.5) + f(1.7) + f(1.9) \right]$$

$$\approx 1.402558$$

(c) $S_{10} = \dfrac{1}{5\cdot 3}\left[f(0) + 4f(0.2) + 2f(0.4) + 4f(0.6) \right.$

$$+ 2f(0.8) + 4f(1) + 2f(1.2) + 4f(1.4)$$

$$\left. + 2f(1.6) + 4f(1.8) + f(2) \right]$$

$$\approx 1.402206$$

23. $f(x) = \dfrac{1}{\ln x}$, $\Delta x = \dfrac{3-2}{10} = \dfrac{1}{10}$

(a) $T_{10} = \dfrac{1}{10\cdot 2}\left[f(2) + 2f(2.1) + 2f(2.2) + \right.$

$$\left. \cdots + 2f(2.9) + f(3) \right] \approx 1.119061$$

(b) $M_{10} = \dfrac{1}{10}\left[f(2.05) + f(2.15) + f(2.25) + \right.$

$$\left. \cdots + f(2.85) + f(2.95) \right] \approx 1.118107$$

(c) $S_{10} = \dfrac{1}{10\cdot 3}\left[f(2) + 4f(2.1) + 2f(2.2) + 4f(2.3) \right.$

$$+ 2f(2.4) + 4f(2.5) + 2f(2.6) + 4f(2.7)$$

$$\left. + 2f(2.8) + 4f(2.9) + f(3) \right]$$

$$\approx 1.118428$$

24. $f(x) = \ln(1 + e^x)$, $\Delta x = \dfrac{1-0}{8} = \dfrac{1}{8}$

(a) $T_8 = \dfrac{1}{8 \cdot 2}\left[f(0) + 2f\left(\dfrac{1}{8}\right) + 2f\left(\dfrac{1}{4}\right) + 2f\left(\dfrac{3}{8}\right)\right.$

$\qquad + 2f\left(\dfrac{1}{2}\right) + 2f\left(\dfrac{5}{8}\right) + 2f\left(\dfrac{3}{4}\right) + 2f\left(\dfrac{7}{8}\right)$

$\qquad \left. + f(1)\right]$

$\qquad \approx 0.984120$

(b) $M_8 = \dfrac{1}{8}\left[f\left(\dfrac{1}{16}\right) + f\left(\dfrac{3}{16}\right) + f\left(\dfrac{5}{16}\right) + \right.$

$\qquad \cdots \left. + f\left(\dfrac{13}{16}\right) + f\left(\dfrac{15}{16}\right)\right] \approx 0.983669$

(c) $S_8 = \dfrac{1}{8 \cdot 3}\left[f(0) + 4f\left(\dfrac{1}{8}\right) + 2f\left(\dfrac{1}{4}\right) + 4f\left(\dfrac{3}{8}\right)\right.$

$\qquad + 2f\left(\dfrac{1}{2}\right) + 4f\left(\dfrac{5}{8}\right) + 2f\left(\dfrac{3}{4}\right) + 4f\left(\dfrac{7}{8}\right)$

$\qquad \left. + f(1)\right]$

$\qquad \approx 0.983819$

8 FURTHER APPLICATIONS OF INTEGRATION

1–3 ■ Find the length of the arc of the given curve from point A to point B.

1. $9y^2 = x(x-3)^2$; $\quad A(0, 0)$, $\quad B\left(4, \dfrac{2}{3}\right)$

2. $y^2 = (x-1)^3$; $\quad A(1, 0)$, $\quad B(2, 1)$

3. $12xy = 4y^4 + 3$; $\quad A\left(\dfrac{7}{12}, 1\right)$, $\quad B\left(\dfrac{67}{24}, 2\right)$

4–10 ■ Find the area of the surface obtained by rotating the curve about the x-axis.

4. $2y = x + 4$, $\quad 0 \le x \le 2$

5. $y = x^3 + \dfrac{1}{12x}$, $\quad 1 \le x \le 2$

6. $x = \dfrac{y^4}{2} + \dfrac{1}{16y^2}$, $\quad 1 \le y \le 3$

7. $y^2 = 4x + 4$, $\quad 0 \le x \le 8$

8. $y = \dfrac{x^2}{4} - \dfrac{\ln x}{2}$, $\quad 1 \le x \le 4$

9. $y = \sin x$, $\quad 0 \le x \le \pi$

10. $2y = 3x^{2/3}$, $\quad 1 \le x \le 8$

11–14 ■ The given curve is rotated about the y-axis. Find the area of the resulting surface.

11. $y = 1 - x^2$, $\quad 0 \le x \le 1$

12. $x = e^{2y}$, $\quad 0 \le y \le \dfrac{1}{2}$

13. $x = \sqrt{2y - y^2}$, $\quad 0 \le y \le 1$

14. $x = \dfrac{1}{2\sqrt{2}}(y^2 - \ln y)$, $\quad 1 \le y \le 2$

15–16 ■ Find the centroid of the region bounded by the curves.

15. $y = \sin 2x$, $\quad y = 0$, $\quad x = 0$, $\quad x = \pi/2$

16. $y = \ln x$, $\quad y = 0$, $\quad x = e$

17. The marginal cost function $C'(x)$ was defined to be the derivative of the cost function. (See Sections 3.3 and 4.8.) If the marginal cost of manufacturing x units of a product is $C'(x) = 0.006x^2 - 1.5x + 8$ (measured in dollars per unit) and the fixed start-up cost is $C(0) = \$1,500,000$, use the Net Change Theorem to find the cost of producing the first 2000 units.

18. The marginal revenue from selling x items is $90 - 0.02x$. The revenue from the sale of the first 100 items is $\$8800$. What is the revenue from the sale of the first 200 items?

19. A supply curve is given by $p = 5 + \dfrac{1}{10}\sqrt{x}$. Find the producer surplus when the selling price is 10.

20. A manufacturer has been selling 1000 television sets a week at $\$450$ each. A market survey indicates that for every $\$10$ that the price is reduced, the number of sets sold will increase by 100 a week. Find the demand function and calculate the consumer surplus when the selling price is set at $\$400$.

8 | ANSWERS TO SELECTED EXERCISES

1. $\dfrac{14}{3}$

2. $\dfrac{13\sqrt{13} - 8}{27}$

3. $\dfrac{59}{24}$

4. $5\sqrt{5}\pi$

5. $\dfrac{12{,}289\pi}{192}$

6. $\dfrac{5813\pi}{30}$

7. $\dfrac{8\pi}{3}(10\sqrt{10} - 2\sqrt{2})$

8. $\pi\left[\dfrac{315}{16} - 8\ln 2 - (\ln 2)^2\right]$

9. $2\pi\left[\sqrt{2} + \ln(\sqrt{2} + 1)\right]$

10. $\dfrac{3\pi}{5}(50\sqrt{5} - 2\sqrt{2})$

11. $\dfrac{\pi}{6}(5\sqrt{5} - 1)$

12. $\dfrac{\pi}{4}\left[2e\sqrt{1 + 4e^2} - 2\sqrt{5} + \ln\left(\dfrac{2e + \sqrt{1 + 4e^2}}{2 + \sqrt{5}}\right)\right]$

13. 2π

14. $\dfrac{\pi}{8}\left[21 - 8\ln 2 - (\ln 2)^2\right]$

15. $\left(\dfrac{\pi}{4}, \dfrac{\pi}{8}\right)$

16. $\left(\dfrac{e^2 + 1}{4}, \dfrac{e - 2}{2}\right)$

17. $14{,}516{,}000

18. $17{,}500

19. $4166.67

20. $p = -\dfrac{1}{10}x + 550, \quad \$112{,}500$

8 | SOLUTIONS TO SELECTED EXERCISES

1. $9y^2 = x(x-3)^2$, $3y = x^{1/2}(x-3)$, $y = \dfrac{1}{3}x^{3/2} - x^{1/2}$

$\Rightarrow y' = \dfrac{1}{2}x^{1/2} - \dfrac{1}{2}x^{-1/2} \Rightarrow (y')^2 = \dfrac{1}{4}x - \dfrac{1}{2} + \dfrac{1}{2}x^{-1}$

$\Rightarrow 1 + (y')^2 = \dfrac{1}{4}x + \dfrac{1}{2} + \dfrac{1}{4}x^{-1} \Rightarrow$

$\sqrt{1 + (y')^2} = \dfrac{1}{2}x^{1/2} + \dfrac{1}{2}x^{-1/2}$. So

$L = \displaystyle\int_0^4 \left(\dfrac{1}{2}x^{1/2} + \dfrac{1}{2}x^{-1/2} \right) dx = \dfrac{1}{2}\left[\dfrac{2}{3}x^{3/2} + 2x^{1/2} \right]_0^4$

$= \dfrac{1}{2}\left(\dfrac{16}{3} + 4 \right) = \dfrac{14}{3}$

2. $y^2 = (x-1)^3$, $y = (x-1)^{3/2}$

$\Rightarrow dy/dx = \dfrac{3}{2}(x-1)^{1/2} \Rightarrow$

$1 + (dy/dx)^2 = 1 + \dfrac{9}{4}(x-1)$. So

$L = \displaystyle\int_1^2 \sqrt{1 + \dfrac{9}{4}(x-1)} \, dx = \int_1^2 \sqrt{\dfrac{9}{4}x - \dfrac{5}{4}} \, dx$

$= \left[\dfrac{4}{9} \cdot \dfrac{2}{3}\left(\dfrac{9}{4}x - \dfrac{5}{4} \right)^{3/2} \right]_1^2 = \dfrac{13\sqrt{13} - 8}{27}$

3. $12xy = 4y^4 + 3$, $x = \dfrac{y^3}{3} + \dfrac{y^{-1}}{4} \Rightarrow \dfrac{dx}{dy} = y^2 - \dfrac{y^{-2}}{4}$,

so $\left(\dfrac{dx}{dy} \right)^2 = y^4 - \dfrac{1}{2} + \dfrac{y^{-4}}{16} \Rightarrow$

$1 + \left(\dfrac{dx}{dy} \right)^2 = y^4 + \dfrac{1}{2} + \dfrac{y^{-4}}{16} \Rightarrow$

$\sqrt{1 + \left(\dfrac{dx}{dy} \right)^2} = y^2 + \dfrac{y^{-2}}{4}$. So

$L = \displaystyle\int_1^2 \left(y^2 + \dfrac{y^{-2}}{4} \right) dy = \left[\dfrac{y^3}{3} - \dfrac{1}{4y} \right]_1^2$

$= \left(\dfrac{8}{3} - \dfrac{1}{8} \right) - \left(\dfrac{1}{3} - \dfrac{1}{4} \right) = \dfrac{59}{24}$

4. $2y = x + 4$, $y = \dfrac{1}{2}x + 2 \Rightarrow$

$y' = \dfrac{1}{2} \Rightarrow \sqrt{1 + (y')^2} = \dfrac{\sqrt{5}}{2}$. So

$S = 2\pi \displaystyle\int_0^2 \dfrac{1}{2}(x+4)\dfrac{\sqrt{5}}{2} \, dx = \dfrac{\pi\sqrt{5}}{2}\left[\dfrac{1}{2}x^2 + 4x \right]_0^2$

$= 5\sqrt{5}\pi$

5. $y = x^3 + \dfrac{1}{12x} \Rightarrow \dfrac{dy}{dx} = 3x^2 - \dfrac{1}{12x^2} \Rightarrow$

$1 + \left(\dfrac{dy}{dx} \right)^2 = 9x^4 + \dfrac{1}{2} + \dfrac{1}{144x^4} = \left(3x^2 + \dfrac{1}{12x^2} \right)^2$.

So

$S = 2\pi \displaystyle\int_1^2 \left(x^3 + \dfrac{1}{12x} \right)\left(3x^2 + \dfrac{1}{12x^2} \right) dx$

$= 2\pi \displaystyle\int_1^2 \left(3x^5 + \dfrac{x}{3} + \dfrac{1}{144x^3} \right) dx$

$= 2\pi \left[\dfrac{x^6}{2} + \dfrac{x^2}{6} - \dfrac{1}{288x^2} \right]_1^2$

$= 2\pi\left[\left(32 + \dfrac{2}{3} - \dfrac{1}{288 \cdot 4} \right) - \left(\dfrac{1}{2} + \dfrac{1}{6} - \dfrac{1}{288} \right) \right]$

$= \dfrac{12{,}289\pi}{192}$

6. $x = \dfrac{y^4}{2} + \dfrac{1}{16y^2} \Rightarrow \dfrac{dx}{dy} = 2y^3 - \dfrac{1}{8y^3} \Rightarrow$

$1 + \left(\dfrac{dx}{dy} \right)^2 = 4y^6 + \dfrac{1}{2} + \dfrac{1}{64y^6} = \left(2y^3 + \dfrac{1}{8y^3} \right)^2$.

So

$S = 2\pi \displaystyle\int_1^3 y\left[2y^3 + \dfrac{1}{8y^3} \right] dy = 2\pi \int_1^3 \left(2y^4 + \dfrac{1}{8}y^{-2} \right) dy$

$= 2\pi \left[\dfrac{2}{5}y^5 - \dfrac{1}{8}y^{-1} \right]_1^3 = 2\pi\left[\dfrac{2}{5}(243) - \dfrac{1}{24} - \dfrac{2}{5} + \dfrac{1}{8} \right]$

$= \dfrac{5813\pi}{30}$

7. The curve $y^2 = 4x + 4$ is symmetric about the x-axis, which is the axis of rotation, so we need only consider the upper half of the curve, given by $y = \sqrt{4x + 4} = 2\sqrt{x + 1}$. Then

$$\frac{dy}{dx} = \frac{1}{\sqrt{x+1}} \Rightarrow \sqrt{1 + \left(\frac{dy}{dx}\right)^2} = \sqrt{1 + \frac{1}{x+1}}. \text{ So}$$

$$S = 2\pi \int_0^8 2\sqrt{x+1}\sqrt{1 + \frac{1}{x+1}}\, dx$$

$$= 4\pi \int_0^8 \sqrt{x+2}\, dx$$

$$= 4\pi \left[\frac{2}{3}(x+2)^{3/2}\right]_0^8 = \frac{8\pi}{3}(10\sqrt{10} - 2\sqrt{2}).$$

Another Method: Use $S = \int_2^6 2\pi y \sqrt{1 + (dx/dy)^2}\, dy$, where $x = \frac{1}{4}y^2 - 1$.

8. $y = \frac{x^2}{4} - \frac{\ln x}{2} \Rightarrow \frac{dy}{dx} = \frac{x}{2} - \frac{1}{2x} \Rightarrow$

$$1 + \left(\frac{dy}{dx}\right)^2 = \frac{x^2}{4} + \frac{1}{2} + \frac{1}{4x^2}. \text{ So}$$

$$S = 2\pi \int_1^4 \left(\frac{x^2}{4} - \frac{\ln x}{2}\right)\left(\frac{x}{2} + \frac{1}{2x}\right) dx$$

$$= \frac{\pi}{2} \int_1^4 \left(\frac{x^2}{2} - \ln x\right)\left(x + \frac{1}{x}\right) dx$$

$$= \frac{\pi}{2} \int_1^4 \left(\frac{x^3}{2} + \frac{x}{2} - x\ln x - \frac{\ln x}{x}\right) dx$$

$$= \frac{\pi}{2} \left[\frac{x^4}{8} + \frac{x^2}{4} - \frac{x^2}{2}\ln x + \frac{x^2}{4} - \frac{1}{2}(\ln x)^2\right]_1^4$$

$$= \frac{\pi}{2}\left[(32 + 4 - 8\ln 4 + 4 - \frac{1}{2}(\ln 4)^2)\right.$$
$$\left. - \left(\frac{1}{8} + \frac{1}{4} - 0 + \frac{1}{4} - 0\right)\right]$$

$$= \pi\left[\frac{315}{16} - 8\ln 2 - (\ln 2)^2\right]$$

9. $y = \sin x \Rightarrow 1 + (dy/dx)^2 = 1 + \cos^2 x$. So

$$S = 2\pi \int_0^\pi \sin x \sqrt{1 + \cos^2 x}\, dx$$

$$= 2\pi \int_{-1}^1 \sqrt{1 + u^2}\, du \ (u = -\cos x, du = \sin x\, dx)$$

$$= 4\pi \int_0^1 \sqrt{1 + u^2}\, du$$

$$= 4\pi \int_0^{\pi/4} \sec^3\theta\, d\theta \ (u = \tan\theta, du = \sec^2\theta\, d\theta)$$

$$= 2\pi\left[\sec\theta\tan\theta + \ln|\sec\theta + \tan\theta|\right]_0^{\pi/4}$$

$$= 2\pi\left[\sqrt{2} + \ln(\sqrt{2} + 1)\right]$$

10. $2y = 3x^{2/3}$, $y = \frac{3}{2}x^{2/3} \Rightarrow dy/dx = x^{-1/3} \Rightarrow$

$1 + (dy/dx)^2 = 1 + x^{-2/3}$. So

$$S = 2\pi \int_1^8 \frac{3}{2}x^{2/3}\sqrt{1 + x^{-2/3}}\, dx$$

$$= 3\pi \int_1^2 u^2\sqrt{1 + 1/u^2}\, 3u^2\, du$$

$$(u = x^{1/3}, x = u^3, dx = 3u^2\, du)$$

$$= 9\pi \int_1^2 u^3\sqrt{u^2 + 1}\, du = \frac{9\pi}{2} \int_1^2 u^2\sqrt{u^2 + 1}\, 2u\, du$$

$$= \frac{9\pi}{2} \int_2^5 (y - 1)\sqrt{y}\, dy \ (y = u^2 + 1, dy = 2u\, du)$$

$$= \frac{9\pi}{2} \int_2^5 (y^{3/2} - y^{1/2})\, dy = \frac{9\pi}{2}\left[\frac{2}{5}y^{5/2} - \frac{2}{3}y^{3/2}\right]_2^5$$

$$= 9\pi\left[\left(\frac{1}{5}\cdot 5^{5/2} - \frac{1}{3}\cdot 5^{3/2}\right) - \left(\frac{1}{5}\cdot 2^{5/2} - \frac{1}{3}\cdot 2^{3/2}\right)\right]$$

$$= 9\pi\left[5\sqrt{5} - \frac{5\sqrt{5}}{3} - \frac{4\sqrt{2}}{5} + \frac{2\sqrt{2}}{3}\right]$$

$$= \frac{3\pi}{5}\left(50\sqrt{5} - 2\sqrt{2}\right)$$

11. $y = 1 - x^2 \Rightarrow 1 + (dy/dx)^2 = 1 + 4x^2 \Rightarrow$

$$S = 2\pi \int_0^1 x\sqrt{1 + 4x^2}\, dx = \frac{\pi}{4} \int_0^1 8x\sqrt{4x^2 + 1}\, dx$$

$$= \frac{\pi}{4}\left[\frac{2}{3}(4x^2 + 1)^{3/2}\right]_0^1 = \frac{\pi}{6}(5\sqrt{5} - 1)$$

12. $x = e^{2y} \Rightarrow 1 + (dx/dy)^2 = 1 + 4e^{4y}$. So

$$S = 2\pi \int_0^{1/2} e^{2y}\sqrt{1 + (2e^{2y})^2}\, dy$$

$$= 2\pi \int_2^{2e} \sqrt{1 + u^2}\, \frac{1}{4}\, du \ (u = 2e^{2y}, du = 4e^{2y}dy)$$

$$= \frac{\pi}{2} \int_2^{2e} \sqrt{1 + u^2}\, du$$

$$= \frac{\pi}{2}\left[\frac{1}{2}u\sqrt{1 + u^2} + \frac{1}{2}\ln|u + \sqrt{1 + u^2}|\right]_2^{2e}$$

$$(u = \tan\theta \text{ or use Formula 21})$$

$$= \frac{\pi}{2}\left[e\sqrt{1 + 4e^2} + \frac{1}{2}\ln(2e + \sqrt{1 + 4e^2})\right.$$
$$\left. - \sqrt{5} - \frac{1}{2}\ln(2 + \sqrt{5})\right]$$

$$= \frac{\pi}{4}\left[2e\sqrt{1 + 4e^2} - 2\sqrt{5} + \ln\left(\frac{2e + \sqrt{1 + 4e^2}}{2 + \sqrt{5}}\right)\right]$$

13. $x = \sqrt{2y - y^2} \Rightarrow \dfrac{dx}{dy} = \dfrac{1 - y}{\sqrt{2y - y^2}} \Rightarrow$

$1 + \left(\dfrac{dx}{dy}\right)^2 = 1 + \dfrac{1 - 2y + y^2}{2y - y^2} = \dfrac{1}{2y - y^2}.$ So

$S = 2\pi \displaystyle\int_0^1 \sqrt{2y - y^2}\left(\dfrac{1}{\sqrt{2y - y^2}}\right) dy$

$\quad = 2\pi \displaystyle\int_0^1 dy = 2\pi$

14. $x = \dfrac{1}{2\sqrt{2}}(y^2 - \ln y) \Rightarrow \dfrac{dx}{dy} = \dfrac{1}{2\sqrt{2}}\left(2y - \dfrac{1}{y}\right) \Rightarrow$

$1 + \left(\dfrac{dx}{dy}\right)^2 = 1 + \dfrac{1}{8}\left(2y - \dfrac{1}{y}\right)^2 = 1 + \dfrac{1}{8}\left(4y^2 - 4 + \dfrac{1}{y^2}\right)$

$\quad = \dfrac{1}{8}\left(4y^2 + 4 + \dfrac{1}{y^2}\right) = \left[\dfrac{1}{2\sqrt{2}}\left(2y + \dfrac{1}{y}\right)\right]^2$

So

$S = 2\pi \displaystyle\int_1^2 \dfrac{1}{2\sqrt{2}}(y^2 - \ln y)\dfrac{1}{2\sqrt{2}}\left(2y + \dfrac{1}{y}\right) dy$

$\quad = \dfrac{\pi}{4}\displaystyle\int_1^2 \left(2y^3 + y - 2y\ln y - \dfrac{\ln y}{y}\right) dy$

$\quad = \dfrac{\pi}{4}\left[\dfrac{1}{2}y^4 + \dfrac{1}{2}y^2 - y^2\ln y + \dfrac{1}{2}y^2 - \dfrac{1}{2}(\ln y)^2\right]_1^2$

$\quad = \dfrac{\pi}{8}\left[y^4 + 2y^2 - 2y^2\ln y - (\ln y)^2\right]_1^2$

$\quad = \dfrac{\pi}{8}\left[16 + 8 - 8\ln 2 - (\ln 2)^2 - 1 - 2\right]$

$\quad = \dfrac{\pi}{8}\left[21 - 8\ln 2 - (\ln 2)^2\right]$

15. From the figure we see that $\bar{x} = \dfrac{\pi}{4}$

$\left(\text{halfway from } x = 0 \text{ to } \dfrac{\pi}{2}\right).$ Now

$A = \displaystyle\int_0^{\pi/2} \sin 2x\, dx = -\dfrac{1}{2}\left[\cos 2x\right]_0^{\pi/2}$

$\quad = -\dfrac{1}{2}(-1 - 1) = 1$

so

$\bar{y} = \dfrac{1}{A}\displaystyle\int_0^{\pi/2} \dfrac{1}{2}\sin^2 2x\, dx = \dfrac{1}{1}\displaystyle\int_0^{\pi/2} \dfrac{1}{2}\cdot\dfrac{1}{2}(1 - \cos 4x)\, dx$

$\quad = \dfrac{1}{4}\left[x - \dfrac{1}{4}\sin 4x\right]_0^{\pi/2} = \dfrac{\pi}{8}.$

Centroid $(\bar{x}, \bar{y}) = \left(\dfrac{\pi}{4}, \dfrac{\pi}{8}\right).$

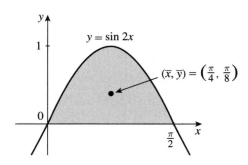

16. $A = \displaystyle\int_1^e \ln x\, dx = \left[x\ln x - x\right]_1^e = 0 - (-1) = 1,$

$\bar{x} = \dfrac{1}{A}\displaystyle\int_1^e x\ln x\, dx = \left[\dfrac{1}{2}x^2\ln x - \dfrac{1}{4}x^2\right]_1^e$

$\quad = \left(\dfrac{1}{2}e^2 - \dfrac{1}{4}e^2\right) - \left(-\dfrac{1}{4}\right) = \dfrac{e^2 + 1}{4}$

$\bar{y} = \dfrac{1}{A}\displaystyle\int_1^e \dfrac{(\ln x)^2}{2}\, dx = \dfrac{1}{2}\displaystyle\int_1^e (\ln x)^2\, dx.$ To evaluate

$\displaystyle\int (\ln x)^2\, dx,$ take $u = \ln x$ and $dv = \ln x\, dx,$ so that

$du = 1/x\, dx$ and $v = x\ln x - x.$ Then

$\displaystyle\int (\ln x)^2\, dx = x(\ln x)^2 - x(\ln x) - \displaystyle\int (x\ln x - x)\dfrac{1}{x}\, dx$

$\quad = x(\ln x)^2 - x(\ln x) - \displaystyle\int (\ln x - 1)\, dx$

$\quad = x(\ln x)^2 - x\ln x - x\ln x + x + x + C$

$\quad = x(\ln x)^2 - 2x\ln x + 2x + C$

Thus

$\bar{y} = \dfrac{1}{2}\left[x(\ln x)^2 - 2x\ln x + 2x\right]_1^e$

$\quad = \dfrac{1}{2}\left[(e - 2e + 2e) - (0 - 0 + 2)\right] = \dfrac{e - 2}{2}$

So $(\bar{x}, \bar{y}) = \left(\dfrac{e^2 + 1}{4}, \dfrac{e - 2}{2}\right).$

17. $C(2000) = C(0) + \displaystyle\int_0^{2000} C'(x)\, dx$

$\quad = 1{,}500{,}000 + \displaystyle\int_0^{2000} (0.006x^2 - 1.5x + 8)\, dx$

$\quad = 1{,}500{,}000 + \left[0.002x^3 - 0.75x^2 + 8x\right]_0^{2000}$

$\quad = \$14{,}516{,}000$

18. $R'(x) = 90 - 0.02x$ and $R(100) = \$8800$, so

$$R(200) = R(100) + \int_{100}^{200} R'(x)\,dx$$

$$= 8800 + \int_{100}^{200} (90 - 0.02x)\,dx$$

$$= 8800 + \left[90x - 0.01x^2 \right]_{100}^{200}$$

$$= 8800 + (18{,}000 - 400) - (9000 - 100)$$

$$= \$17{,}500$$

19. $P = p_S(x) = 10 = 5 + \dfrac{1}{10}\sqrt{x} \Rightarrow 50 = \sqrt{x} \Rightarrow$

$x = 2500$

$$\text{Producer surplus} = \int_0^{2500} \left[P - p_S(x) \right] dx$$

$$= \int_0^{2500} \left(10 - 5 - \frac{1}{10}\sqrt{x} \right) dx$$

$$= \left[5x - \frac{1}{15}x^{3/2} \right]_0^{2500} \approx \$4166.67$$

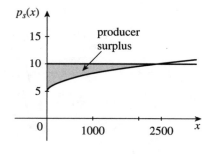

20. The demand function is linear, with slope $\dfrac{-10}{100}$ and $p(1000) = 450$. So its equation is $p - 450 = -\dfrac{1}{10}(x - 1000)$ or $p = -\dfrac{1}{10}x + 550$. A selling price of $\$400 \Rightarrow 400 = -\dfrac{1}{10}x + 550 \Rightarrow x = 1500$.

$$\text{Consumer surplus} = \int_0^{1500} \left(550 - \frac{1}{10}x - 400 \right) dx$$

$$= \left[150x - \frac{1}{20}x^2 \right]_0^{1500}$$

$$= \$112{,}500$$

9 | DIFFERENTIAL EQUATIONS

1. Show that $y = 2 + e^{-x^3}$ is a solution of the differential equation $y' + 3x^2 y = 6x^2$.

2. Verify that $y = (2 + \ln x)/x$ is a solution of the initial-value problem

$$x^2 y' + xy = 1, \qquad y(1) = 2$$

3–6 ■ Solve the differential equation.

3. $\dfrac{dy}{dx} = y^2$

4. $yy' = x$

5. $y' = xy$

6. $\dfrac{dy}{dx} = \dfrac{x + \sin x}{3y^2}$

7. Find a function f such that $f'(x) = x^3 f(x)$ and $f(0) = 1$.

8. Find a function g such that $g'(x) = g(x)(1 + g(x))$ and $g(0) = 1$.

9–15 ■ Solve the differential equation.

9. $y' - 3y = e^x$

10. $y' + 4y = x$

11. $y' - 2xy = x$

12. $xy' + 2y = e^{x^2}$

13. $y' \cos x = y \sin x + \sin 2x, \quad -\pi/2 < x < \pi/2$

14. $xy' + xy + y = e^{-x}, \quad x > 0$

15. $\dfrac{dy}{d\theta} - y \tan \theta = 1, \quad -\pi/2 < \theta < \pi/2$

9 | ANSWERS TO SELECTED EXERCISES

3. $y = \dfrac{-1}{x + C}, y = 0$

4. $x^2 - y^2 = C$

11. $y = Ce^{x^2} - \dfrac{1}{2}$

12. $y = \dfrac{e^{x^2} + C}{2x^2}$

5. $y = Ce^{x^2/2}$

6. $y = \sqrt[3]{\dfrac{1}{2}x^2 - \cos x + C}$

13. $y = \dfrac{\sec x}{2} - \cos x + C \sec x$

7. $f(x) = e^{x/4}$

8. $g(x) = \dfrac{e^x}{2 - e^x}$

14. $y = e^{-x}\left(1 + \dfrac{C}{x}\right)$

9. $y = Ce^{3x} - \dfrac{1}{2}e^x$

10. $y = \dfrac{1}{4}x - \dfrac{1}{16} + Ce^{-4x}$

15. $y = \tan \theta + C \sec \theta$

9 | SOLUTIONS TO SELECTED EXERCISES

1. $y = 2 + e^{-x^3} \implies y' = -3x^2 e^{-x^3}$

$$\begin{aligned} \text{LHS} &= y' + 3x^2 y \\ &= -3x^2 e^{-x^3} + 3x^2(2 + e^{-x^3}) \\ &= -3x^2 e^{-x^3} + 6x^2 + 3x^2 e^{-x^3} \\ &= 6x^2 \\ &= \text{RHS} \end{aligned}$$

2. $y = \dfrac{2 + \ln x}{x} \implies$

$$y' = \frac{x(1/x) - (2 + \ln x)(1)}{(x)^2} = \frac{-1 - \ln x}{x^2} \text{ and}$$

$$y(1) = \frac{2 + \ln 1}{1} = 2.$$

$$\begin{aligned} \text{LHS} &= x^2 y' + xy \\ &= x^2 \left(\frac{-1 - \ln x}{x^2} \right) + x \left(\frac{2 + \ln x}{x} \right) \\ &= (-1 - \ln x) + (2 + \ln x) \\ &= 1 \\ &= \text{RHS} \end{aligned}$$

3. $\dfrac{dy}{dx} = y^2 \implies \dfrac{dy}{y^2} = dx \ (y \neq 0) \implies \displaystyle\int \frac{dy}{y^2} = \int dx$

$$\implies -\frac{1}{y} = x + C \implies -y = \frac{1}{x + C} \implies y = \frac{-1}{x + C},$$

and $y = 0$ is also a solution.

4. $yy' = x \implies \displaystyle\int y \, dy = \int x \, dx \implies$

$$\frac{1}{2}y^2 = \frac{1}{2}x^2 + C_1 \implies y^2 = x^2 + 2C_1 \implies$$

$x^2 - y^2 = C$ (where $C = -2C_1$). This represents a family of hyperbolas.

5. $y' = xy \implies \displaystyle\int \frac{dy}{y} = \int x \, dx \ (y \neq 0) \implies$

$$\ln|y| = \frac{x^2}{2} + C \implies |y| = e^C e^{x^2/2} \implies y = K e^{x^2/2},$$

where $K = \pm e^C$ is a constant. (In our derivation, K was nonzero, but we can restore the excluded case $y = 0$ by allowing K to be zero.)

6. $\dfrac{dy}{dx} = \dfrac{x + \sin x}{3y^2} \implies \displaystyle\int 3y^2 \, dy = \int (x + \sin x) \, dx \implies$

$$y^3 = \frac{x^2}{2} - \cos x + C \implies y = \sqrt[3]{\frac{1}{2}x^2 - \cos x + C}$$

7. Let $y = f(x)$. Then $\dfrac{dy}{dx} = x^3 y$ and $y(0) = 1$.

$$\frac{dy}{y} = x^3 dx \text{ (if } y \neq 0), \text{ so } \int \frac{dy}{y} = \int x^3 \, dx \text{ and}$$

$$\ln|y| = \frac{1}{4}x^4 + C; \ y(0) = 1 \implies C = 0, \text{ so}$$

$\ln|y| = \dfrac{1}{4}x^4$, $|y| = e^{x^4/4}$ and $y = f(x) = e^{x^4/4}$ [since $y(0) = 1$].

8. Let $y = g(x)$. Then $\dfrac{dy}{dx} = y(1 + y)$ and $y(0) = 1$.

$$\int \frac{dy}{y(1 + y)} = \int dx \implies \int \left(\frac{1}{y} - \frac{1}{1 + y} \right) dy = \int dx$$

$$\implies \ln|y| - \ln|1 + y| = x + C \implies \left| \frac{y}{1 + y} \right| = e^C e^x$$

$$\implies \frac{y}{1 + y} = Ae^x. \ y(0) = 1 \implies \tfrac{1}{2} = A, \text{ so } \frac{y}{1 + y} = \frac{e^x}{2}.$$

Solve for y: $y = \dfrac{e^x}{2 - e^x}$.

9. $I(x) = e^{\int -3 \, dx} = e^{-3x}$. Multiplying the differential equation by $I(x)$ gives

$$e^{-3x}y' - 3e^{-3x}y = e^{-2x} \implies (e^{-3x}y)' = e^{-2x} \implies$$

$$y = e^{3x} \left[\int (e^{-2x}) dx + C \right] = Ce^{3x} - \frac{1}{2}e^x.$$

10. $I(x) = e^{\int 4 \, dx} = e^{4x}$. Multiplying the differential equation by $I(x)$ gives $e^{4x}y' + 4e^{4x}y = xe^{4x} \implies$

$(e^{4x}y)' = xe^{4x}$, so

$$y = e^{-4x} \left(\int e^{4x} x \, dx + C \right)$$

$$= e^{-4x} \left(\frac{1}{4}xe^{4x} - \frac{1}{16}e^{4x} + C \right)$$

$$= \frac{1}{4}x - \frac{1}{16} + Ce^{-4x}$$

11. $I(x) = e^{\int (-2x) dx} = e^{-x^2}$. Multiplying the differential equation by $I(x)$ gives

$$e^{-x^2}(y' - 2xy) = xe^{-x^2} \implies (e^{-x^2}y)' = xe^{-x^2} \implies$$

$$y = e^{x^2} \left(\int xe^{-x^2} dx + C \right) = Ce^{x^2} - \frac{1}{2}.$$

12. $y' + \dfrac{2}{x}y = \dfrac{1}{x}e^{x^2}(x \neq 0)$, so

$I(x) = e^{\int 2x^{-1} dx} = e^{\ln x^2} = x^2$. Multiplying the differential equation by $I(x)$ gives $x^2 y' + 2xy = xe^{x^2} \implies$

$(x^2 y)' = x e^{x^2}$ $\Rightarrow$

$$y = x^{-2}\left[\int (x e^{x^2})\, dx + C_1\right] = x^{-2}\left[\left(\frac{1}{2}e^{x^2}\right) + C_1\right]$$

$$= \frac{e^{x^2} + C}{2x^2}$$

13. $y' - y\tan x = \dfrac{\sin 2x}{\cos x} = 2\sin x$, so

$$I(x) = e^{\int -\tan x\, dx} = e^{\ln|\cos x|} = \cos x$$

(since $-\dfrac{\pi}{2} < x < \dfrac{\pi}{2}$). Multiplying
the differential equation by $I(x)$ gives

$$(y' - y\tan x)\cos x = \frac{\sin 2x}{\cos x}\cos x \quad \Rightarrow$$

$$(y\cos x)' = \sin 2x \quad \Rightarrow$$

$$y\cos x = \int \sin 2x\, dx + C = -\frac{1}{2}\cos 2x + C$$

$$= \frac{1}{2} - \cos^2 x + C \quad \Rightarrow$$

$$y = \frac{\sec x}{2} - \cos x + C\sec x.$$

14. $y' + \left(1 + \dfrac{1}{x}\right) y = \dfrac{e^{-x}}{x}$, so $I(x) = e^{\int(1+1/x)dx} = xe^x$.
Multiplying the differential equation by $I(x)$ gives

$$xe^x y' + (xe^x + e^x)\, y = 1 \quad \Rightarrow \quad (xe^x y)' = 1 \quad \Rightarrow$$

$$xe^x y = \int 1\, dx \Rightarrow xe^x y = x + C \quad \Rightarrow$$

$$y = e^{-x}(1 + C/x).$$

15. $I(\theta) = e^{\int -\tan\theta\, d\theta} = e^{-\ln(\sec\theta)} = \cos\theta.$
Multiplying the differential equation by $I(\theta)$ gives
$\cos\theta\,(dy/d\theta) - y\sin\theta = \cos\theta \Rightarrow (y\cos\theta)' = \cos\theta$

$$\Rightarrow \quad y\cos\theta = \int \cos\theta\, d\theta \quad \Rightarrow$$

$$y\cos\theta = \sin\theta + C \quad \Rightarrow$$

$$y = \tan\theta + C\sec\theta.$$

10

PARAMETRIC EQUATIONS AND POLAR COORDINATES

1–4 ■ (a) Sketch the curve by using the parametric equations to plot points. Indicate with an arrow the direction in which the curve is traced as t increases.

(b) Eliminate the parameter to find a Cartesian equaiton of the curve.

1. $x = 2t + 4$, $y = t - 1$

2. $x = 3 - t$, $y = 2t - 3$, $-1 \leq t \leq 4$

3. $x = 1 - 2t$, $y = t^2 + 4$, $0 \leq t \leq 3$

4. $x = t^2$, $y = 6 - 3t$

5–12 ■ Find dy/dx and d^2y/dx^2.

5. $x = t^2 + t$, $y = t^2 + 1$

6. $x = t + 2\cos t$, $y = \sin 2t$

7. $x = t^4 - 1$, $y = t - t^2$

8. $x = t^3 + t^2 + 1$, $y = 1 - t^2$

9. $x = \sin \pi t$, $y = \cos \pi t$

10. $x = 1 + \tan t$, $y = \cos 2t$

11. $x = e^{-t}$, $y = te^{2t}$

12. $x = 1 + t^2$, $y = t \ln t$

13–17 ■ Find a polar equation for the curve represented by the given Cartesian equation.

13. $y = 5$ **14.** $y = 2x - 1$

15. $x^2 + y^2 = 25$ **16.** $x^2 = 4y$

17. $2xy = 1$

18–25 ■ Sketch the curve and find the area that it encloses.

18. $r = 5 \sin \theta$ **19.** $r = 4 - \sin \theta$

20. $r = \sin 3\theta$ **21.** $r = 4(1 - \cos \theta)$

22. $r = 2 \cos \theta$ **23.** $r = 1 + \sin \theta$

24. $r = 3 - \cos \theta$ **25.** $r = \sin 4\theta$

26 ■ Use a calculator or computer to find the length of the loop correct to four decimal places.

26. One loop of the four-leaved rose $r = \cos 2\theta$.

27–34 ■ Find the vertex, focus, and directrix of the parabola and sketch its graph.

27. $x^2 = -8y$ **28.** $x = -5y^2$

29. $y^2 = x$ **30.** $2x^2 = y$

31. $x + 1 = 2(y - 3)^2$ **32.** $x^2 - 6x + 8y = 7$

33. $2x + y^2 - 8y + 12 = 0$

34. $x^2 + 12x - y + 39 = 0$

35. A curve is defined by the parametric equations

$$x = \int_1^t \frac{\cos u}{u} \, du \qquad y = \int_1^t \frac{\sin u}{u} \, du$$

Find the length of the arc of the curve from the origin to the nearest point where there is a vertical tangent line.

10 | ANSWERS TO SELECTED EXERCISES

1. (a) $\dfrac{x^2}{2^2} + \dfrac{y^2}{(1/2)^2} = 1$

(b)

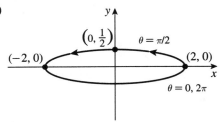

2. (a) $y = 1 - \dfrac{x^2}{4}, \quad -2 \le x \le 2$

(b)

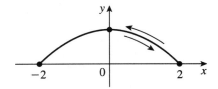

3. (a) $y = -1/x, \, x > 0$

(b)

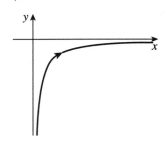

4. (a) $y + 1 = 2x^2, \, -1 \le x \le 1$

(b)

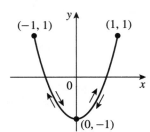

5. $1 - \dfrac{1}{2t+1}, \, \dfrac{2}{(2t+1)^3}$

6. $\dfrac{2\cos 2t}{1-2\sin t}, \, \dfrac{4(\cos t - \sin 2t + \sin t \sin 2t)}{(1-2\sin t)^3}$

7. $\dfrac{1}{4}t^{-3} - \dfrac{1}{2}t^{-2}, \, \dfrac{-3+4t}{16t^7}$

8. $-\dfrac{2}{3t+2}, \, \dfrac{6}{t(3t+2)^3}$

9. $-\tan \pi t, \, -\sec^3 \pi t$

10. $-4\sin t \cos^3 t, \, 4\cos^4 t(3\sin^2 t - \cos^2 t)$

11. $-(2t+1)e^{3t}, \, (6t+5)e^{4t}$

12. $\dfrac{1+\ln t}{2t}, \, -\dfrac{\ln t}{4t^3}$

13. $r\sin\theta = 5$

14. $r = \dfrac{1}{2\cos\theta - \sin\theta}$

15. $r = 5$

16. $r = 4\tan\theta \sec\theta$

17. $r^2 = \csc 2\theta$

18.

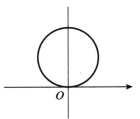

$\dfrac{25}{4}\pi$

19.

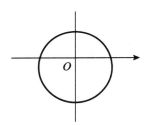

$\dfrac{33\pi}{2}$

20.

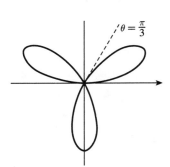

$\dfrac{\pi}{4}$

21.

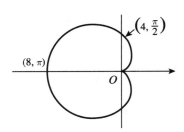

24π

22.

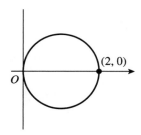

π

23.

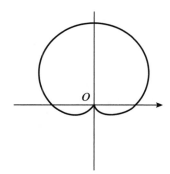

$\dfrac{3\pi}{2}$

24.

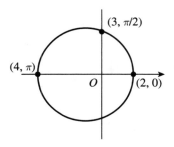

$\dfrac{19\pi}{2}$

25.

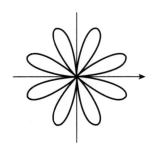

$\dfrac{\pi}{2}$

26. 2.4221

27. $(0, 0)$, $(0, -2)$, $y = 2$

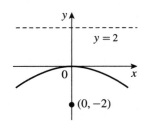

28. $(0, 0)$, $\left(-\dfrac{1}{20}, 0\right)$, $x = \dfrac{1}{20}$

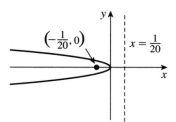

29. $(0, 0)$, $\left(\dfrac{1}{4}, 0\right)$, $x = -\dfrac{1}{4}$

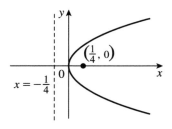

30. $(0, 0)$, $\left(0, \dfrac{1}{8}\right)$, $y = -\dfrac{1}{8}$

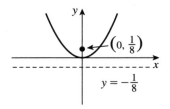

31. $(-1, 3)$, $\left(-\dfrac{7}{8}, 3\right)$, $x = -\dfrac{9}{8}$

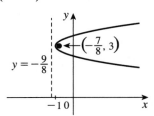

32. $(3, 2)$, $(3, 0)$, $y = 4$

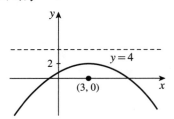

33. $(2, 4), \left(\dfrac{3}{2}, 4\right), x = \dfrac{5}{2}$

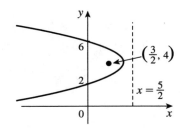

34. $(-6, 3), \left(-6, \dfrac{13}{4}\right), y = \dfrac{11}{4}$

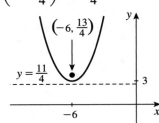

35. $\ln(\pi/2)$

10 | SOLUTIONS TO SELECTED EXERCISES

1. (a) $x = 2\cos\theta$, $y = \dfrac{1}{2}\sin\theta$, $0 \le \theta \le 2\pi$.

$1 = \cos^2\theta + \sin^2\theta = \left(\dfrac{x}{2}\right)^2 + \left(\dfrac{y}{1/2}\right)^2$, so

$\dfrac{x^2}{2^2} + \dfrac{y^2}{(1/2)^2} = 1$.

(b)

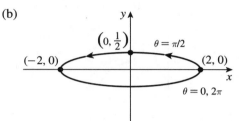

2. (a) $x = 2\cos\theta$, $y = \sin^2\theta$.

$1 = \cos^2\theta + \sin^2\theta = \left(\dfrac{x}{2}\right)^2 + y$, so $y = 1 - \dfrac{x^2}{4}$,

$-2 \le x \le 2$. The curve is at $(2, 0)$ whenever $\theta = 2\pi n$.

(b)

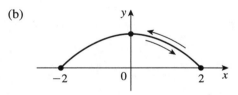

3. (a) $x = \tan\theta + \sec\theta$, $y = \tan\theta - \sec\theta$,

$-\dfrac{\pi}{2} < 0 < \dfrac{\pi}{2}$. $xy = \tan^2\theta - \sec^2\theta = -1 \implies$

$y = -1/x$, $x > 0$.

(b)

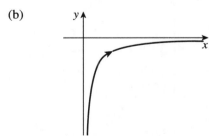

4. (a) $x = \cos t$, $y = \cos 2t$.

$y = \cos 2t = 2\cos^2 t - 1 = 2x^2 - 1$, so

$y + 1 = 2x^2$, $-1 \le x \le 1$.

(b)

5. $x = t^2 + t$, $y = t^2 + 1$.

$\dfrac{dy}{dx} = \dfrac{dy/dt}{dx/dt} = \dfrac{2t}{2t+1} = 1 - \dfrac{1}{2t+1}$;

$\dfrac{d}{dt}\left(\dfrac{dy}{dx}\right) = \dfrac{2}{(2t+1)^2}$;

$\dfrac{d^2y}{dx^2} = \dfrac{d}{dx}\left(\dfrac{dy}{dx}\right) = \dfrac{d\,(dy/dx)/dt}{dx/dt} = \dfrac{2}{(2t+1)^3}$

6. $x = t + 2\cos t$, $y = \sin 2t$. $\dfrac{dy}{dx} = \dfrac{dy/dt}{dx/dt} = \dfrac{2\cos 2t}{1 - 2\sin t}$;

$\dfrac{d}{dt}\left(\dfrac{dy}{dx}\right) = \dfrac{(1 - 2\sin t)(-4\sin 2t) - 2\cos 2t\,(-2\cos t)}{(1 - 2\sin t)^2}$

$\quad = \dfrac{4(\cos t - \sin 2t + \sin t \sin 2t)}{(1 - 2\sin t)^2}$;

$\dfrac{d^2y}{dx^2} = \dfrac{d(dy/dx)/dt}{dx/dt} = \dfrac{4(\cos t - \sin 2t + \sin t \sin 2t)}{(1 - 2\sin t)^3}$.

7. $x = t^4 - 1$, $y = t - t^2 \implies \dfrac{dy}{dt} = 1 - 2t$,

$\dfrac{dx}{dt} = 4t^3$, $\dfrac{dy}{dx} = \dfrac{dy/dt}{dx/dt} = \dfrac{1 - 2t}{4t^3} = \dfrac{1}{4}t^{-3} - \dfrac{1}{2}t^{-2}$;

$\dfrac{d}{dt}\left(\dfrac{dy}{dx}\right) = -\dfrac{3}{4}t^{-4} + t^{-3}$,

$\dfrac{d^2y}{dx^2} = \dfrac{d(dy/dx)/dt}{dx/dt} = \dfrac{-\frac{3}{4}t^{-4} + t^{-3}}{4t^3} \cdot \dfrac{4t^4}{4t^4} = \dfrac{-3 + 4t}{16t^7}$.

8. $x = t^3 + t^2 + 1$, $y = 1 - t^2$. $\dfrac{dy}{dt} = -2t$,

$\dfrac{dx}{dt} = 3t^2 + 2t$; $\dfrac{dy}{dx} = \dfrac{dy/dt}{dx/dt} = \dfrac{-2t}{3t^2 + 2t} = -\dfrac{2}{3t + 2}$;

$\dfrac{d}{dt}\left(\dfrac{dy}{dx}\right) = \dfrac{6}{(3t + 2)^2}$;

$\dfrac{d^2y}{dx^2} = \dfrac{d(dy/dx)\,dt}{dx/dt} = \dfrac{6}{t(3t + 2)^3}$.

9. $x = \sin \pi t$, $y = \cos \pi t$.

$\dfrac{dy}{dx} = \dfrac{dy/dt}{dx/dt} = \dfrac{-\pi \sin \pi t}{\pi \cos \pi t} = -\tan \pi t$;

$\dfrac{d^2y}{dx^2} = \dfrac{d}{dx}\left(\dfrac{dy}{dx}\right) = \dfrac{d(dy/dx)/dt}{dx/dt}$

$\quad = \dfrac{-\pi \sec^2 \pi t}{\pi \cos \pi t} = -\sec^3 \pi t$.

10. $x = 1 + \tan t$, $y = \cos 2t$ $\Rightarrow$ $\dfrac{dy}{dt} = -2 \sin 2t$,

$\dfrac{dx}{dt} = \sec^2 t$,

$\dfrac{dy}{dx} = \dfrac{dy/dt}{dx/dt} = \dfrac{-2 \sin 2t}{\sec^2 t} = -4 \sin t \cos t \cdot \cos^2 t$

$\qquad = -4 \sin t \cos^3 t$;

$\dfrac{d}{dt}\left(\dfrac{dy}{dx}\right) = -4 \sin t \, (3 \cos^2 t)(-\sin t) - 4 \cos^4 t$

$\qquad\qquad = 12 \sin^2 t \cos^2 t - 4 \cos^4 t$,

$\dfrac{d^2 y}{dx^2} = \dfrac{d\,(dy/dx)\,dt}{dx/dt} = \dfrac{4 \cos^2 t \,(3 \sin^2 t - \cos^2 t)}{\sec^2 t}$

$\qquad = 4 \cos^4 t \,(3 \sin^2 t - \cos^2 t).$

11. $x = e^{-t}$, $y = te^{2t}$.

$\dfrac{dy}{dx} = \dfrac{dy/dt}{dx/dt} = \dfrac{(2t + 1)\,e^{2t}}{-e^{-t}} = -(2t + 1)\,e^{3t}$;

$\dfrac{d}{dt}\left(\dfrac{dy}{dx}\right) = -3(2t + 1)\,e^{3t} - 2e^{3t} = -(6t + 5)e^{3t}$;

$\dfrac{d^2 y}{dx^2} = \dfrac{d}{dx}\left(\dfrac{dy}{dx}\right) = \dfrac{d\,(dy/dx)\,dt}{dx/dt} = \dfrac{-(6t + 5)\,e^{3t}}{-e^{-t}}$

$\qquad = (6t + 5)\,e^{4t}.$

12. $x = 1 + t^2$, $y = t \ln t$. $\dfrac{dy}{dx} = \dfrac{dy/dt}{dx/dt} = \dfrac{1 + \ln t}{2t}$;

$\dfrac{d}{dt}\left(\dfrac{dy}{dx}\right) = \dfrac{2t \,(1/t) - (1 + \ln t)\,2}{(2t)^2} = -\dfrac{\ln t}{2t^2}$;

$\dfrac{d^2 y}{dx^2} = \dfrac{d\,(dy/dx)/dt}{dx/dt} = -\dfrac{\ln t}{4t^3}.$

13. $y = 5$ $\Leftrightarrow$ $r \sin \theta = 5$

14. $y = 2x - 1$ $\Leftrightarrow$ $r \sin \theta = 2r \cos \theta - 1$ $\Leftrightarrow$

$r\,(2 \cos \theta - \sin \theta) = 1$ $\Leftrightarrow$ $r = \dfrac{1}{2 \cos \theta - \sin \theta}.$
(We can divide by $2 \cos \theta - \sin \theta$ because it must be nonzero in order that its product with r equals 1.)

15. $x^2 + y^2 = 25$ $\Leftrightarrow$ $r^2 = 25$ $\Leftrightarrow$ $r = 5$

16. $x^2 = 4y$ $\Leftrightarrow$ $r^2 \cos^2 \theta = 4r \sin \theta$ $\Leftrightarrow$
$r \cos^2 \theta = 4 \sin \theta$ $\Leftrightarrow$ $r = 4 \tan \theta \sec \theta$

17. $2xy = 1$ $\Leftrightarrow$ $2r \cos \theta\, r \sin \theta = 1$
$\Leftrightarrow$ $r^2 \sin 2\theta = 1$ $\Leftrightarrow$ $r^2 = \csc 2\theta$

18.

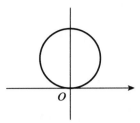

$A = \displaystyle\int_0^\pi \frac{1}{2} (5 \sin \theta)^2 \, d\theta = \frac{25}{4} \int_0^\pi (1 - \cos 2\theta)\, d\theta$

$\qquad = \dfrac{25}{4}\left[\theta - \dfrac{1}{2}\sin 2\theta\right]_0^\pi = \dfrac{25}{4}\pi$

19.

$A = 2 \displaystyle\int_{-\pi/2}^{\pi/2} \frac{1}{2} (4 - \sin \theta)^2 \, d\theta$

$\quad = \displaystyle\int_{-\pi/2}^{\pi/2} (16 - 8 \sin \theta + \sin^2 \theta)\, d\theta$

$\quad = \displaystyle\int_{-\pi/2}^{\pi/2} (16 + \sin^2 \theta)\, d\theta \; \big[\text{by Theorem } 5.5.7\text{(b)}\big]$

$\quad = 2 \displaystyle\int_0^{\pi/2} (16 + \sin^2 \theta)\, d\theta \; \big[\text{by Theorem } 5.5.7\text{(a)}\big]$

$\quad = 2 \displaystyle\int_0^{\pi/2}\left[16 + \frac{1}{2}(1 - \cos 2\theta)\right] d\theta$

$\quad = 2 \left[\dfrac{33}{2}\theta - \dfrac{1}{4}\sin 2\theta\right]_0^{\pi/2} = \dfrac{33\pi}{2}$

20.

$A = 6 \displaystyle\int_0^{\pi/6} \frac{1}{2} \sin^2 3\theta \, d\theta = 3 \int_0^{\pi/6} \frac{1}{2}(1 - \cos 6\theta)\, d\theta$

$\qquad = \dfrac{3}{2}\left[\theta - \dfrac{1}{6}\sin 6\theta\right]_0^{\pi/6} = \dfrac{\pi}{4}$

21.

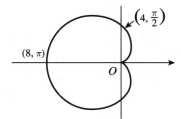

$$A = 2 \int_0^\pi \frac{1}{2} \left[4 \left(1 - \cos \theta \right) \right]^2 d\theta$$

$$= 16 \int_0^\pi (1 - 2 \cos \theta + \cos^2 \theta) \, d\theta$$

$$= 8 \int_0^\pi (3 - 4 \cos \theta + \cos 2\theta) \, d\theta$$

$$= 4 \left[6\theta - 8 \sin \theta + \sin 2\theta \right]_0^\pi = 24\pi$$

22.

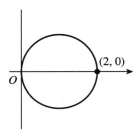

$$A = 2 \int_0^{\pi/2} \frac{1}{2} (2 \cos \theta)^2 \, d\theta = 2 \int_0^{\pi/2} (1 + \cos 2\theta) \, d\theta$$

$$= 2 \left[\theta + \frac{1}{2} \sin 2\theta \right]_0^{\pi/2} = \pi$$

23.

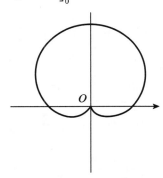

$$A = 2 \int_{-\pi/2}^{\pi/2} \frac{1}{2} (1 + \sin \theta)^2 \, d\theta$$

$$= \int_{-\pi/2}^{\pi/2} (1 + 2 \sin \theta + \sin^2 2\theta) \, d\theta$$

$$= \left[\theta - 2 \cos \theta \right]_{-\pi/2}^{\pi/2} + \int_{-\pi/2}^{\pi/2} \frac{1}{2} (1 - \cos 2\theta) \, d\theta$$

$$= \pi + \frac{1}{2} \left[\theta - \frac{1}{2} \sin 2\theta \right]_{-\pi/2}^{\pi/2} = \pi + \frac{\pi}{2} = \frac{3\pi}{2}$$

24.

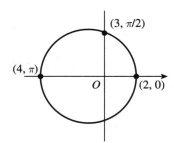

$$A = 2 \int_0^\pi \frac{1}{2} (3 - \cos \theta)^2 \, d\theta$$

$$= \int_0^\pi (9 - 6 \cos \theta + \cos^2 \theta) \, d\theta$$

$$= \left[9\theta - 6 \sin \theta + \frac{1}{2} \theta + \frac{1}{4} \sin 2\theta \right]_0^\pi = \frac{19\pi}{2}$$

25.

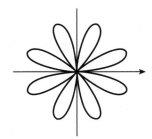

$$A = 8 \int_0^{\pi/4} \frac{1}{2} \sin^2 4\theta \, d\theta = 2 \int_0^{\pi/4} (1 - \cos 8\theta) \, d\theta$$

$$= \left[2\theta - \frac{1}{4} \sin 8\theta \right]_0^{\pi/4} = \frac{\pi}{2}$$

26. From Figure 4 in Example 1,

$$L = \int_{-\pi/4}^{\pi/4} \sqrt{r^2 + (r')^2} \, d\theta$$

$$= 2 \int_0^{\pi/4} \sqrt{\cos^2 2\theta + 4 \sin^2 2\theta} \, d\theta$$

$$\approx 2 \, (1.211056) \approx 2.4221$$

27. $x^2 = -8y$. $4p = -8$, so $p = -2$. The vertex is $(0, 0)$, the focus is $(0, -2)$, and the directrix is $y = 2$.

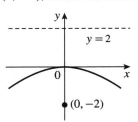

28. $x = -5y^2 \implies y^2 = -\frac{1}{5}x \implies 4p = -\frac{1}{5}$
$\implies p = -\frac{1}{20} \implies$ vertex $(0, 0)$, focus
$\left(-\frac{1}{20}, 0 \right)$, directrix $x = \frac{1}{20}$

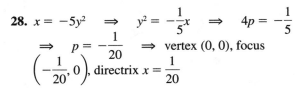

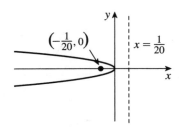

29. $y^2 = x$. $p = \dfrac{1}{4}$ and the vertex is $(0, 0)$, so the focus is $\left(\dfrac{1}{4}, 0\right)$, and the directrix is $x = -\dfrac{1}{4}$.

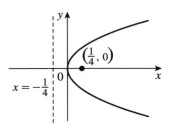

30. $x^2 = \dfrac{1}{2}y \quad \Rightarrow \quad p = \dfrac{1}{8} \quad \Rightarrow \quad$ vertex $(0, 0)$,

focus $\left(0, \dfrac{1}{8}\right)$, directrix $y = -\dfrac{1}{8}$

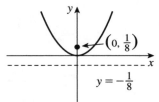

31. $x + 1 = 2(y - 3)^2 \quad \Rightarrow \quad (y - 3)^2 = \dfrac{1}{2}(x + 1) \quad \Rightarrow$

$p = \dfrac{1}{8} \quad \Rightarrow \quad$ vertex $(-1, 3)$, focus $\left(-\dfrac{7}{8}, 3\right)$,

directrix $x = -\dfrac{9}{8}$

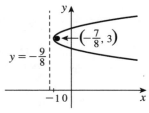

32. $x^2 - 6x + 8y = 7 \quad \Leftrightarrow \quad (x - 3)^2 = -8y + 16 = -8(y - 2) \quad \Rightarrow \quad p = -2 \quad \Rightarrow$ vertex $(3, 2)$, focus $(3, 0)$, directrix $y = 4$

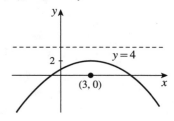

33. $2x + y^2 - 8y + 12 = 0 \quad \Rightarrow \quad (y - 4)^2 = -2(x - 2)$

$\Rightarrow \quad p = -\dfrac{1}{2} \quad \Rightarrow \quad$ vertex $(2, 4)$, focus $\left(\dfrac{3}{2}, 4\right)$,

directrix $x = \dfrac{5}{2}$

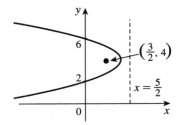

34. $x^2 + 12x - y + 39 = 0 \quad \Leftrightarrow \quad (x + 6)^2 = y - 3 \quad \Rightarrow$

$p = \dfrac{1}{4} \quad \Rightarrow \quad$ vertex $(-6, 3)$, focus $\left(-6, \dfrac{13}{4}\right)$,

directrix $y = \dfrac{11}{4}$

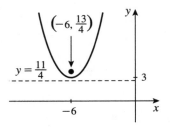

35. $x = \displaystyle\int_1^t \dfrac{\cos u}{u}\, du, \ y = \int_1^t \dfrac{\sin u}{u}\, du$, so by FTC1, we

have $\dfrac{dx}{dt} = \dfrac{\cos t}{t}$ and $\dfrac{dy}{dt} = \dfrac{\sin t}{t}$. Vertical tangent

lines occur when $\dfrac{dx}{dt} = 0 \Leftrightarrow \cos t = 0$. The

parameter value corresponding to $(x, y) = (0, 0)$ is $t = 1$, so the nearest vertical tangent occurs when

$t = \dfrac{\pi}{2}$. Therefore, the arc length between these

points is

$$L = \int_1^{\pi/2} \sqrt{\left(\dfrac{dx}{dt}\right)^2 + \left(\dfrac{dy}{dt}\right)^2}\, dt$$

$$= \int_1^{\pi/2} \sqrt{\dfrac{\cos^2 t}{t^2} + \dfrac{\sin^2 t}{t^2}}\, dt$$

$$= \int_1^{\pi/2} \dfrac{dt}{t} = [\ln t]_1^{\pi/2} = \ln \dfrac{\pi}{2}$$

11 | INFINITE SEQUENCES AND SERIES

1–6 ■ Find a formula for the general term a_n of the sequence, assuming that the pattern of the first few terms continues.

1. $\{1, 4, 7, 10, \dots\}$

2. $\left\{\dfrac{3}{16}, \dfrac{4}{25}, \dfrac{5}{36}, \dfrac{6}{49}, \dots\right\}$

3. $\left\{\dfrac{3}{2}, -\dfrac{9}{4}, \dfrac{27}{8}, -\dfrac{81}{16}, \dots\right\}$

4. $\{-1, 2, -6, 24, \dots\}$

5. $\left\{\dfrac{2}{3}, -\dfrac{3}{5}, \dfrac{4}{7}, -\dfrac{5}{9}, \dots\right\}$

6. $\{0, 2, 0, 2, 0, 2, \dots\}$

7–11 ■ Find the values of x for which the series converges. Find the sum of the series for those values of x.

7. $\displaystyle\sum_{n=0}^{\infty} 3^n x^n$

8. $\displaystyle\sum_{n=2}^{\infty} \dfrac{x^n}{5^n}$

9. $\displaystyle\sum_{n=0}^{\infty} 2^n \sin^n x$

10. $\displaystyle\sum_{n=0}^{\infty} \dfrac{1}{x^n}$

11. $\displaystyle\sum_{n=0}^{\infty} \tan^n x$

12. Use the Integral Test to determine whether the series

$$\frac{1}{3} + \frac{1}{7} + \frac{1}{11} + \frac{1}{15} + \cdots$$

is convergent or divergent.

13–18 ■ Determine whether the series converges or diverges.

13. $\displaystyle\sum_{n=1}^{\infty} \dfrac{n}{\sqrt{n^5 + 4}}$

14. $\displaystyle\sum_{n=1}^{\infty} \dfrac{\arctan n}{n^4}$

15. $\displaystyle\sum_{n=3}^{\infty} \dfrac{1}{n^2 - 4}$

16. $\displaystyle\sum_{n=1}^{\infty} \dfrac{n^2 + 1}{n^4 + 1}$

17. $\displaystyle\sum_{n=1}^{\infty} \dfrac{n+1}{n2^n}$

18. $\displaystyle\sum_{n=1}^{\infty} \dfrac{n^2 - 3n}{\sqrt[3]{n^{10} - 4n^2}}$

19–22 ■ Approximate the sum of the series to the indicated accuracy.

19. $\displaystyle\sum_{n=1}^{\infty} \dfrac{(-1)^{n-1}}{(2n-1)!}$ (four decimal places)

20. $\displaystyle\sum_{n=0}^{\infty} \dfrac{(-1)^n}{(2n)!}$ (four decimal places)

21. $\displaystyle\sum_{n=0}^{\infty} \dfrac{(-1)^n}{2^n n!}$ (four decimal places)

22. $\displaystyle\sum_{n=1}^{\infty} \dfrac{(-1)^{n-1}}{n^6}$ (five decimal places)

23–30 ■ Determine whether the series is absolutely convergent, conditionally convergent, or divergent.

23. $\displaystyle\sum_{n=1}^{\infty} \dfrac{(-1)^{n-1}}{n\sqrt{n}}$

24. $\displaystyle\sum_{n=1}^{\infty} \dfrac{(-1)^n}{\sqrt{n}}$

25. $\displaystyle\sum_{n=1}^{\infty} \dfrac{(-3)^n}{n^3}$

26. $\displaystyle\sum_{n=0}^{\infty} \dfrac{(-3)^n}{n!}$

27. $\displaystyle\sum_{n=1}^{\infty} \dfrac{(-1)^n}{5+n}$

28. $\displaystyle\sum_{n=1}^{\infty} \dfrac{(-1)^{n-1}}{n!}$

29. $1 - \dfrac{2!}{1\cdot 3} + \dfrac{3!}{1\cdot 3\cdot 5} - \dfrac{4!}{1\cdot 3\cdot 5\cdot 7} + \cdots$
$$+ \dfrac{(-1)^{n-1}n!}{1\cdot 3\cdot 5\cdots\cdot(2n-1)} + \cdots$$

30. $\dfrac{1}{3} + \dfrac{1\cdot 4}{3\cdot 5} + \dfrac{1\cdot 4\cdot 7}{3\cdot 5\cdot 7} + \dfrac{1\cdot 4\cdot 7\cdot 10}{3\cdot 5\cdot 7\cdot 9} + \cdots$
$$+ \dfrac{1\cdot 4\cdot 7\cdots\cdot(3n-2)}{3\cdot 5\cdot 7\cdots\cdot(2n+1)} + \cdots$$

31–34 ■ Find the radius of convergence and interval of convergence of the series.

31. $\displaystyle\sum_{n=0}^{\infty} \dfrac{x^n}{n+2}$

32. $\displaystyle\sum_{n=1}^{\infty} \dfrac{(-1)^n x^n}{\sqrt[3]{n}}$

33. $\displaystyle\sum_{n=1}^{\infty} \dfrac{(-1)^n x^n}{n2^n}$

34. $\displaystyle\sum_{n=1}^{\infty} n5^n x^n$

35–38 ■ Find the Taylor series for $f(x)$ centered at the given value of a. [Assume that f has a power series expansion. Do not show that $R_n(x) \to 0$.]

35. $f(x) = 1/x, \quad a = 1$

36. $f(x) = \sqrt{x}, \quad a = 4$

37. $f(x) = \sin x, \quad a = \pi/4$

38. $f(x) = \cos x, \quad a = -\pi/4$

39–42 ■ Use a Maclaurin series derived in this section to obtain the Maclaurin series for the given function.

39. $f(x) = e^{3x}$

40. $f(x) = \sin 2x$

41. $f(x) = x^2 \cos x$

42. $f(x) = \cos(x^3)$

11 | ANSWERS TO SELECTED EXERCISES

1. $a_n = 3n - 2$

2. $a_n = \dfrac{n + 2}{(n + 3)^2}$

3. $a_n = (-1)^{n+1}\left(\dfrac{3}{2}\right)^n$

4. $a_n = (-1)^n\, n!$

5. $a_n = (-1)^{n+1}\dfrac{n + 1}{2n + 1}$

6. $a_n = 1 - (-1)^{n-1}$ or $a_n = 1 + (-1)^n$

7. $-\dfrac{1}{3} < x < \dfrac{1}{3}$; $\dfrac{1}{1 - 3x}$

8. $-5 < x < 5$; $\dfrac{x^2}{25 - 5x}$

9. $n\pi - \dfrac{\pi}{6} < x < n\pi + \dfrac{\pi}{6}$ (n any integer); $\dfrac{1}{1 - 2\sin x}$

10. $|x| > 1$; $\dfrac{x}{x - 1}$

11. $n\pi - \dfrac{\pi}{4} < x < n\pi + \dfrac{\pi}{4}$ (n any integer); $\dfrac{1}{1 - \tan x}$

12. Divergent

13. Converges

14. Converges

15. Converges

16. Converges

17. Converges

18. Converges

19. 0.8415

20. 0.5403

21. 0.6065

22. 0.98555

23. Absolutely convergent

24. Conditionally convergent

25. Divergent

26. Absolutely convergent

27. Conditionally convergent

28. Absolutely convergent

29. Absolutely convergent

30. Divergent

31. $1, [-1, 1)$

32. $2, (-1, 1]$

33. $2, (-2, 2]$

34. $\dfrac{1}{5}, \left(-\dfrac{1}{5}, \dfrac{1}{5}\right)$

35. $\displaystyle\sum_{n=0}^{\infty} (-1)^n (x - 1)^n,\ R = 1$

36. $2 + \dfrac{x - 4}{4}$
$\qquad + \displaystyle\sum_{n=2}^{\infty} \dfrac{(-1)^{n-1}1\cdot 3\cdot 5\cdot\cdots\cdot(2n - 3)}{2^{3n-1}n!}(x - 4)^n,$
$R = 4$

37. $\dfrac{\sqrt{2}}{2}\displaystyle\sum_{n=0}^{\infty}(-1)^n\left[\dfrac{1}{(2n)!}\left(x - \dfrac{\pi}{4}\right)^{2n}\right.$
$\qquad\qquad \left. + \dfrac{1}{(2n + 1)!}\left(x - \dfrac{\pi}{4}\right)^{2n+1}\right],\ R = \infty$

38. $\dfrac{\sqrt{2}}{2}\displaystyle\sum_{n=0}^{\infty}\dfrac{(-1)^{n(n-1)/2}\left(x + \dfrac{\pi}{4}\right)^n}{n!},\ R = \infty$

39. $\displaystyle\sum_{n=0}^{\infty}\dfrac{3^n x^n}{n!},\ R = \infty$

40. $\displaystyle\sum_{n=0}^{\infty}\dfrac{(-1)^n 2^{2n+1} x^{2n+1}}{(2n + 1)!},\ R = \infty$

41. $\displaystyle\sum_{n=0}^{\infty}\dfrac{(-1)^n x^{2n+2}}{(2n)!},\ R = \infty$

42. $\displaystyle\sum_{n=0}^{\infty}\dfrac{(-1)^n x^{6n}}{(2n)!},\ R = \infty$

11 | SOLUTIONS TO SELECTED EXERCISES

1. $a_n = 3n - 2$

2. $a_n = \dfrac{n + 2}{(n + 3)^2}$

3. $a_n = (-1)^{n+1} \left(\dfrac{3}{2}\right)^n$

4. $a_n = (-1)^n \, n!$

5. $a_n = (-1)^{n+1} \dfrac{n + 1}{2n + 1}$

6. $\{0, 2, 0, 2, 0, 2, \ldots\}$. 1 is halfway between 0 and 2, so we can think of alternately subtracting and adding 1 (from 1 and to 1) to obtain the given sequence: $a_n = 1 - (-1)^{n-1}$.

7. $\displaystyle\sum_{n=0}^{\infty} (3x)^n$ is geometric with $r = 3x$, so converges for $|3x| < 1 \Leftrightarrow -\dfrac{1}{3} < x < \dfrac{1}{3}$ to $\dfrac{1}{1 - 3x}$.

8. $\displaystyle\sum_{n=2}^{\infty} \left(\dfrac{x}{5}\right)^n$ is a geometric series with $r = \dfrac{x}{5}$, so converges whenever $\left|\dfrac{x}{5}\right| < 1 \Leftrightarrow -5 < x < 5$. The sum is $\dfrac{(x/5)^2}{1 - x/5} = \dfrac{x^2}{25 - 5x}$.

9. $\displaystyle\sum_{n=0}^{\infty} (2 \sin x)^n$ is geometric so converges whenever $|2 \sin x| < 1 \Leftrightarrow -\dfrac{1}{2} < \sin x < \dfrac{1}{2} \Leftrightarrow n\pi - \dfrac{\pi}{6} < x < n\pi + \dfrac{\pi}{6}$, where the sum is $\dfrac{1}{1 - 2 \sin x}$.

10. $\displaystyle\sum_{n=0}^{\infty} \left(\dfrac{1}{x}\right)^n$ is geometric with $r = \dfrac{1}{x}$, so it converges whenever $\left|\dfrac{1}{x}\right| < 1 \Leftrightarrow |x| > 1 \Leftrightarrow x > 1$ or $x < -1$, and the sum is $\dfrac{1}{1 - 1/x} = \dfrac{x}{x - 1}$.

11. $\displaystyle\sum_{n=0}^{\infty} \tan^n x$ is geometric and converges when $|\tan x| < 1 \Leftrightarrow -1 < \tan x < 1 \Leftrightarrow n\pi - \dfrac{\pi}{4} < x < n\pi + \dfrac{\pi}{4}$ (n any integer). On these intervals the sum is $\dfrac{1}{1 - \tan x}$.

12. $\dfrac{1}{3} + \dfrac{1}{7} + \dfrac{1}{11} + \dfrac{1}{15} + \cdots = \displaystyle\sum_{n=1}^{\infty} \dfrac{1}{4n - 1}$. The function $f(x) = \dfrac{1}{4x - 1}$ is positive, continuous, and decreasing on $[1, \infty)$, so the Intergal Test applies.

$$\int_1^{\infty} \frac{dx}{4x - 1} = \lim_{b \to \infty} \int_1^b \frac{dx}{4x - 1} = \lim_{b \to \infty} \left[\frac{1}{4} \ln (4x - 1)\right]_1^b$$

$$= \lim_{b \to \infty} \left[\frac{1}{4} \ln (4b - 1) - \frac{1}{4} \ln 3\right] = \infty$$

so the improper integral diverges, and so does the series.

13. $\dfrac{n}{\sqrt{n^5 + 4}} < \dfrac{n}{\sqrt{n^5}} = \dfrac{1}{n^{3/2}}$. $\displaystyle\sum_{n=1}^{\infty} \dfrac{1}{n^{3/2}}$ is a convergent p-series $\left(p = \dfrac{3}{2} > 1\right)$ so $\displaystyle\sum_{n=1}^{\infty} \dfrac{n}{\sqrt{n^5 + 4}}$ converges by the Comparison Test.

14. $\dfrac{\arctan n}{n^4} < \dfrac{\pi/2}{n^4}$ and $\dfrac{\pi}{2} \displaystyle\sum_{n=1}^{\infty} \dfrac{1}{n^4}$ converges ($p = 4 > 1$) so $\displaystyle\sum_{n=1}^{\infty} \dfrac{\arctan n}{n^4}$ converges by the Comparison Test.

15. Use the Limit Comparison Test with $a_n = \dfrac{1}{n^2 - 4}$ and $b_n = \dfrac{1}{n^2}$: $\displaystyle\lim_{n \to \infty} \dfrac{a_n}{b_n} = \lim_{n \to \infty} \dfrac{n^2}{n^2 - 4} = 1 > 0$. Since $\displaystyle\sum_{n=3}^{\infty} b_n$ converges ($p = 2 > 1$), $\displaystyle\sum_{n=3}^{\infty} \dfrac{1}{n^2 - 4}$ also converges.

16. Let $a_n = \dfrac{n^2 + 1}{n^4 + 1}$ and $b_n = \dfrac{1}{n^2}$. Then $\displaystyle\lim_{n \to \infty} \dfrac{a_n}{b_n} = \lim_{n \to \infty} \dfrac{n^4 + n^2}{n^4 + 1} = 1 > 0$. Since $\displaystyle\sum_{n=1}^{\infty} \dfrac{1}{n^2}$ is a convergent p-series ($p = 2 > 1$), so is $\displaystyle\sum_{n=1}^{\infty} \dfrac{n^2 + 1}{n^4 + 1}$ by the Limit Comparison Test.

17. Let $a_n = \dfrac{n + 1}{n2^n}$ and $b_n = \dfrac{1}{2^n}$. Then $\displaystyle\lim_{n \to \infty} \dfrac{a_n}{b_n} = \lim_{n \to \infty} \dfrac{n + 1}{n} = 1 > 0$. Since $\displaystyle\sum_{n=1}^{\infty} \dfrac{1}{2^n}$ is a convergent geometric series $\left(|r| = \dfrac{1}{2} < 1\right)$, $\displaystyle\sum_{n=1}^{\infty} \dfrac{n + 1}{n2^n}$ converges by the Limit Comparison Test.

18. Use the Limit Comparison Test with

$$a_n = \frac{n^2 - 3n}{\sqrt[3]{n^{10} - 4n^2}} \text{ and } b_n = \frac{1}{n^{4/3}}.$$

$$\lim_{n\to\infty} \frac{a_n}{b_n} = \lim_{n\to\infty} \frac{n^{10/3} - 3n^{7/3}}{\sqrt[3]{n^{10} - 4n^2}} = \lim_{n\to\infty} \frac{1 - 3/n}{\sqrt[3]{1 - 4n^{-8}}}$$

$$= 1 > 0$$

so since $\sum_{n=1}^{\infty} b_n$ converges $\left(p = \frac{4}{3} > 1\right)$, so does

$$\sum_{n=1}^{\infty} \frac{n^2 - 3n}{\sqrt[3]{n^{10} - 4n^2}}.$$

19. $\sum_{n=1}^{\infty} \frac{(-1)^{n-1}}{(2n-1)!}.$

$$b_5 = \frac{1}{(2 \cdot 5 - 1)!}$$

$$= \frac{1}{362{,}880} < 0.00001, \text{ so}$$

$$\sum_{n=1}^{\infty} \frac{(-1)^{n-1}}{(2n-1)!} \approx \sum_{n=1}^{4} \frac{(-1)^{n-1}}{(2n-1)!} \approx 0.8415.$$

20. $b_4 = \frac{1}{(2 \cdot 4)!} = \frac{1}{40{,}320} \approx 0.000025$ and

$$s_3 = 1 - \frac{1}{2} + \frac{1}{24} - \frac{1}{720} \approx 0.54028, \text{ so, correct to}$$

four decimal places, $\sum_{n=0}^{\infty} \frac{(-1)^n}{(2n)!} \approx 0.5403.$

21. $b_6 = \frac{1}{2^6 6!} = \frac{1}{46{,}080} \approx 0.000022 < 0.0001, \text{ so}$

$$\sum_{n=0}^{\infty} \frac{(-1)^n}{2^n n!} \approx \sum_{n=0}^{5} \frac{(-1)^n}{2^n n!} \approx 0.6065.$$

22. $b_8 = 1/8^6 \approx 0.0000038 < 0.00001$ and

$$s_7 = 1 - \frac{1}{64} + \frac{1}{729} - \frac{1}{4096} + \frac{1}{15{,}625}$$

$$- \frac{1}{46{,}656} + \frac{1}{117{,}649}$$

$$\approx 0.9855537$$

so correct to five decimal places,

$$\sum_{n=1}^{\infty} \frac{(-1)^{n-1}}{n^6} \approx 0.98555.$$

23. $\sum_{n=1}^{\infty} \frac{1}{n\sqrt{n}} = \sum_{n=1}^{\infty} \frac{1}{n^{3/2}}$ is a convergent p-series

$\left(p = \frac{3}{2} > 1\right)$, so the given series is absolutely

convergent.

24. $\sum_{n=1}^{\infty} \frac{(-1)^n}{n^{1/2}}$ converges by the Alternating Series Test,

but $\sum_{n=1}^{\infty} \frac{1}{n^{1/2}}$ is a divergent p-series $\left(p = \frac{1}{2} < 1\right)$, so

$\sum_{n=1}^{\infty} \frac{(-1)^n}{n^{1/2}}$ converges conditionally.

25. Using the Ratio Test,

$$\lim_{n\to\infty}\left|\frac{a_{n+1}}{a_n}\right| = \lim_{n\to\infty}\left|\frac{(-3)^{n+1}/(n+1)^3}{(-3)^n/n^3}\right|$$

$$= 3\lim_{n\to\infty}\left(\frac{n}{n+1}\right)^3 = 3 > 1$$

so the series diverges.

26. Using the Ratio Test,

$$\lim_{n\to\infty}\left|\frac{a_{n+1}}{a_n}\right| = \lim_{n\to\infty}\left|\frac{(-3)^{n+1}/(n+1)!}{(-3)^n/n!}\right|$$

$$= 3\lim_{n\to\infty}\frac{1}{n+1} = 0 < 1,$$

so the series is absolutely convergent.

27. $\sum_{n=1}^{\infty} \frac{(-1)^n}{5+n}$ converges by the Alternating Series Test,

but $\sum_{n=1}^{\infty} \frac{1}{5+n}$ diverges by the Limit Comparison

Test with the harmonic series $\sum_{n=1}^{\infty} \frac{1}{n}$, so the given

series is conditionally convergent.

28. $\lim_{n\to\infty}\left|\frac{a_{n+1}}{a_n}\right| = \lim_{n\to\infty}\left|\frac{n!}{(n+1)!}\right| = \lim_{n\to\infty}\frac{1}{n+1} = 0 < 1,$

so the series $\sum_{n=1}^{\infty} \frac{(-1)^{n-1}}{n!}$ is absolutely convergent

by the Ratio Test.

29. $\lim_{n\to\infty}\left|\frac{a_{n+1}}{a_n}\right| = \lim_{n\to\infty}\frac{(n+1)!/[1\cdot3\cdot5\cdots\cdots(2n+1)]}{n!/[1\cdot3\cdot5\cdots\cdots(2n-1)]}$

$$= \lim_{n\to\infty}\frac{n+1}{2n+1} = \frac{1}{2} < 1$$

so the series converges absolutely by the Ratio Test.

30. $\lim_{n\to\infty}\left|\frac{a_{n+1}}{a_n}\right| = \lim_{n\to\infty}\left|\dfrac{\dfrac{1\cdot4\cdot7\cdots\cdots(3n-2)(3n+1)}{3\cdot5\cdot7\cdots\cdots(2n+1)(2n+3)}}{\dfrac{1\cdot4\cdot7\cdots\cdots(3n-2)}{3\cdot5\cdot7\cdots\cdots(2n+1)}}\right|$

$$= \lim_{n\to\infty}\frac{3n+1}{2n+3} = \frac{3}{2} > 1$$

so the series diverges by the Ratio Test.

"R" stands for "radius of convergence" and "I" stands for "interval of convergence" in this section.

31. If $a_n = \dfrac{x^n}{n+2}$, then

$$\lim_{n\to\infty}\left|\frac{a_{n+1}}{a_n}\right| = \lim_{n\to\infty}\left|\frac{x^{n+1}}{n+3}\cdot\frac{n+2}{x^n}\right|$$

$$= |x|\lim_{n\to\infty}\frac{n+2}{n+3} = |x| < 1$$

for convergence (by the Ratio Test). So $R = 1$.

When $x = 1$, the series is $\displaystyle\sum_{n=0}^{\infty}\frac{1}{n+2}$ which diverges (Integral Test or Comparison Test), and when $x = -1$, it is $\displaystyle\sum_{n=0}^{\infty}\frac{(-1)^n}{n+2}$ which converges (Alternating Series Test), so $I = [-1, 1)$.

32. If $a_n = \dfrac{(-1)^n x^n}{\sqrt[3]{n}}$, then

$$\lim_{n\to\infty}\left|\frac{a_{n+1}}{a_n}\right| = |x|\lim_{n\to\infty}\left(\frac{n}{n+1}\right)^{1/3} = |x| < 1 \text{ for}$$

convergence (by the Ratio Test), and $R = 1$. When $x = 1$, $\displaystyle\sum_{n=1}^{\infty}a_n = \sum_{n=1}^{\infty}\frac{(-1)^n}{\sqrt[3]{n}}$ which is a convergent alternating series, but when $x = -1$,

$$\sum_{n=1}^{\infty}a_n = \sum_{n=1}^{\infty}\frac{1}{n^{1/3}} \text{ which is a divergent } p\text{-series}$$

$\left(p = \dfrac{1}{3} < 1\right)$, so $I = (-1, 1]$.

33. If $a_n = \dfrac{(-1)^n x^n}{n2^n}$, then

$$\lim_{n\to\infty}\left|\frac{a_{n+1}}{a_n}\right| = \lim_{n\to\infty}\left|\frac{x^{n+1}/[(n+1)2^{n+1}]}{x^n/(n2^n)}\right|$$

$$= \left|\frac{x}{2}\right|\lim_{n\to\infty}\frac{n}{n+1} = \left|\frac{x}{2}\right| < 1$$

for convergence, so $|x| < 2$ and $R = 2$.

When $x = 2$, $\displaystyle\sum_{n=1}^{\infty}\frac{(-1)^n x^n}{n2^n} = \sum_{n=1}^{\infty}\frac{(-1)^n}{n}$ which converges by the Alternating Series Test. When $x = -2$, $\displaystyle\sum_{n=1}^{\infty}\frac{(-1)^n x^n}{n2^n} = \sum_{n=1}^{\infty}\frac{1}{n}$ which diverges (harmonic series), so $I = (-2, 2]$.

34. If $a_n = n5^n x^n$, then

$$\lim_{n\to\infty}\left|\frac{a_{n+1}}{a_n}\right| = 5|x|\lim_{n\to\infty}\frac{n+1}{n} = 5|x| < 1 \text{ for}$$

convergence (by the Ratio Test), so $R = \dfrac{1}{5}$. If $x = \pm\dfrac{1}{5}$,

$|a_n| = n \to \infty$ as $n \to \infty$, so $\displaystyle\sum_{n=1}^{\infty}a_n$ diverges by the Test for Divergence and $I = \left(-\dfrac{1}{5}, \dfrac{1}{5}\right)$.

35.

n	$f^{(n)}(x)$	$f^{(n)}(1)$
0	x^{-1}	1
1	$-x^{-2}$	-1
2	$2x^{-3}$	2
3	$-3\cdot 2x^{-4}$	$-3\cdot 2$
4	$4\cdot 3\cdot 2x^{-5}$	$4\cdot 3\cdot 2$
...	...	...

So $f^{(n)}(1) = (-1)^n n!$, and

$$\frac{1}{x} = \sum_{n=0}^{\infty}\frac{(-1)^n}{n!}(x-1)^n = \sum_{n=0}^{\infty}(-1)^n(x-1)^n. \text{ If}$$

$a_n = (-1)^n(x-1)^n$ then $\displaystyle\lim_{n\to\infty}\left|\frac{a_{n+1}}{a_n}\right| = |x-1| < 1$

for convergence, so $0 < x < 2$ and $R = 1$.

36.

n	$f^{(n)}(x)$	$f^{(n)}(4)$
0	$x^{1/2}$	2
1	$\dfrac{1}{2}x^{-1/2}$	2^{-2}
2	$-\dfrac{1}{4}x^{-3/2}$	-2^{-5}
3	$\dfrac{3}{8}x^{-5/2}$	$3\cdot 2^{-8}$
4	$-\dfrac{15}{16}x^{-7/2}$	$-15\cdot 2^{-11}$
...	...	...

$$f^{(n)}(4) = \frac{(-1)^{n-1}1\cdot 3\cdot 5\cdots (2n-3)}{2^{3n-1}}$$

for $n \geq 2$, so $\sqrt{x} = 2 + \dfrac{x-4}{4}$

$$+ \sum_{n=2}^{\infty}\frac{(-1)^{n-1}1\cdot 3\cdot 5\cdots(2n-3)}{2^{3n-1}n!}(x-4)^n;$$

$$\lim_{n\to\infty}\left|\frac{a_{n+1}}{a_n}\right| = \frac{|x-4|}{8}\lim_{n\to\infty}\left(\frac{2n-1}{n+1}\right) = \frac{|x-4|}{4} < 1$$

for convergence, so $|x-4| < 4 \implies R = 4$.

37.

n	$f^{(n)}(x)$	$f^{(n)}\left(\dfrac{\pi}{4}\right)$
0	$\sin x$	$\sqrt{2}/2$
1	$\cos x$	$\sqrt{2}/2$
2	$-\sin x$	$-\sqrt{2}/2$
3	$-\cos x$	$-\sqrt{2}/2$
4	$\sin x$	$\sqrt{2}/2$
...	...	...

$$\sin x = f\left(\frac{\pi}{4}\right) + f'\left(\frac{\pi}{4}\right)\left(x - \frac{\pi}{4}\right) + \frac{f''\left(\frac{\pi}{4}\right)}{2!}\left(x - \frac{\pi}{4}\right)^2$$

$$+ \frac{f^{(3)}\left(\frac{\pi}{4}\right)}{3!}\left(x - \frac{\pi}{4}\right)^3 + \frac{f^{(4)}\left(\frac{\pi}{4}\right)}{4!}\left(x - \frac{\pi}{4}\right)^4 + \cdots$$

$$= \frac{\sqrt{2}}{2}\left[1 + \left(x - \frac{\pi}{4}\right) - \frac{1}{2!}\left(x - \frac{\pi}{4}\right)^2 \right.$$

$$\left. - \frac{1}{3!}\left(x - \frac{\pi}{4}\right)^3 + \frac{1}{4!}\left(x - \frac{\pi}{4}\right)^4 + \cdots \right]$$

$$= \frac{\sqrt{2}}{2}\left[1 - \frac{1}{2!}\left(x - \frac{\pi}{4}\right)^2 + \frac{1}{4!}\left(x - \frac{\pi}{4}\right)^4 - \cdots \right]$$

$$+ \frac{\sqrt{2}}{2}\left[\left(x - \frac{\pi}{4}\right) - \frac{1}{3!}\left(x - \frac{\pi}{4}\right)^3 + \cdots \right]$$

$$= \frac{\sqrt{2}}{2}\sum_{n=0}^{\infty}(-1)^n\left[\frac{1}{(2n)!}\left(x - \frac{\pi}{4}\right)^{2n}\right.$$

$$\left. + \frac{1}{(2n+1)!}\left(x - \frac{\pi}{4}\right)^{2n+1}\right]$$

The series can also be written in the more elegant form

$$\sin x = \frac{\sqrt{2}}{2}\sum_{n=0}^{\infty}\frac{(-1)^{n(n-1)/2}\left(x - \frac{\pi}{4}\right)^n}{n!}.$$

If $a_n = \dfrac{(-1)^{n(n-1)/2}\left(x - \frac{\pi}{4}\right)^n}{n!}$, then

$$\lim_{n\to\infty}\left|\frac{a_{n+1}}{a_n}\right| = \lim_{n\to\infty}\frac{\left|x - \frac{\pi}{4}\right|}{n+1} = 0 < 1 \text{ for all } x,$$

so $R = \infty$.

38.

n	$f^{(n)}(x)$	$f^{(n)}\left(-\dfrac{\pi}{4}\right)$
0	$\cos x$	$\dfrac{\sqrt{2}}{2}$
1	$-\sin x$	$\dfrac{\sqrt{2}}{2}$
2	$-\cos x$	$-\dfrac{\sqrt{2}}{2}$
3	$\sin x$	$-\dfrac{\sqrt{2}}{2}$
4	$\cos x$	$\dfrac{\sqrt{2}}{2}$
...	...	...

$$f^{(n)}\left(-\frac{\pi}{4}\right) = (-1)^{n(n-1)/2}\frac{\sqrt{2}}{2}, \text{ so}$$

$$\cos x = \sum_{n=0}^{\infty}\frac{f^{(n)}\left(-\frac{\pi}{4}\right)}{n!}\left(x + \frac{\pi}{4}\right)^n$$

$$= \frac{\sqrt{2}}{2}\sum_{n=0}^{\infty}\frac{(-1)^{n(n-1)/2}\left(x + \frac{\pi}{4}\right)^n}{n!}$$

with $R = \infty$ by the Ratio Test (as in Problem 37).

39. $e^{3x} = \displaystyle\sum_{n=0}^{\infty}\frac{(3x)^n}{n!} = \sum_{n=0}^{\infty}\frac{3^n x^n}{n!}$, with $R = \infty$.

40. $\sin 2x = \displaystyle\sum_{n=0}^{\infty}\frac{(-1)^n(2x)^{2n+1}}{(2n+1)!} = \sum_{n=0}^{\infty}\frac{(-1)^n 2^{2n+1}x^{2n+1}}{(2n+1)!}$, $R = \infty$

41. $x^2\cos x = x^2\displaystyle\sum_{n=0}^{\infty}\frac{(-1)^n x^{2n}}{(2n)!} = \sum_{n=0}^{\infty}\frac{(-1)^n x^{2n+2}}{(2n)!}$, $R = \infty$

42. $\cos(x^3) = \displaystyle\sum_{n=0}^{\infty}\frac{(-1)^n(x^3)^{2n}}{(2n)!} = \sum_{n=0}^{\infty}\frac{(-1)^n x^{6n}}{(2n)!}$, $R = \infty$

12 VECTORS AND THE GEOMETRY OF SPACE

1–3 ■ Show that the equation represents a sphere and find its center and radius.

1. $x^2 + y^2 + z^2 + 2x + 8y - 4z = 28$

2. $2x^2 + 2y^2 + 2z^2 + 4y - 2z = 1$

3. $x^2 + y^2 + z^2 = 6x + 4y + 10z$

4–9 ■ Find a unit vector that has the same direction as the given vector.

4. $\langle 1, 2 \rangle$ **5.** $\langle 3, -5 \rangle$

6. $\langle -2, 4, 3 \rangle$ **7.** $\langle 1, -4, 8 \rangle$

8. $\mathbf{i} + \mathbf{j}$ **9.** $2\mathbf{i} - 4\mathbf{j} + 7\mathbf{k}$

10–15 ■ Find the angle between the vectors. (First find an exact expression and then approximate to the nearest degree.)

10. $\mathbf{a} = \langle 1, 2, 2 \rangle$, $\mathbf{b} = \langle 3, 4, 0 \rangle$

11. $\mathbf{a} = \langle 6, 0, 2 \rangle$, $\mathbf{b} = \langle 5, 3, -2 \rangle$

12. $\mathbf{a} = \langle 1, 2 \rangle$, $\mathbf{b} = \langle 12, -5 \rangle$

13. $\mathbf{a} = \langle 3, 1 \rangle$, $\mathbf{b} = \langle 2, 4 \rangle$

14. $\mathbf{a} = 6\mathbf{i} - 2\mathbf{j} - 3\mathbf{k}$, $\mathbf{b} = \mathbf{i} + \mathbf{j} + \mathbf{k}$

15. $\mathbf{a} = \mathbf{i} + \mathbf{j} + 2\mathbf{k}$, $\mathbf{b} = 2\mathbf{j} - 3\mathbf{k}$

16–18 ■ (a) Find a vector orthogonal to the plane through the points P, Q, and R, and (b) find the area of triangle PQR.

16. $P(1, 0, -1)$, $Q(2, 4, 5)$, $R(3, 1, 7)$

17. $P(0, 0, 0)$, $Q(1, -1, 1)$, $R(4, 3, 7)$

18. $P(-4, -4, -4)$, $Q(0, 5, -1)$, $R(3, 1, 2)$

19–22 ■ Find an equation of the plane passing through the given point and with normal vector $\mathbf{n}$.

19. $(1, 4, 5)$, $\mathbf{n} = \langle 7, 1, 4 \rangle$

20. $(-5, 1, 2)$, $\mathbf{n} = \langle 3, -5, 2 \rangle$

21. $(1, 2, 3)$, $\mathbf{n} = 15\mathbf{i} + 9\mathbf{j} - 12\mathbf{k}$

22. $(-1, -6, -4)$, $\mathbf{n} = -5\mathbf{i} + 2\mathbf{j} - 2\mathbf{k}$

23–27 ■ Find the traces of the given surface in the planes $x = k$, $y = k$, $z = k$. Then identify the surface and sketch it.

23. $x = y^2 + z^2$

24. $2x^2 + z^2 = 4$

25. $x^2 - y^2 + z^2 = 1$

26. $4z^2 - x^2 - y^2 = 1$

27. $9x^2 - y^2 - z^2 = 9$

12 | ANSWERS TO SELECTED EXERCISES

1. $(-1, -4, 2)$, 7

2. $\left(0, -1, \dfrac{1}{2}\right)$, $\dfrac{\sqrt{7}}{2}$

3. $(3, 2, 5)$, $\sqrt{38}$

4. $\left\langle \dfrac{1}{\sqrt{5}}, \dfrac{2}{\sqrt{5}} \right\rangle$

5. $\left\langle \dfrac{3}{\sqrt{34}}, -\dfrac{5}{\sqrt{34}} \right\rangle$

6. $\left\langle -\dfrac{2}{\sqrt{29}}, \dfrac{4}{\sqrt{29}}, \dfrac{3}{\sqrt{29}} \right\rangle$

7. $\left\langle \dfrac{1}{9}, -\dfrac{4}{9}, \dfrac{8}{9} \right\rangle$

8. $\dfrac{1}{\sqrt{2}}\mathbf{i} + \dfrac{1}{\sqrt{2}}\mathbf{j}$

9. $\dfrac{2}{\sqrt{69}}\mathbf{i} - \dfrac{4}{\sqrt{69}}\mathbf{j} + \dfrac{7}{\sqrt{69}}\mathbf{k}$

10. $\cos^{-1}\left(\dfrac{11}{15}\right) \approx 43°$

11. $\cos^{-1}\left(\dfrac{13}{2\sqrt{95}}\right) \approx 48°$ **12.** $\cos^{-1}\left(\dfrac{2}{13\sqrt{5}}\right) \approx 86°$

13. $\cos^{-1}\left(\dfrac{\sqrt{2}}{2}\right) = 45°$ **14.** $\cos^{-1}\left(\dfrac{1}{7\sqrt{3}}\right) \approx 85°$

15. $\cos^{-1}\left(-\dfrac{4}{\sqrt{78}}\right) \approx 117°$

16. (a) $\langle 26, 4, -7 \rangle$ (b) $\dfrac{1}{2}\sqrt{741}$

17. (a) $\langle -10, -3, 7 \rangle$ (b) $\dfrac{1}{2}\sqrt{158}$

18. (a) $\langle 39, -3, -43 \rangle$ (b) $\dfrac{1}{2}\sqrt{3379}$

19. $7x + y + 4z = 31$

20. $3x - 5y + 2z = -16$

21. $5x + 3y - 4z = -1$

22. $-5x + 2y - 2z = 1$

23. $x = k$, $y^2 + z^2 = k$, circle $(k > 0)$; $y = k$, $x - k^2 = z^2$, parabola; $z = k$, $x - k^2 = y^2$, parabola
Circular paraboloid with axis the x-axis

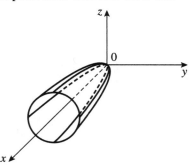

24. $x = k$, $z = \pm\sqrt{4 - 2k^2}$, two parallel lines $(|k| < \sqrt{2})$;
$y = k$, $2x^2 + z^2 = 4$, ellipse;
$z = k$, $x = \pm\sqrt{2 - (k^2/2)}$, two parallel lines $(|k| < 2)$
Elliptic cylinder with axis the y-axis

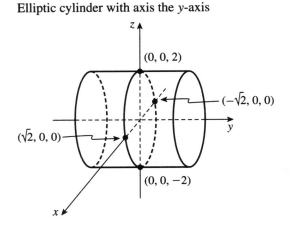

25. $x = k$, $z^2 - y^2 = 1 - k^2$, hyperbola;
$y = k$, $x^2 + z^2 = 1 + k^2$, circle;
$z = k$, $x^2 - y^2 = 1 - k^2$, hyperbola
Hyperboloid of one sheet with axis the y-axis

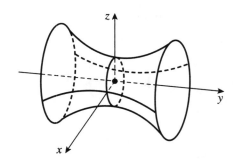

26. $x = k$, $4z^2 - y^2 = 1 + k^2$, hyperbola;
$y = k$, $4z^2 - x^2 = 1 + k^2$, hyperbola;
$z = k$, $x^2 + y^2 = 4k^2 - 1$, circle $\left(|k| > \dfrac{1}{2}\right)$
Hyperboloid of two sheets with axis the z-axis

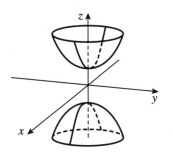

27. $x = k$, $y^2 + z^2 = 9\,(k^2 - 1)$, circle $(|k| > 1)$;
$y = k$, $9x^2 - z^2 = 9 + k^2$, hyperbola;
$z = k$, $9x^2 - y^2 = 9 + k^2$, hyperbola
Hyperboloid of two sheets with axis the x-axis

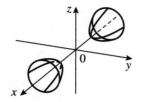

12 | SOLUTIONS TO SELECTED EXERCISES

1. Completing squares in the equation gives
$$(x^2 + 2x + 1) + (y^2 + 8y + 16) + (z^2 - 4z + 4)$$
$$= 28 + 1 + 16 + 4 \Rightarrow$$
$(x + 1)^2 + (y + 4)^2 + (z - 2)^2 = 49$, which we recognize as an equation of a sphere with center $(-1, -4, 2)$ and radius 7.

2. Completing squares in the equation gives
$$2x^2 + 2(y^2 + 2y + 1) + 2\left(z^2 - z + \frac{1}{4}\right)$$
$$= 1 + 2 + \frac{1}{2} = \frac{7}{2} \Rightarrow$$
$(x - 0)^2 + (y + 1)^2 + \left(z - \frac{1}{2}\right)^2 = \frac{7}{4}$, which we recognize as an equation of a sphere with center $\left(0, -1, \frac{1}{2}\right)$ and radius $\frac{\sqrt{7}}{2}$.

3. $(x^2 - 6x + 9) + (y^2 - 4y + 4) + (z^2 - 10z + 25)$
$$= 9 + 4 + 25 \Rightarrow$$
$(x - 3)^2 + (y - 2)^2 + (z - 5)^2 = 38 \Rightarrow C(3, 2, 5)$, and $r = \sqrt{38}$.

4. $|\langle 1, 2 \rangle| = \sqrt{1^2 + 2^2} = \sqrt{5}$. Thus
$$\mathbf{u} = \frac{1}{\sqrt{5}} \langle 1, 2 \rangle = \left\langle \frac{1}{\sqrt{5}}, \frac{2}{\sqrt{5}} \right\rangle.$$

5. $|\langle 3, -5 \rangle| = \sqrt{3^2 + (-5)^2} = \sqrt{34}$. Thus
$$\mathbf{u} = \frac{1}{\sqrt{34}} \langle 3, -5 \rangle = \left\langle \frac{3}{\sqrt{34}}, -\frac{5}{\sqrt{34}} \right\rangle.$$

6. $|\langle -2, 4, 3 \rangle| = \sqrt{(-2)^2 + 4^2 + 3^2} = \sqrt{29}$. Thus
$$\mathbf{u} = \frac{1}{\sqrt{29}} \langle -2, 4, 3 \rangle = \left\langle -\frac{2}{\sqrt{29}}, \frac{4}{\sqrt{29}}, \frac{3}{\sqrt{29}} \right\rangle.$$

7. $|\langle 1, -4, 8 \rangle| = \sqrt{1^2 + (-4)^2 + 8^2} = \sqrt{81} = 9$.
Thus $\mathbf{u} = \frac{1}{9} \langle 1, -4, 8 \rangle = \left\langle \frac{1}{9}, -\frac{4}{9}, \frac{8}{9} \right\rangle$.

8. $|\mathbf{i} + \mathbf{j}| = \sqrt{1^2 + 1^2} = \sqrt{2}$. Thus
$$\mathbf{u} = \frac{1}{\sqrt{2}} (\mathbf{i} + \mathbf{j}) = \frac{1}{\sqrt{2}} \mathbf{i} + \frac{1}{\sqrt{2}} \mathbf{j}.$$

9. $|2\mathbf{i} - 4\mathbf{j} + 7\mathbf{k}| = \sqrt{2^2 + (-4)^2 + 7^2} = \sqrt{69}$. Thus
$$\mathbf{u} = \frac{1}{\sqrt{69}} (2\mathbf{i} - 4\mathbf{j} + 7\mathbf{k}) = \frac{2}{\sqrt{69}} \mathbf{i} - \frac{4}{\sqrt{69}} \mathbf{j} + \frac{7}{\sqrt{69}} \mathbf{k}.$$

10. $|\mathbf{a}| = \sqrt{1^2 + 2^2 + 2^2} = 3$,
$|\mathbf{b}| = \sqrt{3^2 + 4^2 + 0^2} = 5$, $\mathbf{a} \cdot \mathbf{b} = 3 + 8 + 0 = 11$,
$\cos\theta = \frac{11}{3 \cdot 5}$, so $\theta = \cos^{-1}\left(\frac{11}{15}\right) \approx 43°$.

11. $|\mathbf{a}| = \sqrt{6^2 + 0^2 + 2^2} = 2\sqrt{10}$,
$|\mathbf{b}| = \sqrt{5^2 + 3^2 + (-2)^2} = \sqrt{38}$,

$\mathbf{a} \cdot \mathbf{b} = 30 + 0 + (-4) = 26$, $\cos\theta = \frac{26}{2\sqrt{10}\sqrt{38}}$,
so $\theta = \cos^{-1}\left(\frac{13}{2\sqrt{95}}\right) \approx 48°$.

12. $|\mathbf{a}| = \sqrt{1^2 + 2^2} = \sqrt{5}$,
$|\mathbf{b}| = \sqrt{12^2 + (-5)^2} = 13$, $\mathbf{a} \cdot \mathbf{b} = 12 - 10 = 2$,
$\cos\theta = \frac{2}{13\sqrt{5}}$, so $\theta = \cos^{-1}\left(\frac{2}{13\sqrt{5}}\right) \approx 86°$.

13. $|\mathbf{a}| = \sqrt{3^2 + 1^2} = \sqrt{10}$, $|\mathbf{b}| = \sqrt{2^2 + 4^2} = 2\sqrt{5}$,
$\mathbf{a} \cdot \mathbf{b} = 6 + 4 = 10$, $\cos\theta = \frac{10}{\sqrt{10} \cdot 2\sqrt{5}} = \frac{\sqrt{2}}{2}$ and
$\theta = \cos^{-1}\left(\frac{\sqrt{2}}{2}\right) = 45°$.

14. $|\mathbf{a}| = \sqrt{36 + 4 + 9} = 7$, $|\mathbf{b}| = \sqrt{3}$,
$\mathbf{a} \cdot \mathbf{b} = 6 - 2 - 3 = 1$, $\cos\theta = \frac{1}{7\sqrt{3}}$, so
$\theta = \cos^{-1}\left(\frac{1}{7\sqrt{3}}\right) \approx 85°$.

15. $|\mathbf{a}| = \sqrt{1 + 1 + 4} = \sqrt{6}$, $|\mathbf{b}| = \sqrt{4 + 9} = \sqrt{13}$,
$\mathbf{a} \cdot \mathbf{b} = 0 + 2 - 6 = -4$, $\cos\theta = -\frac{4}{\sqrt{78}}$, so
$\theta = \cos^{-1}\left(-\frac{4}{\sqrt{78}}\right) \approx 117°$.

16. (a) $\vec{PQ} = \langle 1, 4, 6 \rangle$ and $\vec{PR} = \langle 2, 1, 8 \rangle$, so a vector orthogonal to the plane through P, Q, and R is
$$\vec{PQ} \times \vec{PR} = \langle 4 \cdot 8 - 6 \cdot 1, 6 \cdot 2 - 1 \cdot 8, 1 \cdot 1 - 4 \cdot 2 \rangle$$
$$= \langle 26, 4, -7 \rangle \text{ (or any scalar multiple thereof).}$$

(b) The area of the parallelogram determined by $\vec{PQ}$ and $\vec{PR}$ is
$$|\vec{PQ} \times \vec{PR}| = |\langle 26, 4, -7 \rangle| = \sqrt{676 + 16 + 49}$$
$$= \sqrt{741}.$$
So the area of triangle PQR is $\frac{1}{2}\sqrt{741}$.

17. (a) $\vec{PQ} = \langle 1, -1, 1 \rangle$ and $\vec{PR} = \langle 4, 3, 7 \rangle$, so a vector orthogonal to the plane through P, Q, and R is
$$\vec{PQ} \times \vec{PR}$$
$$= \langle (-1) \cdot 7 - 1 \cdot 3, 1 \cdot 4 - 1 \cdot 7, 1 \cdot 3 - (-1) \cdot 4 \rangle$$
$$= \langle -10, -3, 7 \rangle \text{ (or any scalar multiple thereof).}$$

(b) The area of the parallelogram determined by $\vec{PQ}$ and $\vec{PR}$ is
$$|\vec{PQ} \times \vec{PR}| = |\langle -10, -3, 7 \rangle| = \sqrt{100 + 9 + 49}$$
$$= \sqrt{158}$$
so the area of triangle PQR is $\frac{1}{2}\sqrt{158}$.

18. (a) $\overrightarrow{PQ} = \langle 4, 9, 3 \rangle$ and $\overrightarrow{PR} = \langle 7, 5, 6 \rangle \implies$
$\overrightarrow{PQ} \times \overrightarrow{PR} = \langle 9 \cdot 6 - 3 \cdot 5, 3 \cdot 7 - 4 \cdot 6, 4 \cdot 5 - 9 \cdot 7 \rangle$
$\qquad = \langle 39, -3, -43 \rangle$

(b) $|\overrightarrow{PQ} \times \overrightarrow{PR}| = \sqrt{1521 + 9 + 1849} = \sqrt{3379}$,
so the area of the triangle is $\dfrac{1}{2}\sqrt{3379}$.

19. Setting $a = 7, b = 1, c = 4, x_0 = 1, y_0 = 4, z_0 = 5$ in Equation 7 gives $7(x - 1) + 1(y - 4) + 4(z - 5) = 0$ or $7x + y + 4z = 31$ to be an equation of the plane.

20. Setting $a = 3, b = -5, c = 2, x_0 = -5$, $y_0 = 1, z_0 = 2$ in Equation 7 gives $3(x + 5) - 5(y - 1) + 2(z - 2) = 0$ or $3x - 5y + 2z = -16$ to be an equation of the plane.

21. Setting $a = 15, b = 9, c = -12, x_0 = 1$, $y_0 = 2, z_0 = 3$ in Equation 7 gives $15(x - 1) + 9(y - 2) - 12(z - 3) = 0$ or $5x + 3y - 4z = -1$ to be an equation of the plane.

22. Setting $a = -5, b = 2, c = -2, x_0 = -1$, $y_0 = -6, z_0 = -4$ in Equation 7 gives $-5(x + 1) + 2(y + 6) - 2(z + 4) = 0$ or $-5x + 2y - 2z = 1$ to be an equation of the plane.

23. Traces: $x = k, y^2 + z^2 = k$, a circle for $k > 0$; $y = k$, $x - k^2 = z^2$, a parabola; $z = k, x - k^2 = y^2$, a parabola. Thus the surface is a circular paraboloid (a paraboloid of revolution) with axis the x-axis and vertex at $(0, 0, 0)$.

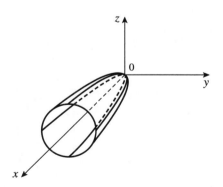

24. Traces: $x = k, z^2 = 4 - 2k^2$ or $z = \pm\sqrt{4 - 2k^2}$, two parallel lines for $|k| < \sqrt{2}$; $y = k, 2x^2 + z^2 = 4$, an ellipse; $z = k, 2x^2 = 4 - k^2$ or $x = \pm\sqrt{2 - (k^2/2)}$, two parallel lines for $|k| < 2$. Thus the surface is an elliptic cylinder with axis the y-axis.

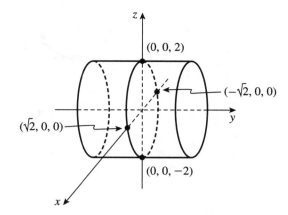

25. The trace in any plane $x = k$ is given by $z^2 - y^2 = 1 - k^2, x = k$, whose graph is a hyperbola. The trace in any plane $y = k$ is the circle given by $x^2 + z^2 = 1 + k^2, y = k$, and the trace in any plane $z = k$ is the hyperbola given by $x^2 - y^2 = 1 - k^2$, $z = k$. Thus the surface is a hyperboloid of one sheet with axis the y-axis.

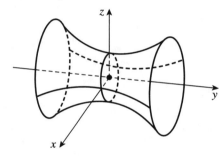

26. Traces: $x = k, 4z^2 - y^2 = 1 + k^2$, a hyperbola; $y = k, 4z^2 - x^2 = 1 + k^2$, a hyperbola; $z = k$, $-x^2 - y^2 = 1 - 4k^2$ or $x^2 + y^2 = 4k^2 - 1$, a circle for $k > \dfrac{1}{2}$ or $k < -\dfrac{1}{2}$. Thus the surface is a hyperboloid of two sheets with axis the z-axis.

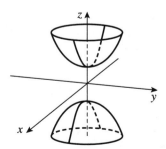

27. Traces: $x = k$, $y^2 + z^2 = 9(k^2 - 1)$, a circle for $|k| > 1$; $y = k$, $9x^2 - z^2 = 9 + k^2$, a hyperbola; $z = k$, $9x^2 - y^2 = 9 + k^2$, a hyperbola. Thus the surface is a hyperboloid of two sheets with axis the x-axis.

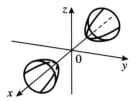

13 | VECTOR FUNCTIONS

1–4 ■ Find the limit.

1. $\lim\limits_{t \to 0} \langle t, \cos t, 2 \rangle$

2. $\lim\limits_{t \to 0} \left\langle \dfrac{1 - \cos t}{t}, t^3, e^{-1/t^2} \right\rangle$

3. $\lim\limits_{t \to 1} \left\langle \sqrt{t + 3}\, \mathbf{i} + \dfrac{t - 1}{t^2 - 1}\, \mathbf{j} + \dfrac{\tan t}{t}\, \mathbf{k} \right\rangle$

4. $\lim\limits_{t \to \infty} \left\langle e^{-t}\, \mathbf{i} + \dfrac{t - 1}{t + 1}\, \mathbf{j} + \tan^{-1} t\, \mathbf{k} \right\rangle$

5–10 ■ Find parametric equations for the tangent line to the curve with the given parametric equations at the specified point.

5. $x = t,\ y = t^2,\ z = t^3;\quad (1, 1, 1)$

6. $x = 1 + 2t,\ y = 1 + t - t^2,\ z = 1 - t + t^2 - t^3;$
    $(1, 1, 1)$

7. $x = t \cos 2\pi t,\ y = t \sin 2\pi t,\ z = 4t;\quad \left(0, \dfrac{1}{4}, 1 \right)$

8. $x = \sin \pi t,\ y = \sqrt{t},\ z = \cos \pi t;\quad (0, 1, -1)$

9. $x = t,\ y = \sqrt{2} \cos t,\ z = \sqrt{2} \sin t;\quad (\pi/4, 1, 1)$

10. $x = \cos t,\ y = 3e^{2t},\ z = 3e^{-2t};\quad (1, 3, 3)$

11–13 ■ Evaluate the integral.

11. $\displaystyle\int_0^1 (t\, \mathbf{i} + t^2\, \mathbf{j} + t^3\, \mathbf{k})\, dt$

12. $\displaystyle\int_1^2 \left[(1 + t^2)\, \mathbf{i} - 4t^4 \mathbf{j} - (t^2 - 1)\, \mathbf{k} \right] dt$

13. $\displaystyle\int_0^{\pi/4} (\cos 2t\, \mathbf{i} + \sin 2t\, \mathbf{j} + t \sin t\, \mathbf{k})\, dt$

14–18 ■ Use Theorem 10 to find the curvature.

14. $\mathbf{r}(t) = \mathbf{i} + t\, \mathbf{j} + t^2 \mathbf{k}$

15. $\mathbf{r}(t) = (1 + t)\, \mathbf{i} + (1 - t)\, \mathbf{j} + 3t^2 \mathbf{k}$

16. $\mathbf{r}(t) = 2t^3 \mathbf{i} - 3t^2 \mathbf{j} + 6t\, \mathbf{k}$

17. $\mathbf{r}(t) = (t^2 + 2)\, \mathbf{i} + (t^2 - 4t)\, \mathbf{j} + 2t\, \mathbf{k}$

18. $\mathbf{r}(t) = \sin t\, \mathbf{i} + \cos t\, \mathbf{j} + \sin t\, \mathbf{k}$

19–24 ■ Find the velocity, acceleration, and speed of a particle with the given position function.

19. $\mathbf{r}(t) = \langle t, t^2, t^3 \rangle$

20. $\mathbf{r}(t) = \langle t^3, t^2 + 1, t^3 - 1 \rangle$

21. $\mathbf{r}(t) = \langle \sqrt{t}, t, t\sqrt{t} \rangle$

22. $\mathbf{r}(t) = (1/t)\, \mathbf{i} + \mathbf{j} + t^2 \mathbf{k}$

23. $\mathbf{r}(t) = e^t \mathbf{i} + 2t\, \mathbf{j} + e^{-t} \mathbf{k}$

24. $\mathbf{r}(t) = \cosh t\, \mathbf{i} + \sinh t\, \mathbf{j} + t\, \mathbf{k}$

13 | ANSWERS TO SELECTED EXERCISES

1. $\langle 0, 1, 2 \rangle$

2. $\langle 0, 0, 0 \rangle$

3. $\left\langle 2, \dfrac{1}{2}, \tan 1 \right\rangle$

4. $\left\langle 0, 1, \dfrac{\pi}{2} \right\rangle$

5. $x = 1 + t,\, y = 1 + 2t,\, z = 1 + 3t$

6. $x = 1 + 2t,\, y = 1 + t,\, z = 1 - t$

7. $x = -\dfrac{\pi}{2} t,\, y = \dfrac{1}{4} + t,\, z = 1 + 4t$

8. $x = -\pi t,\, y = 1 + \dfrac{1}{2} t,\, z = -1$

9. $x = \dfrac{\pi}{4} + t,\, y = 1 - t,\, z = 1 + t$

10. $x = 1,\, y = 3 + 6t,\, z = 3 - 6t$

11. $\dfrac{1}{2}\mathbf{i} + \dfrac{1}{3}\mathbf{j} + \dfrac{1}{4}\mathbf{k}$

12. $\dfrac{10}{3}\mathbf{i} - \dfrac{124}{5}\mathbf{j} - \dfrac{4}{3}\mathbf{k}$

13. $\dfrac{1}{2}\mathbf{i} + \dfrac{1}{2}\mathbf{j} + \dfrac{4 - \pi}{4\sqrt{2}}\mathbf{k}$

14. $\dfrac{2}{(4t^2 + 1)^{3/2}}$

15. $\dfrac{3}{(1 + 18t^2)^{3/2}}$

16. $\dfrac{\sqrt{1 + 4t^2 + t^4}}{6\,(t^4 + t^2 + 1)^{3/2}}$

17. $\dfrac{\sqrt{6}}{2\,(2t^2 - 4t + 5)^{3/2}}$

18. $\dfrac{\sqrt{2}}{(1 + \cos^2 t)^{3/2}}$

19. $\langle 1, 2t, 3t^2 \rangle,\ \langle 0, 2, 6t \rangle,\ \sqrt{1 + 4t^2 + 9t^4}$

20. $\langle 3t^2, 2t, 3t^2 \rangle,\ \langle 6t, 2, 6t \rangle,\ |t|\,\sqrt{18t^2 + 4}$

21. $\left\langle \dfrac{1}{2} t^{-1/2}, 1, \dfrac{3}{2} t^{1/2} \right\rangle,\ \left\langle -\dfrac{1}{4} t^{-3/2}, 0, \dfrac{3}{4} t^{-1/2} \right\rangle,$
$\dfrac{1}{2}\sqrt{\dfrac{1 + 4t + 9t^2}{t}}$

22. $\langle -t^{-2}, 0, 2t \rangle,\ \langle 2t^{-3}, 0, 2 \rangle,\ \dfrac{1}{t^2}\sqrt{4t^6 + 1}$

23. $\langle e^t, 2, -e^{-t} \rangle,\ \langle e^t, 0, e^{-t} \rangle,\ \sqrt{e^{2t} + 4 + e^{-2t}}$

24. $\langle \sinh t, \cosh t, 1 \rangle,\ \langle \cosh t, \sinh t, 0 \rangle,\ \sqrt{\cosh 2t + 1}$

13 | SOLUTIONS TO SELECTED EXERCISES

1. $\lim_{t\to 0}\langle t,\cos t,2\rangle=\langle \lim_{t\to 0}t,\lim_{t\to 0}\cos t,\lim_{t\to 0}2\rangle=\langle 0,1,2\rangle$

2. $\lim_{t\to 0}\left\langle \dfrac{1-\cos t}{t},t^3,e^{-1/t^2}\right\rangle=$

$\left\langle \lim_{t\to 0}\dfrac{1-\cos t}{t},\lim_{t\to 0}t^3,\lim_{t\to 0}e^{-1/t^2}\right\rangle=\langle 0,0,0\rangle$

3. $\lim_{t\to 1}\sqrt{t+3}=2,\ \lim_{t\to 1}\dfrac{t-1}{t^2-1}=\lim_{t\to 1}\dfrac{1}{t+1}=\dfrac{1}{2}$,

$\lim_{t\to 1}\left(\dfrac{\tan t}{t}\right)=\tan 1$.

Thus the given limit equals $\left\langle 2,\dfrac{1}{2},\tan 1\right\rangle$.

4. $\lim_{t\to\infty}e^{-t}=0,\ \lim_{t\to\infty}\dfrac{t-1}{t+1}=1,\ \lim_{t\to\infty}\tan^{-1}t=\dfrac{\pi}{2}$, so the

given limit equals $\left\langle 0,1,\dfrac{\pi}{2}\right\rangle$.

5. The vector equation of the curve is
$\mathbf{r}(t)=t\,\mathbf{i}+t^2\,\mathbf{j}+t^3\,\mathbf{k}$, so $\mathbf{r}'(t)=\mathbf{i}+2t\,\mathbf{j}+3t^2\,\mathbf{k}$. At
the point $(1,1,1)$, $t=1$, so the tangent vector here
is $\mathbf{i}+2\,\mathbf{j}+3\,\mathbf{k}$. The tangent line goes through the
point $(1,1,1)$ and has direction vector $\mathbf{i}+2\,\mathbf{j}+3\,\mathbf{k}$.
Thus parametric equations are $x=1+t,\ y=1+2t$,
$z=1+3t$.

6. $\mathbf{r}(t)=\langle 1+2t,1+t-t^2,1-t+t^2-t^3\rangle$,
$\mathbf{r}'(t)=\langle 2,1-2t,-1+2t-3t^2\rangle$. At $(1,1,1)$, $t=0$
and $\mathbf{r}'(0)=\langle 2,1,-1\rangle$. Thus the tangent line goes
through the point $(1,1,1)$ and has direction vector
$\langle 2,1,-1\rangle$. The parametric equations are $x=1+2t$,
$y=1+t,\ z=1-t$.

7. $\mathbf{r}(t)=\langle t\cos 2\pi t,t\sin 2\pi t,4t\rangle$,
$\mathbf{r}'(t)=\langle \cos 2\pi t-2\pi t\sin 2\pi t,\sin 2\pi t$
$+2\pi t\cos 2\pi t,4\rangle$. At $\left(0,\dfrac{1}{4},1\right)$, $t=\dfrac{1}{4}$ and

$\mathbf{r}'\left(\dfrac{1}{4}\right)=\left\langle 0-\dfrac{\pi}{2},1+0,4\right\rangle=\left\langle -\dfrac{\pi}{2},1,4\right\rangle$.
Thus, parametric equations of the tangent line are

$x=-\dfrac{\pi}{2}t,\ y=\dfrac{1}{4}+t,\ z=1+4t$.

8. $\mathbf{r}(t)=\langle \sin\pi t,\sqrt{t},\cos\pi t\rangle$,
$\mathbf{r}'(t)=\langle \pi\cos\pi t,1/(2\sqrt{t}),-\pi\sin\pi t\rangle$. At

$(0,1,-1)$, $t=1$ and $\mathbf{r}'(1)=\left\langle -\pi,\dfrac{1}{2},0\right\rangle$. Thus,

parametric equations of the tangent line are
$x=-\pi t,\ y=1+\dfrac{1}{2}t,\ z=-1$.

9. $\mathbf{r}(t)=\langle t,\sqrt{2}\cos t,\sqrt{2}\sin t\rangle$,
$\mathbf{r}'(t)=\langle 1,-\sqrt{2}\sin t,\sqrt{2}\cos t\rangle$. At $\left(\dfrac{\pi}{4},1,1\right)$,
$t=\dfrac{\pi}{4}$ and $\mathbf{r}'\left(\dfrac{\pi}{4}\right)=\langle 1,-1,1\rangle$. Thus, parametric equations of the tangent line are $x=\dfrac{\pi}{4}+t$,
$y=1-t,\ z=1+t$.

10. $\mathbf{r}(t)=\langle \cos t,3e^{2t},3e^{-2t}\rangle$,
$\mathbf{r}'(t)=\langle -\sin t,6e^{2t},-6e^{-2t}\rangle$. At $(1,3,3)$, $t=0$ and
$\mathbf{r}'(0)=\langle 0,6,-6\rangle$. Thus, parametric equations of
the tangent line are $x=1,\ y=3+6t,\ z=3-6t$.

11. $\displaystyle\int_0^1(t\,\mathbf{i}+t^2\,\mathbf{j}+t^3\,\mathbf{k})\,dt$

$=\left(\displaystyle\int_0^1 t\,dt\right)\mathbf{i}+\left(\displaystyle\int_0^1 t^2\,dt\right)\mathbf{j}+\left(\displaystyle\int_0^1 t^3\,dt\right)\mathbf{k}$

$=\left[\dfrac{t^2}{2}\right]_0^1\mathbf{i}+\left[\dfrac{t^3}{3}\right]_0^1\mathbf{j}+\left[\dfrac{t^4}{4}\right]_0^1\mathbf{k}$

$=\dfrac{1}{2}\mathbf{i}+\dfrac{1}{3}\mathbf{j}+\dfrac{1}{4}\mathbf{k}$

12. $\displaystyle\int_1^2\left[(1+t^2)\,\mathbf{i}-4t^4\,\mathbf{j}-(t^2-1)\,\mathbf{k}\right]dt$

$=\left[\left(t+\dfrac{1}{3}t^3\right)\mathbf{i}-\dfrac{4}{5}t^5\,\mathbf{j}-\left(\dfrac{1}{3}t^3-t\right)\mathbf{k}\right]_1^2$

$=\left[\left(2+\dfrac{8}{3}\right)\mathbf{i}-\dfrac{128}{5}\mathbf{j}-\left(\dfrac{8}{3}-2\right)\mathbf{k}\right]$

$-\left[\left(1+\dfrac{1}{3}\right)\mathbf{i}-\dfrac{4}{5}\mathbf{j}-\left(\dfrac{1}{3}-1\right)\mathbf{k}\right]$

$=\dfrac{10}{3}\mathbf{i}-\dfrac{124}{5}\mathbf{j}-\dfrac{4}{3}\mathbf{k}$

13. $\displaystyle\int_0^{\pi/4}(\cos 2t\,\mathbf{i}+\sin 2t\,\mathbf{j}+t\sin t\,\mathbf{k})\,dt$

$=\left[\dfrac{1}{2}\sin 2t\,\mathbf{i}-\dfrac{1}{2}\cos 2t\,\mathbf{j}\right]_0^{\pi/4}$

$+\left[[-t\cos t]_0^{\pi/4}+\displaystyle\int_0^{\pi/4}\cos t\,dt\right]\mathbf{k}$

$=\dfrac{1}{2}\mathbf{i}+\dfrac{1}{2}\mathbf{j}+\left[-\dfrac{\pi}{4}\cos\dfrac{\pi}{4}+\sin\dfrac{\pi}{4}\right]\mathbf{k}$

$=\dfrac{1}{2}\mathbf{i}+\dfrac{1}{2}\mathbf{j}+\dfrac{1}{\sqrt{2}}\left(1-\dfrac{\pi}{4}\right)\mathbf{k}$

$=\dfrac{1}{2}\mathbf{i}+\dfrac{1}{2}\mathbf{j}+\dfrac{4-\pi}{4\sqrt{2}}\mathbf{k}$

14. $\mathbf{r}'(t) = \mathbf{j} - 2t\,\mathbf{k}$, $\mathbf{r}''(t) = -2\,\mathbf{k}$, $|\mathbf{r}'(t)|^3 = (4t^2 + 1)^{3/2}$,
$|\mathbf{r}'(t) \times \mathbf{r}''(t)| = |-2\mathbf{i}| = 2$,
$$\kappa(t) = \frac{|\mathbf{r}'(t) \times \mathbf{r}''(t)|}{|\mathbf{r}'(t)|^3} = \frac{2}{(4t^2 + 1)^{3/2}}$$

15. $\mathbf{r}'(t) = \langle 1, -1, 6t \rangle$, $\mathbf{r}''(t) = \langle 0, 0, 6 \rangle$,
$|\mathbf{r}'(t)|^3 = (\sqrt{2 + 36t^2})^3 = [2(1 + 18t^2)]^{3/2}$,
$|\mathbf{r}'(t) \times \mathbf{r}''(t)| = |\langle -6, -6, 0 \rangle| = 6\sqrt{2}$,
$$\kappa(t) = \frac{|\mathbf{r}'(t) \times \mathbf{r}''(t)|}{|\mathbf{r}'(t)|^3} = \frac{6\sqrt{2}}{[2(1 + 18t^2)]^{3/2}}$$
$$= \frac{3}{(1 + 18t^2)^{3/2}}$$

16. $\mathbf{r}'(t) = \langle 6t^2, -6t, 6 \rangle$, $\mathbf{r}''(t) = \langle 12t, -6, 0 \rangle$,
$|\mathbf{r}'(t)|^3 = 6^3 (t^4 + t^2 + 1)^{3/2}$,
$|\mathbf{r}'(t) \times \mathbf{r}''(t)| = |36 \langle 1, 2t, t^2 \rangle| = 36\sqrt{1 + 4t^2 + t^4}$,
$$\kappa(t) = \frac{|\mathbf{r}'(t) \times \mathbf{r}''(t)|}{|\mathbf{r}'(t)|^3} = \frac{36\sqrt{1 + 4t^2 + t^4}}{6^3 (t^4 + t^2 + 1)^{3/2}}$$
$$= \frac{\sqrt{1 + 4t^2 + t^4}}{6(t^4 + t^2 + 1)^{3/2}}$$

17. $\mathbf{r}'(t) = \langle 2t, 2t - 4, 2 \rangle$, $\mathbf{r}''(t) = \langle 2, 2, 0 \rangle$,
$|\mathbf{r}'(t)|^3 = (4t^2 + 4t^2 - 16t + 16 + 4)^{3/2}$
$= 8(2t^2 - 4t + 5)^{3/2}$,
$|\mathbf{r}'(t) \times \mathbf{r}''(t)| = 4|\langle -1, 1, 2 \rangle| = 4\sqrt{6}$,
$$\kappa(t) = \frac{|\mathbf{r}'(t) \times \mathbf{r}''(t)|}{|\mathbf{r}'(t)|^3} = \frac{4\sqrt{6}}{8(2t^2 - 4t + 5)^{3/2}}$$
$$= \frac{\sqrt{6}}{2(2t^2 - 4t + 5)^{3/2}}$$

18. $\mathbf{r}'(t) = \langle \cos t, -\sin t, \cos t \rangle$,
$\mathbf{r}''(t) = \langle -\sin t, -\cos t, -\sin t \rangle$,
$|\mathbf{r}'(t)|^3 = (\sqrt{\cos^2 t + 1})^3$,
$|\mathbf{r}'(t) \times \mathbf{r}''(t)| = |\langle 1, 0, -1 \rangle| = \sqrt{2}$,
$$\kappa(t) = \frac{|\mathbf{r}'(t) \times \mathbf{r}''(t)|}{|\mathbf{r}'(t)|^3} = \frac{\sqrt{2}}{(1 + \cos^2 t)^{3/2}}$$

19. $\mathbf{r}(t) = \langle t, t^2, t^3 \rangle$ $\implies$ $\mathbf{v}(t) = \mathbf{r}'(t) = \langle 1, 2t, 3t^2 \rangle$,
$\mathbf{a}(t) = \mathbf{v}'(t) = \langle 0, 2, 6t \rangle$,
$|\mathbf{v}(t)| = \sqrt{1^2 + (2t)^2 + (3t^2)^2} = \sqrt{1 + 4t^2 + 9t^4}$

20. $\mathbf{r}(t) = \langle t^3, t^2 + 1, t^3 - 1 \rangle$ $\implies$ $\mathbf{v}(t) = \langle 3t^2, 2t, 3t^2 \rangle$,
$\mathbf{a}(t) = \langle 6t, 2, 6t \rangle$,
$|\mathbf{v}(t)| = \sqrt{9t^4 + 4t^2 + 9t^4} = \sqrt{18t^4 + 4t^2}$
$= |t|\sqrt{18t^2 + 4}$

21. $\mathbf{r}(t) = \langle \sqrt{t}, t, t\sqrt{t} \rangle$ $\implies$ $\mathbf{v}(t) = \left\langle \frac{1}{2}t^{-1/2}, 1, \frac{3}{2}t^{1/2} \right\rangle$,
$\mathbf{a}(t) = \left\langle -\frac{1}{4}t^{-3/2}, 0, \frac{3}{4}t^{-1/2} \right\rangle$,
$|\mathbf{v}(t)| = \sqrt{\frac{1}{4}t^{-1} + 1 + \frac{9}{4}t} = \frac{1}{2}\sqrt{\frac{1 + 4t + 9t^2}{t}}$

22. $\mathbf{r}(t) = \langle 1/t, 1, t^2 \rangle$ $\implies$ $\mathbf{v}(t) = \langle -t^{-2}, 0, 2t \rangle$,
$\mathbf{a}(t) = \langle 2t^{-3}, 0, 2 \rangle$,
$|\mathbf{v}(t)| = \sqrt{t^{-4} + 4t^2} = \frac{1}{t^2}\sqrt{4t^6 + 1}$

23. $\mathbf{r}(t) = \langle e^t, 2t, e^{-t} \rangle$ $\implies$ $\mathbf{v}(t) = \langle e^t, 2, -e^{-t} \rangle$,
$\mathbf{a}(t) = \langle e^t, 0, e^{-t} \rangle$, $|\mathbf{v}(t)| = \sqrt{e^{2t} + 4 + e^{-2t}}$

24. $\mathbf{r}(t) = \langle \cosh t, \sinh t, t \rangle$ $\implies$ $\mathbf{v}(t) = \langle \sinh t, \cosh t, 1 \rangle$,
$\mathbf{a}(t) = \langle \cosh t, \sinh t, 0 \rangle$,
$|\mathbf{v}(t)| = \sqrt{\sinh^2 t + \cosh^2 t + 1} = \sqrt{\cosh 2t + 1}$
Recall that $\cosh^2 t + \sinh^2 t = \cosh 2t$.

14 PARTIAL DERIVATIVES

1–5 ∎ Sketch the graph of the function.

1. $f(x, y) = x$

2. $f(x, y) = \sin y$

3. $f(x, y) = x^2 + 9y^2$

4. $f(x, y) = y^2$

5. $f(x, y) = \sqrt{16 - x^2 - 16y^2}$

6–11 ∎ Find the limit, if it exists, or show that the limit does not exist.

6. $\lim\limits_{(x, y) \to (2, 3)} (x^2 y^2 - 2xy^5 + 3y)$

7. $\lim\limits_{(x, y) \to (-3, 4)} (x^3 + 3x^2 y^2 - 5y^3 + 1)$

8. $\lim\limits_{(x, y) \to (0, 0)} \dfrac{x^2 y^3 + x^3 y^2 - 5}{2 - xy}$

9. $\lim\limits_{(x, y) \to (-2, 1)} \dfrac{x^2 + xy + y^2}{x^2 - y^2}$

10. $\lim\limits_{(x, y) \to (\pi, \pi)} x \sin\left(\dfrac{x + y}{4}\right)$

11. $\lim\limits_{(x, y) \to (1, 4)} e^{\sqrt{x+2y}}$

12. Use polar coordinates to find

$$\lim\limits_{(x, y) \to (0, 0)} \dfrac{\sin(x^2 + y^2)}{x^2 + y^2}$$

[If (r, θ) are polar coordinates of the point (x, y) with $r \geq 0$, note that $r \to 0^+$ as $(x, y) \to (0, 0)$.]

13–18 ∎ Find the first partial derivatives of the function.

13. $g(x, y) = y \tan(x^2 y^3)$

14. $g(x, y) = \ln(x + \ln y)$

15. $f(x, y) = e^{xy} \cos x \sin y$

16. $f(s, t) = \sqrt{2 - 3s^2 - 5t^2}$

17. $z = \sinh \sqrt{3x + 4y}$

18. $z = \log_x y$

19–24 ∎ Find an equation of the tangent plane to the given surface at the specified point.

19. $z = x^2 + 4y^2$, $(2, 1, 8)$

20. $z = x^2 - y^2$, $(3, -2, 5)$

21. $z = 5 + (x - 1)^2 + (y + 2)^2$, $(2, 0, 10)$

22. $z = xy$, $(-1, 2, -2)$

23. $z = \sqrt{x - y}$, $(5, 1, 2)$

24. $z = y^2 - x^2$, $(-4, 5, 9)$

25–28 ∎ Use the Chain Rule to find the indicated partial derivatives.

25. $w = x^2 + y^2 + z^2$, $x = st$, $y = s \cos t$, $z = s \sin t$; $\dfrac{\partial w}{\partial s}, \dfrac{\partial w}{\partial t}$ when $s = 1$, $t = 0$

26. $u = xy + yz + zx$, $x = st$, $y = e^{st}$, $z = t^2$; $\dfrac{\partial u}{\partial s}, \dfrac{\partial u}{\partial t}$ when $s = 0$, $t = 1$

27. $z = y^2 \tan x$, $x = t^2 uv$, $y = u + tv^2$; $\dfrac{\partial z}{\partial t}, \dfrac{\partial z}{\partial u}, \dfrac{\partial z}{\partial v}$ when $t = 2$, $u = 1$, $v = 0$

28. $z = \dfrac{x}{y}$, $x = re^{st}$, $y = rse^t$; $\dfrac{\partial z}{\partial r}, \dfrac{\partial z}{\partial s}, \dfrac{\partial z}{\partial t}$ when $r = 1$, $s = 2$, $t = 0$

29–34 ∎ Find the maximum rate of change of f at the given point and the direction in which it occurs.

29. $f(x, y) = \sqrt{x^2 + 2y}$, $(4, 10)$

30. $f(x, y) = \cos(3x + 2y)$, $(\pi/6, -\pi/8)$

31. $f(x, y) = xe^{-y} + 3y$, $(1, 0)$

32. $f(x, y) = \ln(x^2 + y^2)$, $(1, 2)$

33. $f(x, y, z) = x + y/z$, $(4, 3, -1)$

34. $f(x, y, z) = \dfrac{x}{y} + \dfrac{y}{z}$, $(4, 2, 1)$

35–38 ■ Find the absolute maximum and minimum values of f on the set D.

35. $f(x, y) = 5 - 3x + 4y$, D is the closed triangular region with vertices $(0, 0)$, $(4, 0)$, and $(4, 5)$

36. $f(x, y) = x^2 + 2xy + 3y^2$, D is the closed triangular region with vertices $(-1, 1)$, $(2, 1)$, and $(-1, -2)$

37. $f(x, y) = 1 + xy - x - y$, D is the region bounded by the parabola $y = x^2$ and the line $y = 4$

38. $f(x, y) = 2x^2 + x + y^2 - 2$, $D = \{(x, y) \mid x^2 + y^2 \leq 4\}$

14 | ANSWERS TO SELECTED EXERCISES

1.
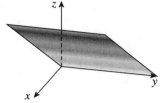

2.
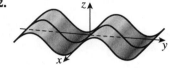

3.
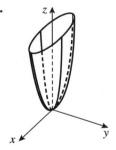

4.
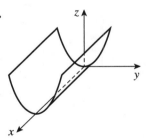

5.
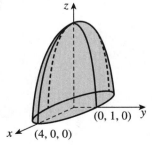

6. -927

7. 86

8. $-\dfrac{5}{2}$

9. 1

10. π

11. e^3

12. 1

13. $g_x(x, y) = 2xy^4 \sec^2(x^2 y^3)$,
$g_y(x, y) = \tan(x^2 y^3) + 3x^2 y^3 \sec^2(x^2 y^3)$

14. $g_x(x, y) = \dfrac{1}{x + \ln y}, g_y(x, y) = \dfrac{1}{y(x + \ln y)}$

15. $f_x(x, y) = e^{xy} \sin y\,(y \cos x - \sin x)$,
$f_y(x, y) = e^{xy} \cos x\,(x \sin y + \cos y)$

16. $f_s(s, t) = -\dfrac{3s}{\sqrt{2 - 3s^2 - 5t^2}}$,

$f_t(s, t) = -\dfrac{5t}{\sqrt{2 - 3s^2 - 5t^2}}$

17. $\dfrac{\partial z}{\partial x} = \dfrac{3 \cosh \sqrt{3x + 4y}}{2\sqrt{3x + 4y}}, \dfrac{\partial z}{\partial x} = \dfrac{2 \cosh \sqrt{3x + 4y}}{\sqrt{3x + 4y}}$

18. $\dfrac{\partial z}{\partial x} = -\dfrac{\ln y}{x(\ln x)^2}, \dfrac{\partial z}{\partial y} = \dfrac{1}{y \ln x}$

19. $4x + 8y - z = 8$

20. $6x + 4y - z = 5$

21. $2x + 4y - z = -6$

22. $2x - y - z = -2$

23. $x - y - 4z = -4$

24. $z = 8x + 10y - 9$

25. $2, 0$

26. $3, 2$

27. $0, 0, 4$

28. $0, -\dfrac{1}{4}, \dfrac{1}{2}$

29. $\dfrac{\sqrt{17}}{6}, \langle 4, 1 \rangle$

30. $\sqrt{\dfrac{13}{2}}, \langle -3, -2 \rangle$

31. $\sqrt{5}, \langle 1, 2 \rangle$

32. $\dfrac{2\sqrt{5}}{5}$, $\langle 1, 2 \rangle$

33. $\sqrt{11}$, $\langle 1, -1, -3 \rangle$

34. $\dfrac{\sqrt{17}}{2}$, $\langle 1, 0, -4 \rangle$

35. Maximum $f(4, 5) = 13$, minimum $f(4, 0) = -7$

36. Maximum $f(-1, -2) = 17$, minimum $f(0, 0) = 0$

37. Maximum $f(2, 4) = 3$, minimum $f(-2, 4) = -9$

38. Maximum $f(2, 0) = 8$, minimum $f\left(-\dfrac{1}{4}, 0\right) = -\dfrac{17}{8}$

14 | SOLUTIONS TO SELECTED EXERCISES

1. $z = x$, a plane which intersects the xz-plane in the line $z = x$, $y = 0$. The portion of this plane that lies in the first octant is shown.

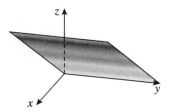

2. $z = \sin y$, a "wave."

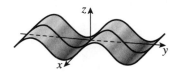

3. $z = x^2 + 9y^2$, an elliptic paraboloid with vertex the origin.

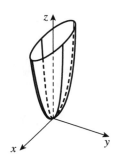

4. $z = y^2$, a parabolic cylinder.

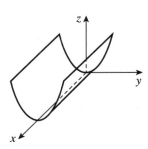

5. $z = \sqrt{16 - x^2 - 16y^2}$ so $z \geq 0$ and $z^2 + x^2 + 16y^2 = 16$, the top half of an ellipsoid.

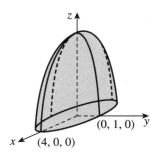

6. The function is a polynomial, so the limit equals $(2^2)(3^2) - 2(2)(3^5) + 3(3) = -927$.

7. The function is a polynomial, so the limit equals $(-3)^3 + 3(-3)^2(4)^2 - 5(4)^3 + 1 = 86$.

8. Since this is a rational function defined at $(0, 0)$, the limit equals $(0 + 0 - 5)/(2 - 0) = -\dfrac{5}{2}$.

9. This is a rational function defined at $(-2, 1)$, so the limit equals $(4 - 2 + 1)/(4 - 1) = 1$.

10. This is the product of two functions continuous at (π, π), so the limit equals $\pi \sin \dfrac{\pi + \pi}{4} = \pi$.

11. This is the composition of two continuous functions, so the limit equals $e^{\sqrt{1+8}} = e^3$.

12. $\lim\limits_{(x, y) \to (0, 0)} \dfrac{\sin(x^2 + y^2)}{x^2 + y^2} = \lim\limits_{r \to 0^+} \dfrac{\sin(r^2)}{r^2}$, which is an indeterminate form of type $\dfrac{0}{0}$. Using l'Hospital's Rule, we get

$$\lim\limits_{r \to 0^+} \dfrac{\sin(r^2)}{r^2} = \lim\limits_{r \to 0^+} \dfrac{2r \cos(r^2)}{2r}$$

$$= \lim\limits_{r \to 0^+} \cos(r^2) = 1$$

Or: Use the fact that $\lim\limits_{\theta \to 0} \dfrac{\sin \theta}{\theta} = 1$.

13. $g(x, y) = y \tan(x^2 y^3) \implies$
$g_x(x, y) = \left[y \sec^2(x^2 y^3) \right](2xy^3) = 2xy^4 \sec^2(x^2 y^3)$,
$g_y(x, y) = \tan(x^2 y^3) + \left[y \sec^2(x^2 y^3) \right](3x^2 y^2)$
$\qquad = \tan(x^2 y^3) + 3x^2 y^3 \sec^2(x^2 y^3)$

14. $g(x, y) = \ln(x + \ln y) \implies$
$g_x(x, y) = \dfrac{1}{x + \ln y}(1) = \dfrac{1}{x + \ln y}$,
$g_y(x, y) = \dfrac{1}{x + \ln y}\left(\dfrac{1}{y}\right) = \dfrac{1}{y(x + \ln y)}$

15. $f(x, y) = e^{xy} \cos x \sin y \Rightarrow$
$$f_x(x, y) = ye^{xy} \cos x \sin y + e^{xy}(-\sin x) \sin y$$
$$= e^{xy} \sin y \, (y \cos x - \sin x),$$
$$f_y(x, y) = xe^{xy} \cos x \sin y + e^{xy} \cos x \cos y$$
$$= e^{xy} \cos x \, (x \sin y + \cos y)$$

16. $f(s, t) = \sqrt{2 - 3s^2 - 5t^2} \Rightarrow$
$$f_s(s, t) = \frac{1}{2}(2 - 3s^2 - 5t^2)^{-1/2}(-6s)$$
$$= -\frac{3s}{\sqrt{2 - 3s^2 - 5t^2}},$$
$$f_t(s, t) = \frac{1}{2}(2 - 3s^2 - 5t^2)^{-1}(-10t)$$
$$= -\frac{5t}{\sqrt{2 - 3s^2 - 5t^2}}$$

17. $z = \sinh \sqrt{3x + 4y} \Rightarrow$
$$\frac{\partial z}{\partial x} = \left(\cosh \sqrt{3x + 4y}\right)\left(\frac{1}{2}\right)(3x + 4y)^{-1/2}(3)$$
$$= \frac{3 \cosh \sqrt{3x + 4y}}{2\sqrt{3x + 4y}},$$
$$\frac{\partial z}{\partial y} = \left(\cosh \sqrt{3x + 4y}\right)\left(\frac{1}{2}\right)(3x + 4y)^{-1/2}(4)$$
$$= \frac{2 \cosh \sqrt{3x + 4y}}{\sqrt{3x + 4y}}$$

18. Since $z = \log_x y$, $x^z = y$ and $z \ln x = \ln y$. Then
$$\frac{\partial z}{\partial x} \ln x + z\left(\frac{1}{x}\right) = 0, \text{ so } \frac{\partial z}{\partial x} = -\frac{z}{x \ln x} = -\frac{\ln y}{x (\ln x)^2}.$$
Also, $(\ln x)\dfrac{\partial z}{\partial y} = \dfrac{1}{y}$, so $\dfrac{\partial z}{\partial y} = \dfrac{1}{y \ln x}$.

19. $z = f(x, y) = x^2 + 4y^2 \Rightarrow f_x(x, y) = 2x$,
$f_y(x, y) = 8y$, $f_x(2, 1) = 4$, $f_y(2, 1) = 8$.
Thus the equation of the tangent plane is
$z - 8 = 4(x - 2) + 8(y - 1)$ or $4x + 8y - z = 8$.

20. $z = f(x, y) = x^2 - y^2 \Rightarrow f_x(x, y) = 2x$,
$f_y(x, y) = -2y$, $f_x(3, -2) = 6$, $f_y(3, -2) = 4$. Thus
the equation is $z - 5 = 6(x - 3) + 4(y + 2)$ or
$6x + 4y - z = 5$.

21. $z = f(x, y) = 5 + (x - 1)^2 + (y + 2)^2 \Rightarrow$
$f_x(x, y) = 2(x - 1)$, $f_y(x, y) = 2(y + 2)$,
$f_x(2, 0) = 2$, $f_y(2, 0) = 4$ and the equation is
$z - 10 = 2(x - 2) + 4y$ or $2x + 4y - z = -6$.

22. $f_x(-1, 2) = 2$ and $f_y(-1, 2) = -1$,
so an equation of the tangent plane is
$z + 2 = 2(x + 1) + (-1)(y - 2)$ or
$2x - y - z = -2$.

23. $f_x(x, y) = \dfrac{1}{2}(x - y)^{-1/2}$, $f_x(5, 1) = \dfrac{1}{4}$,
$f_x(x, y) = -\dfrac{1}{2}(x - y)^{-1/2}$, and $f_y(5, 1) = -\dfrac{1}{4}$,
so an equation of the tangent plane is
$z - 2 = \dfrac{1}{4}(x - 5) - \dfrac{1}{4}(y - 1)$ or $x - y - 4z = -4$.

24. $z = f(x, y) = y^2 - x^2 \Rightarrow f_x(x, y) = -2x$,
$f_y(x, y) = 2y$, so $f_x(-4, 5) = 8$, $f_y(-4, 5) = 10$.
By Equation 2, an equation of the tangent plane is
$z - 9 = f_x(-4, 5) \left[x - (-4)\right] + f_y(-4, 5)(y - 5) \Rightarrow$
$z - 9 = 8(x + 4) + 10(y - 5)$ or $z = 8x + 10y - 9$.

25. $w = x^2 + y^2 + z^2$, $x = st$, $y = s \cos t$, $z = s \sin t \Rightarrow$
$$\frac{\partial w}{\partial s} = \frac{\partial w}{\partial x}\frac{\partial x}{\partial s} + \frac{\partial w}{\partial y}\frac{\partial y}{\partial s} + \frac{\partial w}{\partial z}\frac{\partial z}{\partial s}$$
$$= 2xt + 2y \cos t + 2z \sin t$$
when $s = 1$, $t = 0$, we have $x = 0$, $y = 1$ and
$z = 0$, so $\partial w/\partial s = 2 \cos 0 = 2$. Similarly
$\partial w/\partial t = 2xs + 2y(-s \sin t) + 2z(s \cos t)$
$= 0 + (-2) \sin 0 + 0 = 0$
when $s = 1$ and $t = 0$.

26. $u = xy + yz + zx$, $x = st$, $y = e^{st}$, $z = t^2 \Rightarrow$
$\partial u/\partial s = (y + z)t + (x + z)te^{st} + (x + y)(0)$ and
$\partial u/\partial t = (y + z)s + (x + z)se^{st} + (x + y)(2t)$.
When $s = 0$, $t = 1$, we have $x = 0$, $y = 1$,
$z = 1$, so $\partial u/\partial s = 2 + 1 + 0 = 3$ and
$\partial u/\partial t = 0 + 0 + (1)(2) = 2$.

27. $z = y^2 \tan x$, $x = t^2 uv$, $y = u + tv^2 \Rightarrow$
$\partial z/\partial t = (y^2 \sec^2 x) 2tuv + (2y \tan x) v^2$,
$\partial z/\partial u = (y^2 \sec^2 x) t^2 v + 2y \tan x$,
$\partial z/\partial v = (y^2 \sec^2 x) t^2 u + (2y \tan x) 2tv$. When $t = 2$,
$u = 1$, and $v = 0$, we have $x = 0$, $y = 1$, so
$\partial z/\partial t = 0$, $\partial z/\partial u = 0$, $\partial z/\partial v = 4$.

28. $z = \dfrac{x}{y}$, $x = re^{st}$, $y = rse^t \Rightarrow$
$$\frac{\partial z}{\partial r} = \frac{1}{y}e^{st} + \frac{-x}{y^2}se^t, \quad \frac{\partial z}{\partial s} = \frac{1}{y}rte^{st} - \frac{x}{y^2}re^t,$$
$$\frac{\partial z}{\partial t} = \frac{1}{y}rse^{st} - \frac{x}{y^2}rse^t. \text{ When } r = 1, s = 2, \text{ and } t = 0,$$
we have $x = 1$, $y = 2$, so $\partial z/\partial r = \dfrac{1}{2} + \dfrac{-1}{4} \cdot 2 = 0$,
$\partial z/\partial s = 0 - \dfrac{1}{4} = -\dfrac{1}{4}$ and $\partial z/\partial t = \dfrac{1}{2} \cdot 2 - \dfrac{1}{4} \cdot 2 = \dfrac{1}{2}$.

29. $f(x, y) = \sqrt{x^2 + 2y} \Rightarrow$
$$\nabla f(x, y) = \left\langle \frac{x}{\sqrt{x^2 + 2y}}, \frac{1}{\sqrt{x^2 + 2y}} \right\rangle. \text{ Thus the}$$
maximum rate of change is $|\nabla f(4, 10)| = \dfrac{\sqrt{17}}{6}$ in
the direction $\left\langle \dfrac{2}{3}, \dfrac{1}{6} \right\rangle$ or $\langle 4, 1 \rangle$.

30. $f(x, y) = \cos(3x + 2y) \Rightarrow$
$\nabla f(x, y) = \langle -3 \sin(3x + 2y), -2 \sin(3x + 2y) \rangle$,
so the maximum rate of change is
$$\left| \nabla f\left(\frac{\pi}{6}, -\frac{\pi}{8}\right) \right| = \sqrt{\frac{13}{2}} \text{ in the direction}$$
$$\left\langle -\frac{3\sqrt{2}}{2}, -\sqrt{2} \right\rangle \text{ or } \langle -3, -2 \rangle.$$

31. $f(x, y) = xe^{-y} + 3y \implies \nabla f(x, y) = \langle e^{-y}, 3 - xe^{-y} \rangle$, $\nabla f(1, 0) = \langle 1, 2 \rangle$ is the direction of maximum rate of change and the maximum rate is $|\nabla f(1, 0)| = \sqrt{5}$.

32. $f(x, y) = \ln(x^2 + y^2) \implies$
$$\nabla f(x, y) = \left\langle \frac{2x}{x^2 + y^2}, \frac{2y}{x^2 + y^2} \right\rangle,$$
$$\nabla f(1, 2) = \left\langle \frac{2}{5}, \frac{4}{5} \right\rangle.$$
Thus the maximum rate of change is
$|\nabla f(1, 2)| = \dfrac{2\sqrt{5}}{5}$ in the direction $\left\langle \dfrac{2}{5}, \dfrac{4}{5} \right\rangle$ or $\langle 1, 2 \rangle$.

33. $f(x, y, z) = x + y/z \implies$
$\nabla f(x, y, z) = \left\langle 1, \dfrac{1}{z}, -\dfrac{y}{z^2} \right\rangle$, so the maximum rate of change is $|\nabla f(4, 3, -1)| = \sqrt{11}$ in the direction $\langle 1, -1, -3 \rangle$.

34. $f(x, y, z) = \dfrac{x}{y} + \dfrac{y}{z} \implies$
$\nabla f(x, y, z) = \left\langle \dfrac{1}{y}, \dfrac{1}{z} - \dfrac{x}{y^2}, -\dfrac{y}{z^2} \right\rangle$, so the maximum rate of change is $|\nabla f(4, 2, 1)| = \dfrac{\sqrt{17}}{2}$ in the direction $\left\langle \dfrac{1}{2}, 0, -2 \right\rangle$ or $\langle 1, 0, -4 \rangle$.

35. Since f is a polynomial it is continuous on D, so an absolute maximum and minimum exist.

Here $f_x = -3$, $f_y = 4$ so there are no critical points inside D. Thus the absolute extrema must both occur on the boundary. Along L_1, $y = 0$ and $f(x, 0) = 5 - 3x$, a decreasing function in x, so the maximum value is $f(0, 0) = 5$ and the minimum value is $f(4, 0) = -7$. Along L_2, $x = 4$ and $f(4, y) = -7 + 4y$, an increasing function in y, so the minimum value is $f(4, 0) = -7$ and the maximum value is $f(4, 5) = 13$. Along L_3, $y = \dfrac{5}{4}x$ and $f\left(x, \dfrac{5}{4}x\right) = 5 + 2x$, an increasing function in x, so the minimum value is $f(0, 0) = 5$ and the maximum value is $f(4, 5) = 13$. Thus the absolute minimum of f on D is $f(4, 0) = -7$ and the absolute maximum is $f(4, 5) = 13$.

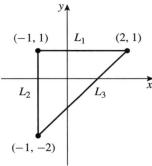

36. $f_x = 2x + 2y$ and $f_y = 2x + 6y$. Setting $f_x = f_y = 0$ gives $x = y = 0$ which yields the critical point $(0, 0)$ where $f(0, 0) = 0$. Along $L_1 : y = 1$ and $f(x, 1) = x^2 + 2x + 3, -1 \le x \le 2$, which has a maximum at $x = 2$ where $f(2, 1) = 11$, and a minimum at $x = -1$ where $f(-1, 1) = 2$. Along $L_2 : x = -1$ and $f(-1, y) = 1 - 2y + 3y^2$, $-2 \le y \le 1$, which has a maximum at $y = -2$ where $f(-1, -2) = 17$ and a minimum at $y = \dfrac{1}{3}$ where $f\left(-1, \dfrac{1}{3}\right) = \dfrac{2}{3}$. Along $L_3 : y = x - 1$ and $f(x, x - 1) = 6x^2 - 8x + 3$, $-1 \le x \le 2$, which has a maximum at $x = -1$, where $f(-1, -2) = 17$ and a minimum at $x = \dfrac{2}{3}$, where $f\left(\dfrac{2}{3}, -\dfrac{1}{3}\right) = \dfrac{1}{3}$. As a result, the absolute maximum value of f on D is $f(-1, -2) = 17$ and the minimum value is $f(0, 0) = 0$.

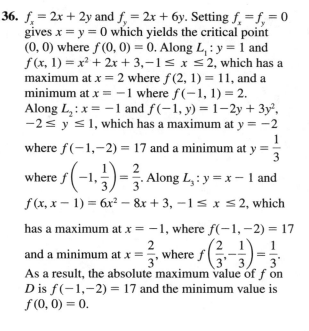

37. $f_x(x, y) = y - 1$ and $f_y(x, y) = x - 1$ and so the critical point is $(1, 1)$ (in D), where $f(1, 1) = 0$.

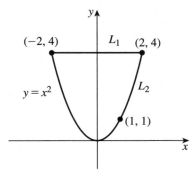

Along $L_1 : y = 4$, so $f(x, 4) = 1 + 4x - x - 4 = 3x - 3$, $-2 \le x \le 2$, which is an increasing function and has a maximum value when $x = 2$, where $f(2, 4) = 3$ and a minimum of $f(-2, 4) = -9$. Along $L_2 : y = x^2$, so let $g(x) = f(x, x^2) = x^3 - x^2 - x + 1$. Then
$g'(x) = 3x^2 - 2x - 1 = 0 \Leftrightarrow x = -\dfrac{1}{3}$ or $x = 1$.
$f\left(-\dfrac{1}{3}, \dfrac{1}{9}\right) = \dfrac{32}{27}$ and $f(1, 1) = 0$. As a result, the

absolute maximum and minimum values of f on D are $f(2, 4) = 3$ and $f(-2, 4) = -9$.

38. $f_x = 4x + 1$, $f_y = 2y$ and the only critical point is $\left(-\dfrac{1}{4}, 0\right)$ (and this point is in D) and $f\left(-\dfrac{1}{4}, 0\right) = -\dfrac{17}{8}$. On the circle $x^2 + y^2 = 4$,

$f(x, y) = x^2 + x + 2$, a quadratic in x which attains its minimum at $\left(-\dfrac{1}{2}, \pm\dfrac{\sqrt{15}}{2}\right)$, $f\left(-\dfrac{1}{2}, \pm\dfrac{\sqrt{15}}{2}\right) = \dfrac{7}{4}$ and its maximum at $(2, 0)$, $f(2, 0) = 8$. Thus the absolute maximum of f on D is $f(2, 0) = 8$, while the absolute minimum is $f\left(-\dfrac{1}{4}, 0\right) = -\dfrac{17}{8}$.

15 MULTIPLE INTEGRALS

1–8 ■ Calculate the iterated integral.

1. $\displaystyle\int_0^4 \int_0^2 x\sqrt{y}\,dx\,dy$

2. $\displaystyle\int_0^2 \int_0^3 e^{x-y}\,dy\,dx$

3. $\displaystyle\int_{-1}^1 \int_0^1 (x^3 y^3 + 3xy^2)\,dy\,dx$

4. $\displaystyle\int_0^1 \int_1^2 (x^4 - y^2)\,dx\,dy$

5. $\displaystyle\int_0^{\pi/4} \int_0^3 \sin x\,dy\,dx$

6. $\displaystyle\int_0^{\pi/2} \int_0^{\pi/2} \sin x \cos y\,dy\,dx$

7. $\displaystyle\int_0^3 \int_0^1 \sqrt{x+y}\,dx\,dy$

8. $\displaystyle\int_0^{\pi/2} \int_0^{\pi/2} \sin(x+y)\,dy\,dx$

9–14 ■ Evaluate the double integral.

9. $\displaystyle\iint_D xy\,dA, \quad D = \{(x,y)\,|\,0 \le x \le 1,\, x^2 \le y \le \sqrt{x}\}$

10. $\displaystyle\iint_D (x - 2y)\,dA,$
$D = \{(x, y)\,|\,1 \le x \le 3,\, 1 + x \le y \le 2x\}$

11. $\displaystyle\iint_D (x^2 - 2xy)\,dA,$
$D = \{(x, y)\,|\,0 \le x \le 1,\, \sqrt{x} \le y \le 2 - x\}$

12. $\displaystyle\iint_D x \sin y\,dA,$
$D = \{(x, y)\,|\,0 \le y \le \pi/2,\, 0 \le x \le \cos y\}$

13. $\displaystyle\iint_D \frac{1}{x}\,dA,$
$D = \{(x, y)\,|\,1 \le y \le e,\, y^2 \le x \le y^4\}$

14. $\displaystyle\iint_D (3x + y)\,dA,$
$D = \{(x, y)\,|\,\pi/6 \le x \le \pi/4,\, \sin x \le y \le \cos x\}$

15–18 ■ Use a double integral to find the area of the region.

15. The region enclosed by the cardioid $r = 1 - \sin\theta$

16. The region enclosed by the lemniscate $r^2 = 4\cos 2\theta$

17. The region inside the circle $r = 3\cos\theta$ and outside the cardioid $r = 1 + \cos\theta$

18. The smaller region bounded by the spiral $r\theta = 1$, the circles $r = 1$ and $r = 3$, and the polar axis

19. Evaluate the iterated integral
$$\int_0^3 \int_0^{\sqrt{9-x^2}} \arctan\frac{y}{x}\,dy\,dx$$
by converting to polar coordinates.

20–22 ■ Find the mass and center of mass of the lamina that occupies the region D and has the given density function ρ.

20. D is bounded by the cardioid $r = 1 + \sin\theta$;
$\rho(x, y) = 2$

21. $D = \{(x, y)\,|\,0 \le y \le \sin x,\, 0 \le x \le \pi\}$; $\rho(x, y) = y$

22. $D = \{(x, y)\,|\,0 \le y \le \cos x,\, 0 \le x \le \pi/2\}$;
$\rho(x, y) = x$

23–26 ■ Use a triple integral to find the volume of the given solid.

23. The tetrahedron bounded by the coordinate planes and the plane $2x + 3y + 6z = 12$

24. The solid bounded by the elliptic cylinder $4x^2 + z^2 = 4$ and the planes $y = 0$ and $y = z + 2$

25. The solid bounded by the cylinder $x = y^2$ and the planes $z = 0$ and $x + z = 1$

26. The solid enclosed by the paraboloids $z = x^2 + y^2$ and $z = 18 - x^2 - y^2$

27. Evaluate $\iiint_E (x^2 + y^2)\, dV$, where E is the region bounded by the cylinder $x^2 + y^2 = 4$ and the planes $z = -1$ and $z = 2$.

28. Evaluate $\iiint_E \sqrt{x^2 + y^2}\, dV$, where E is the solid bounded by the paraboloid $z = 9 - x^2 - y^2$ and the xy-plane.

29–30 ■ Use spherical coordinates.

29. Evaluate $\iiint_E xe^{(x^2 + y^2 + z^2)^2}\, dV$, where E is the solid that lies between the spheres $x^2 + y^2 + z^2 = 1$ and $x^2 + y^2 + z^2 = 4$ in the first octant.

30. Evaluate $\iiint_E \sqrt{x^2 + y^2 + z^2}\, dV$, where E is bounded below by the cone $\phi = \pi/6$ and above by the sphere $\rho = 2$.

31–36 ■ Find the Jacobian of the transformation.

31. $x = u - 2v, \quad y = 2u - v$

32. $x = u - v^2, \quad y = u + v^2$

33. $x = e^{2u} \cos v, \quad y = e^{2u} \sin v$

34. $x = se^t, \quad y = se^{-t}$

35. $x = u + v + w, \quad y = u + v - w, \quad z = u - v + w$

36. $x = 2u, \quad y = 3v^2, \quad z = 4w^3$

15 | ANSWERS TO SELECTED EXERCISES

1. $\dfrac{32}{3}$

2. $e^2 - e^{-1} - 1 + e^{-3}$

3. 0

4. $\dfrac{88}{15}$

5. $3\left(1 - \dfrac{1}{\sqrt{2}}\right)$

6. 1

7. $\dfrac{4}{15}(31 - 9\sqrt{3})$

8. 2

9. $\dfrac{1}{12}$

10. $-\dfrac{34}{3}$

11. $-\dfrac{19}{42}$

12. $\dfrac{1}{6}$

13. 2

14. $\dfrac{3\sqrt{2} - 1 - \sqrt{3}}{4}\pi + \dfrac{14 - 13\sqrt{3}}{8}$

15. $\dfrac{3\pi}{2}$

16. 4

17. π

18. 2

19. $\dfrac{9}{4}\pi^2$

20. $3\pi, \left(0, \dfrac{5}{6}\right)$

21. $\dfrac{\pi}{4}, \left(\dfrac{\pi}{2}, \dfrac{16}{9\pi}\right)$

22. $\dfrac{\pi - 2}{2}, \left(\dfrac{\pi^2 - 8}{2(\pi - 2)}, \dfrac{\pi}{4}\right)$

23. 8

24. 4π

25. $\dfrac{8}{15}$

26. 81π

27. 24π

28. $\dfrac{324\pi}{5}$

29. $\dfrac{1}{16}\pi(e^{16} - e)$

30. $4\pi(2 - \sqrt{3})$

31. 3

32. $4v$

33. $2e^{4u}$

34. $-2s$

35. -4

36. $144vw^2$

15 | SOLUTIONS TO SELECTED EXERCISES

1. $\displaystyle\int_0^4\int_0^2 x\sqrt{y}\,dx\,dy = \int_0^4 \sqrt{y}\left[\frac{1}{2}x^2\right]_0^2 dy = \int_0^4 2\sqrt{y}\,dy$

$\displaystyle\qquad = \left[\frac{4}{3}y^{3/2}\right]_0^4 = \frac{32}{3}$

2. $\displaystyle\int_0^2\int_0^3 e^{x-y}\,dy\,dx = \int_0^2 \left[-e^{x-y}\right]_0^3 dx$

$\displaystyle\qquad = \int_0^2 e^x(1-e^{-3})\,dx$

$\displaystyle\qquad = e^2 - e^{-1} - 1 + e^{-3}$

3. $\displaystyle\int_{-1}^1\int_0^1 (x^3y^2 + 3xy^2)\,dy\,dx$

$\displaystyle\qquad = \int_{-1}^1 \left[\frac{1}{4}x^3y^4 + xy^3\right]_{y=0}^{y=1} dx = \int_{-1}^1\left[\frac{1}{4}x^3 + x\right]dx$

$\displaystyle\qquad = \left[\frac{1}{16}x^4 + \frac{1}{2}x^2\right]_{-1}^1 = 0$

Alternate Solution: Applying Fubini's Theorem, the integral equals

$\displaystyle\int_0^1\int_{-1}^1 (x^3y^2 + 3xy^2)\,dx\,dy$

$\displaystyle\qquad = \int_0^1\left[\frac{1}{4}y^2x^4 + \frac{3}{2}y^2x^2\right]_{x=-1}^{x=1} dy = \int_0^1 0\,dy = 0$

4. $\displaystyle\int_0^1\int_1^2 (x^4 - y^2)\,dx\,dy = \int_1^2\int_0^1 (x^4 - y^2)\,dy\,dx$

$\displaystyle\qquad = \int_1^2\left[x^4 y - \frac{1}{3}y^3\right]_{y=0}^{y=1} dx = \int_1^2\left[x^4 - \frac{1}{3}\right]dx$

$\displaystyle\qquad = \left[\frac{1}{5}x^5 - \frac{1}{3}x\right]_1^2 = \frac{88}{15}$

5. $\displaystyle\int_0^{\pi/4}\int_0^3 \sin x\,dy\,dx = 3\int_0^{\pi/4}\sin x\,dx = 3\left[-\cos x\right]_0^{\pi/4}$

$\displaystyle\qquad = 3\left(1 - \frac{1}{\sqrt{2}}\right)$

6. $\displaystyle\int_0^{\pi/2}\int_0^{\pi/2} \sin x\,\cos y\,dy\,dx$

$\displaystyle\qquad = \int_0^{\pi/2} \sin x\,dx \int_0^{\pi/2} \cos y\,dy \ \text{(as in Example 5)}$

$\displaystyle\qquad = \left[-\cos x\right]_0^{\pi/2}\left[\sin y\right]_0^{\pi/2} = -(0-1)(1-0) = 1$

7. $\displaystyle\int_0^3\int_0^1 \sqrt{x+y}\,dx\,dy = \int_0^3\left[\frac{2}{3}(x+y)^{3/2}\right]_{x=0}^{x=1} dy$

$\displaystyle\qquad = \frac{2}{3}\int_0^3 \left[(1+y)^{3/2} - y^{3/2}\right]dy$

$\displaystyle\qquad = \frac{2}{3}\left[\frac{2}{5}(1+y)^{5/2} - \frac{2}{5}y^{5/2}\right]_0^3$

$\displaystyle\qquad = \frac{4}{15}\left[32 - 3^{5/2} - 1\right] = \frac{4}{15}(31 - 9\sqrt{3})$

8. $\displaystyle\int_0^{\pi/2}\int_0^{\pi/2} \sin(x+y)\,dy\,dx$

$\displaystyle\qquad = \int_0^{\pi/2}\left[-\cos(x+y)\right]_{y=0}^{y=\pi/2} dx$

$\displaystyle\qquad = \int_0^{\pi/2}\left[\cos x - \cos\left(x + \frac{\pi}{2}\right)\right]dx$

$\displaystyle\qquad = \left[\sin x - \sin\left(x + \frac{\pi}{2}\right)\right]_0^{\pi/2}$

$\displaystyle\qquad = (1-0) - (0-1) = 2$

9. $\displaystyle\int_0^1\int_{x^2}^{\sqrt{x}} xy\,dy\,dx = \int_0^1\left[\frac{1}{2}xy^2\right]_{x^2}^{\sqrt{x}} dx$

$\displaystyle\qquad = \frac{1}{2}\int_0^1 (x^2 - x^5)\,dx = \frac{1}{2}\left[\frac{1}{3}x^3 - \frac{1}{6}x^6\right]_0^1 = \frac{1}{12}$

10. $\displaystyle\int_1^3\int_{1+x}^{2x} (x - 2y)\,dy\,dx$

$\displaystyle\qquad = \int_1^3 \left[xy - y^2\right]_{1+x}^{2x} dx$

$\displaystyle\qquad = \int_1^3\left[(1+x)^2 - 3x^2 - x\right]dx$

$\displaystyle\qquad = \left[\frac{1}{3}(1+x)^3 - x^3 - \frac{1}{2}x^2\right]_1^3 = -\frac{34}{3}$

11. $\displaystyle\int_0^1\int_{\sqrt{x}}^{2-x} (x^2 - 2xy)\,dy\,dx$

$\displaystyle\qquad = \int_0^1 \left[x^2 y - xy^2\right]_{\sqrt{x}}^{2-x} dx$

$\displaystyle\qquad = \int_0^1 (-2x^3 + 7x^2 - 4x - x^{5/2})\,dx$

$\displaystyle\qquad = \left[-\frac{1}{2}x^4 + \frac{7}{3}x^3 - 2x^2 - \frac{2}{7}x^{7/2}\right]_0^1 = -\frac{19}{42}$

12. $\displaystyle\int_0^{\pi/2}\int_0^{\cos y} x\sin y\,dx\,dy = \int_0^{\pi/2}\frac{1}{2}(\cos^2 y\sin y)\,dy$

$$= -\frac{1}{6}\cos^3 y\Big|_0^{\pi/2} = \frac{1}{6}$$

13. $\displaystyle\int_1^e\int_{y^2}^{y^4}(1/x)\,dx\,dy = \int_1^e(\ln y^4 - \ln y^2)\,dy$

$$= \int_1^e 2\ln y\,dy = 2\big[y\ln y - y\big]_1^e = 2$$

14. $\displaystyle\int_{\pi/6}^{\pi/4}\int_{\sin x}^{\cos x}(3x+y)\,dy\,dx$

$$= \int_{\pi/6}^{\pi/4}\Big[3xy+\frac{1}{2}y^2\Big]_{y=\sin x}^{y=\cos x}dx$$

$$= \int_{\pi/6}^{\pi/4}\Big[3x(\cos x-\sin x)+\frac{1}{2}\cos^2 x-\frac{1}{2}\sin^2 x\Big]dx$$

$$= 3x(\sin x+\cos x)\Big|_{\pi/6}^{\pi/4} - 3\int_{\pi/6}^{\pi/4}(\sin x+\cos x)\,dx$$

$$\qquad + \Big[\frac{1}{4}\sin 2x\Big]_{\pi/6}^{\pi/4}$$

$$= 3\Big(\frac{\pi}{4}\Big)\sqrt{2} - \frac{\pi}{2}\cdot\frac{1+\sqrt{3}}{2} + 3\Big[0+\frac{1-\sqrt{3}}{2}\Big]$$

$$\qquad + \frac{1}{4}\Big(1-\frac{\sqrt{3}}{2}\Big)$$

$$= \frac{3\sqrt{2}-1-\sqrt{3}}{4}\pi + \frac{14-13\sqrt{3}}{8}$$

15. By symmetry,

$$A = 2\int_{-\pi/2}^{\pi/2}\int_0^{1-\sin\theta} r\,dr\,d\theta$$

$$= \int_{-\pi/2}^{\pi/2}\big[r^2\big]_{r=0}^{r=1-\sin\theta}d\theta$$

$$= \int_{-\pi/2}^{\pi/2}(1-2\sin\theta+\sin^2\theta)\,d\theta$$

$$= \int_{-\pi/2}^{\pi/2}\Big[1+\frac{1}{2}(1-\cos 2\theta)\Big]d\theta$$

$$= \int_{-\pi/2}^{\pi/2}\Big(\frac{3}{2}-\frac{1}{2}\cos 2\theta\Big)d\theta$$

since $2\sin\theta$ is an odd function. But $\dfrac{3}{2}-\dfrac{1}{2}\cos 2\theta$ is an even function, so

$$A = \int_0^{\pi/2}(3-\cos 2\theta)\,d\theta = \Big[3\theta-\frac{1}{2}\sin 2\theta\Big]_0^{\pi/2} = \frac{3\pi}{2}.$$

16. By symmetry, the two loops of the lemniscate are equal in area, so

12. $\displaystyle A = 2\int_{-\pi/4}^{\pi/4}\int_0^{2\sqrt{\cos 2\theta}} r\,dr\,d\theta = \int_{-\pi/4}^{\pi/4}\big[r^2\big]_{r=0}^{r=2\sqrt{\cos 2\theta}}d\theta$

$$= \int_{-\pi/4}^{\pi/4} 4\cos 2\theta\,d\theta = 8\int_0^{\pi/4}\cos 2\theta\,d\theta$$

$$= 4\sin 2\theta\Big|_0^{\pi/4} = 4$$

17. $3\cos\theta = 1+\cos\theta$ implies $\cos\theta = \dfrac{1}{2}$, so $\theta = \pm\dfrac{\pi}{3}$. Then by symmetry

$$A = 2\int_0^{\pi/3}\int_{1+\cos\theta}^{3\cos\theta} r\,dr\,d\theta$$

$$= 2\int_0^{\pi/3}\Big[\frac{1}{2}r^2\Big]_{1+\cos\theta}^{3\cos\theta}d\theta$$

$$= \int_0^{\pi/3}(9\cos^2\theta-1-2\cos\theta-\cos^2\theta)\,d\theta$$

$$= \int_0^{\pi/3}\Big[8\cdot\frac{1}{2}(1+\cos 2\theta)-2\cos\theta-1\Big]d\theta$$

$$= \big[4\theta+2\sin 2\theta-2\sin\theta-\theta\big]_0^{\pi/3} = \pi$$

18.

C is the point $r=1$, $\theta=1$ rad; the arrow indicates the direction of increasing θ. B is the point $r=3$, $\theta = \dfrac{1}{3}$ rad. The region, as a type I polar region, is $\{(r,\theta)\,|\,1\le r\le 3,\ 0\le\theta\le 1/r\}$, so by Formula 3, we have $A = \displaystyle\int_1^3\int_0^{1/r} r\,d\theta\,dr = \int_1^3 1\,dr = 2.$

19. $\displaystyle\int_{-3}^3\int_0^{\sqrt{9-x^2}}\arctan(y/x)\,dy\,dx$

$$= \int_0^\pi\int_0^3\arctan(\tan\theta)\,r\,dr\,d\theta = \int_0^\pi\int_0^3\theta r\,dr\,d\theta$$

$$= \int_0^\pi\Big[\frac{1}{2}r^2\Big]_0^3 d\theta = \frac{9}{4}\theta^2\Big|_0^\pi = \frac{9}{4}\pi^2$$

20. Working in polar coordinates,

$$m = \int_0^{2\pi} \int_0^{1+\sin\theta} 2r\,dr\,d\theta = \int_0^{2\pi} (1+\sin\theta)^2\,d\theta$$

$$= \int_0^{2\pi} \left[1 + 2\sin\theta + \frac{1}{2}(1-\cos2\theta)\right]d\theta$$

$$= \left[\frac{3}{2}\theta - 2\cos\theta - \frac{1}{4}\sin2\theta\right]_0^{2\pi} = 3\pi$$

$M_y = 0$ since the lamina is homogeneous and symmetric with respect to the y-axis, and

$$M_x = \int_0^{2\pi} \int_0^{1+\sin\theta} (2r^2\sin\theta)\,dr\,d\theta$$

$$= \frac{2}{3}\int_0^{2\pi} (1+\sin\theta)^3 \sin\theta\,d\theta$$

$$= \frac{2}{3}\int_0^{2\pi} (\sin\theta + 3\sin^2\theta + 3\sin^3\theta + \sin^4\theta)\,d\theta$$

$$= \frac{2}{3}\left(3\pi + \frac{3}{4}\pi\right) = \frac{5\pi}{2}.$$

Hence $m = 3\pi$, $(\bar{x},\bar{y}) = \left(0, \dfrac{5}{6}\right)$.

21. $m = \displaystyle\int_0^{\pi}\int_0^{\sin x} y\,dy\,dx = \int_0^{\pi}\frac{1}{2}\sin^2 x\,dx$

$$= \left[\frac{1}{4}x - \frac{1}{8}\sin2x\right]_0^{\pi} = \frac{1}{4}\pi$$

$$M_y = \int_0^{\pi}\int_0^{\sin x} xy\,dy\,dx = \int_0^{\pi}\frac{1}{2}x\sin^2 x\,dx$$

$$= \left[\frac{1}{8}x^2 - \frac{1}{8}x\sin2x - \frac{1}{16}\cos2x\right]_0^{\pi} = \frac{1}{8}\pi^2$$

and

$$M_x = \int_0^{\pi}\int_0^{\sin x} y^2\,dy\,dx = \int_0^{\pi}\frac{1}{3}\sin^3 x\,dx$$

$$= \frac{1}{3}\left[-\cos x + \frac{1}{3}\cos^3 x\right]_0^{\pi} = \frac{4}{9}$$

Hence $m = \dfrac{\pi}{4}$, $(\bar{x},\bar{y}) = \left(\dfrac{\pi}{2}, \dfrac{16}{9\pi}\right)$.

22. $m = \displaystyle\int_0^{\pi/2}\int_0^{\cos x} x\,dy\,dx = \int_0^{\pi/2} x\cos x\,dx$

$$= \left[x\sin x + \cos x\right]_0^{\pi/2} = \frac{\pi}{2} - 1$$

$$M_y = \int_0^{\pi/2}\int_0^{\cos x} x^2\,dy\,dx = \int_0^{\pi/2} x^2\cos x\,dx$$

$$= \left[x^2\sin x + 2x\cos x - 2\sin x\right]_0^{\pi/2} = \frac{\pi^2}{4} - 2$$

and

$$M_x = \int_0^{\pi/2}\int_0^{\cos x} xy\,dy\,dx = \int_0^{\pi/2}\frac{1}{2}x\cos^2 x\,dx$$

$$= \frac{1}{2}\left[x^2 - x + (x-1)\sin x\cos x\right]_0^{\pi/2} = \frac{\pi^2}{8} - \frac{\pi}{4}$$

Hence $m = \dfrac{\pi-2}{2}$, $(\bar{x},\bar{y}) = \left(\dfrac{\pi^2-8}{2(\pi-2)}, \dfrac{\pi}{4}\right)$.

23. The plane $2x + 3y + 6z = 12$ intersects the xy-plane when $2x + 3y + 6(0) = 12 \implies y = 4 - \dfrac{2}{3}x$. So

$$E = \left\{(x,y,z)\mid 0 \le x \le 6,\ 0 \le y \le 4 - \frac{2}{3}x,\right.$$

$$\left. 0 \le z \le \frac{1}{6}(12 - 2x - 3y)\right\}$$

and

$$V = \int_0^6 \int_0^{4-2x/3} \int_0^{(12-2x-3y)/6} dz\,dy\,dx$$

$$= \frac{1}{6}\int_0^6 \int_0^{4-2x/3} (12 - 2x - 3y)\,dy\,dx$$

$$= \frac{1}{6}\int_0^6 \left[12y - 2xy - \frac{3}{2}y^2\right]_{y=0}^{y=4-2x/3} dx$$

$$= \frac{1}{6}\int_0^6 \left[\frac{(12-2x)^2}{3} - \frac{3}{2}\frac{12-2x}{9}\right]dx$$

$$= \frac{1}{36}\int_0^6 (12-2x)^2\,dx = \left[\frac{1}{36}\left(-\frac{1}{6}\right)(12-2x)^3\right]_0^6 = 8.$$

24.

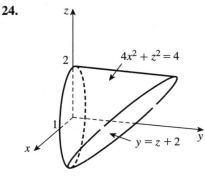

$$V = \int_{-1}^1 \int_{-\sqrt{4-4x^2}}^{\sqrt{4-4x^2}} \int_0^{z+2} dy\,dz\,dx$$

$$= 2\int_0^1 \int_{-\sqrt{4-4x^2}}^{\sqrt{4-4x^2}} \int_0^{z+2} dy\,dz\,dx$$

$$= 2\int_0^1 \int_{-\sqrt{4-4x^2}}^{\sqrt{4-4x^2}} (z+2)\,dz\,dx$$

$$= 2\int_0^1 \left[\frac{1}{2}z^2 + 2z\right]_{z=-2\sqrt{1-x^2}}^{z=2\sqrt{1-x^2}} dx$$

$$= 2 \int_0^1 8\sqrt{1-x^2}\, dx$$

$$= 16\left[\frac{1}{2}x\sqrt{1-x^2} + \frac{1}{2}\sin^{-1}x\right]_0^1 = 4\pi$$

25.

$$V = \int_0^1 \int_{-\sqrt{x}}^{\sqrt{x}} \int_0^{1-x} dz\, dy\, dx = \int_0^1 \int_{-\sqrt{x}}^{\sqrt{x}} (1-x)\, dy\, dx$$

$$= \int_0^1 2\sqrt{x}\,(1-x)\, dx = \int_0^1 2(\sqrt{x} - x^{3/2})\, dx$$

$$= 2\left[\frac{2}{3}x^{3/2} - \frac{2}{5}x^{5/2}\right]_0^1 = 2\left(\frac{2}{3} - \frac{2}{5}\right) = \frac{8}{15}$$

26. The paraboloids $z = x^2 + y^2$ and $z = 18 - x^2 - y^2$ intersect when $x^2 + y^2 = 18 - x^2 - y^2$ $\Rightarrow$ $2x^2 + 2y^2 = 18$ $\Rightarrow$ $x^2 + y^2 = 9$. Thus,

$$E = \left\{(x,y,z) \mid x^2 + y^2 \le 9,\right.$$
$$\left. x^2 + y^2 \le z \le 18 - x^2 - y^2\right\}$$

Let $D = \left\{(x,y) \mid x^2 + y^2 \le 9\right\}$. Then

$$V = \iiint_E dV = \iint_D \left(\int_{x^2+y^2}^{18-x^2-y^2} dz\right) dA$$

$$= \iint_D (18 - 2x^2 - 2y^2)\, dA$$

$$= \int_0^{2\pi} \int_0^3 (18 - 2r^2)\, r\, dr\, d\theta$$

$$= \int_0^{2\pi} \left[9r^2 - \frac{1}{2}r^4\right]_{r=0}^{r=3} d\theta = \int_0^{2\pi} \frac{81}{2} d\theta = 81\pi$$

27. $\displaystyle\iiint_E (x^2 + y^2)\, dV = \int_{-1}^2 \int_0^{2\pi} \int_0^2 (r^2)\, r\, dr\, d\theta\, dz$

$$= (3)(2\pi)\left[\frac{1}{4}r^4\right]_0^2 = 24\pi$$

28. $\displaystyle\iiint_E \sqrt{x^2 + y^2}\, dV = \int_0^{2\pi} \int_0^3 \int_0^{9-r^2} r^2\, dz\, dr\, d\theta$

$$= 2\pi \int_0^3 (9r^2 - r^4)\, dr = 2\pi\left(81 - \frac{243}{5}\right) = \frac{324\pi}{5}$$

29. $\displaystyle\iiint_E xe^{(x^2+y^2+z^2)^2}\, dV$

$$= \int_0^{\pi/2} \int_0^{\pi/2} \int_1^2 (\rho\sin\phi\cos\theta)\, e^{\rho^4}(\rho^2\sin\phi)\, d\rho\, d\phi\, d\theta$$

$$= \int_0^{\pi/2} \cos\theta\, d\theta \int_0^{\pi/2} \sin^2\phi\, d\phi \int_1^2 \rho^3 e^{\rho^4}\, d\rho$$

$$= \left[\sin\theta\right]_0^{\pi/2}\left[\frac{1}{2}\phi - \frac{1}{4}\sin 2\phi\right]_0^{\pi/2}\left[\frac{1}{4}e^{\rho^4}\right]_1^2$$

$$= (1)\left(\frac{\pi}{4}\right)\left[\frac{1}{4}(e^{16} - e)\right] = \frac{1}{16}\pi(e^{16} - e)$$

30. $\displaystyle\iiint_E \sqrt{x^2 + y^2 + z^2}\, dV$

$$= \int_0^{2\pi} \int_0^{\pi/6} \int_0^2 (\rho)\,\rho^2 \sin\phi\, d\rho\, d\phi\, d\theta$$

$$= \int_0^{2\pi} d\theta \int_0^{\pi/6} \sin\phi\, d\phi \int_0^2 \rho^3\, d\rho$$

$$= \left[\theta\right]_0^{2\pi}\left[-\cos\phi\right]_0^{\pi/6}\left[\frac{1}{4}\rho^4\right]_0^2 = (2\pi)\left(1 - \frac{\sqrt{3}}{2}\right)(4)$$

$$= 8\pi\left(1 - \frac{\sqrt{3}}{2}\right) = 4\pi(2 - \sqrt{3})$$

31. $\displaystyle\frac{\partial(x,y)}{\partial(u,v)} = \begin{vmatrix} \partial x/\partial u & \partial x/\partial v \\ \partial y/\partial u & \partial y/\partial v \end{vmatrix} = \begin{vmatrix} 1 & -2 \\ 2 & -1 \end{vmatrix}$

$$= 1(-1) - 2(-2) = 3$$

32. $\displaystyle\frac{\partial(x,y)}{\partial(u,v)} = \begin{vmatrix} \partial x/\partial u & \partial x/\partial v \\ \partial y/\partial u & \partial y/\partial v \end{vmatrix} = \begin{vmatrix} 1 & -2v \\ 1 & 2v \end{vmatrix}$

$$= 2v - (-2v) = 4v$$

33. $\displaystyle\frac{\partial(x,y)}{\partial(u,v)} = \begin{vmatrix} \partial x/\partial u & \partial x/\partial v \\ \partial y/\partial u & \partial y/\partial v \end{vmatrix} = \begin{vmatrix} 2e^{2u}\cos v & -e^{2u}\sin v \\ 2e^{2u}\sin v & e^{2u}\cos v \end{vmatrix}$

$$= 2e^{4u}(\cos^2 v + \sin^2 v) = 2e^{4u}$$

34. $\displaystyle\frac{\partial(x,y)}{\partial(u,v)} = \begin{vmatrix} \partial x/\partial u & \partial x/\partial v \\ \partial y/\partial u & \partial y/\partial v \end{vmatrix} = \begin{vmatrix} e^t & se^t \\ e^{-t} & -se^{-t} \end{vmatrix}$

$$= -s - s = -2s$$

35. $\displaystyle\frac{\partial(x,y,z)}{\partial(u,v,w)} = \begin{vmatrix} 1 & 1 & 1 \\ 1 & 1 & -1 \\ 1 & -1 & 1 \end{vmatrix}$

$$= 1(1-1) - 1(1+1) + 1(-1-1) = -4$$

36. $\displaystyle\frac{\partial(x,y,z)}{\partial(u,v,w)} = \begin{vmatrix} 2 & 0 & 0 \\ 0 & 6v & 0 \\ 0 & 0 & 12w^2 \end{vmatrix}$

$$= (2)(6v)(12w^2) = 144vw^2$$

16 | VECTOR CALCULUS

1–2 ■ Find the gradient vector field ∇f of f and sketch it.

1. $f(x, y) = x^2 - \dfrac{1}{2}y^2$

2. $f(x, y) = \ln\sqrt{x^2 + y^2}$

3–8 ■ Evaluate the line integral, where C is the given curve.

3. $\displaystyle\int_C x\, ds, \quad C: x = t^3, y = t, 0 \le t \le 1$

4. $\displaystyle\int_C y\, ds, \quad C: x = t^3, y = t^2, 0 \le t \le 1$

5. $\displaystyle\int_C xy\, ds, \quad C$ is the line segment joining $(-1, 1)$ to $(2, 3)$

6. $\displaystyle\int_C (x - 2y^2)\, dy, \quad C$ is the arc of the parabola $y = x^2$ from $(-2, 4)$ to $(1, 1)$

7. $\displaystyle\int_C \sin x\, dx, \quad C$ is the arc of the curve $x = y^4$ from $(1, -1)$ to $(1, 1)$

8. $\displaystyle\int_C x\sqrt{y}\, dx + 2y\sqrt{x}\, dy, \quad C$ consists of the shortest arc of the circle $x^2 + y^2 = 1$ from $(1, 0)$ to $(0, 1)$ and the line segment from $(0, 1)$ to $(4, 3)$

9–10 ■ Show that the line integral is independent of path and evaluate the integral.

9. $\displaystyle\int_C 2x \sin y\, dx + (x^2 \cos y - 3y^2)\, dy, \quad C$ is any path from $(-1, 0)$ to $(5, 1)$

10. $\displaystyle\int_C (2y^2 - 12x^3y^3)\, dx + (4xy - 9x^4y^2)\, dy,$

C is any path from $(1, 1)$ to $(3, 2)$

11–16 ■ Use Green's Theorem to evaluate the line integral along the given positively oriented curve.

11. $\displaystyle\int_C xy\, dx + y^5\, dy, \quad C$ is the triangle with vertices $(0, 0)$, $(2, 0)$, and $(2, 1)$

12. $\displaystyle\int_C x^2y\, dx + xy^5\, dy, \quad C$ is the square with vertices $(\pm 1, \pm 1)$

13. $\displaystyle\int_C x^2\, dx + y^2\, dy, \quad C$ is the curve $x^6 + y^6 = 1$

14. $\displaystyle\int_C x^2y\, dx - 3y^2\, dy, \quad C$ is the circle $x^2 + y^2 = 1$

15. $\displaystyle\int_C 2xy\, dx + x^2\, dy, \quad C$ is the cardioid $r = 1 + \cos\theta$.

16. $\displaystyle\int_C (xy + e^{x^2})\, dx + (x^2 - \ln(1 + y))\, dy, \quad C$ consists of the line segment from $(0, 0)$ to $(\pi, 0)$, and the curve $y = \sin x, 0 \le x \le \pi$

17–22 ■ Find (a) the curl and (b) the divergence of the vector field.

17. $\mathbf{F}(x, y, z) = xy\,\mathbf{j} + xyz\,\mathbf{k}$

18. $\mathbf{F}(x, y, z) = \sin x\,\mathbf{i} + \cos x\,\mathbf{j} + z^2\,\mathbf{k}$

19. $\mathbf{F}(x, y, z) = e^{xz}\,\mathbf{i} - 2e^{yz}\,\mathbf{j} + 3xe^y\,\mathbf{k}$

20. $\mathbf{F}(x, y, z) = (x + 3y - 5z)\,\mathbf{i} + (z - 3y)\,\mathbf{j} + (5x + 6y - z)\,\mathbf{k}$

21. $\mathbf{F}(x, y, z) = xe^y\,\mathbf{i} - ze^{-y}\,\mathbf{j} + y \ln z\,\mathbf{k}$

22. $\mathbf{F}(x, y, z) = e^{xyz}\,\mathbf{i} + \sin(x - y)\,\mathbf{j} - \dfrac{xy}{z}\,\mathbf{k}$

23–26 ■ Find a parametric representation for the surface.

23. The part of the hyperboloid $-x^2 - y^2 + z^2 = 1$ that lies below the rectangle $[-1, 1] \times [-3, 3]$

24. The part of the elliptic paraboloid $y = 6 - 3x^2 - 2z^2$ that lies to the right of the xz-plane

25. The part of the cylinder $x^2 + z^2 = 1$ that lies between the planes $y = -1$ and $y = 3$

26. The part of the plane $z = 5$ that lies inside the cylinder $x^2 + y^2 = 16$

27–31 ■ Evaluate the surface integral $\iint_S \mathbf{F} \cdot d\mathbf{S}$ for the given vector field $\mathbf{F}$ and the oriented surface S. In other words, find the flux of $\mathbf{F}$ across S. For closed surfaces, use the positive (outward) orientation.

27. $\mathbf{F}(x, y, z) = e^y\mathbf{i} + ye^x\mathbf{j} + x^2y\,\mathbf{k}$, S is the part of the paraboloid $z = x^2 + y^2$ that lies above the square $0 \le x \le 1$, $0 \le y \le 1$ and has upward orientation

28. $\mathbf{F}(x, y, z) = x^2y\,\mathbf{i} - 3xy^2\mathbf{j} + 4y^3\,\mathbf{k}$, S is the part of the elliptic paraboloid $z = x^2 + y^2 - 9$ that lies below the rectangle $0 \le x \le 2$, $0 \le y \le 1$ and has downward orientation

29. $\mathbf{F}(x, y, z) = -x\mathbf{i} - y\mathbf{j} + z^2\,\mathbf{k}$, S is the part of the cone $z = \sqrt{x^2 + y^2}$ between the planes $z = 1$ and $z = 2$ with upward orientation

30. $\mathbf{F}(x, y, z) = x\mathbf{i} + y\mathbf{j} + z\,\mathbf{k}$, S is the sphere $x^2 + y^2 + z^2 = 9$

31. $\mathbf{F}(x, y, z) = -y\mathbf{i} + x\mathbf{j} + 3z\,\mathbf{k}$, S is the hemisphere $z = \sqrt{16 - x^2 - y^2}$ with upward orientation

32–34 ■ Use Stokes' Theorem to evaluate $\int_C \mathbf{F} \cdot d\mathbf{r}$. In each case C is oriented counterclockwise as viewed from above.

32. $\mathbf{F}(x, y, z) = xz\,\mathbf{i} + 2xy\,\mathbf{j} + 3xy\,\mathbf{k}$, C is the boundary of the part of the plane $3x + y + z = 3$ in the first octant

33. $\mathbf{F}(x, y, z) = z^2\mathbf{i} + y^2\mathbf{j} + xy\,\mathbf{k}$, C is the triangle with vertices $(1, 0, 0)$, $(0, 1, 0)$, and $(0, 0, 2)$

34. $\mathbf{F}(x, y, z) = 2z\mathbf{i} + 4x\mathbf{j} + 5y\,\mathbf{k}$, C is the curve of intersection of the plane $z = x + 4$ and the cylinder $x^2 + y^2 = 4$

35–39 ■ Use the Divergence Theorem to calculate the surface integral $\iint_S \mathbf{F} \cdot d\mathbf{S}$; that is, calculate the flux of $\mathbf{F}$ across S.

35. $\mathbf{F}(x, y, z) = 3y^2z^3\mathbf{i} + 9x^2yz^2\mathbf{j} - 4xy^2\mathbf{k}$,
S is the surface of the cube with vertices $(\pm 1, \pm 1, \pm 1)$

36. $\mathbf{F}(x, y, z) = x^2y\mathbf{i} - x^2z\mathbf{j} + z^2y\,\mathbf{k}$,
S is the surface of the rectangular box bounded by the planes $x = 0$, $x = 3$, $y = 0$, $y = 2$, $z = 0$, and $z = 1$

37. $\mathbf{F}(x, y, z) = -xz\mathbf{i} - yz\mathbf{j} + z^2\,\mathbf{k}$,
S is the ellipsoid $x^2/a^2 + y^2/b^2 + z^2/c^2 = 1$

38. $\mathbf{F}(x, y, z) = 3xy\mathbf{i} + y^2\mathbf{j} - x^2y^4\mathbf{k}$,
S is the surface of the tetrahedron with vertices $(0, 0, 0)$, $(1, 0, 0)$, $(0, 1, 0)$, and $(0, 0, 1)$

39. $\mathbf{F}(x, y, z) = x^3\mathbf{i} + y^3\mathbf{j} + z^3\,\mathbf{k}$,
S is the sphere $x^2 + y^2 + z^2 = 1$

16 | ANSWERS TO SELECTED EXERCISES

1. $2x\mathbf{i} - y\mathbf{j}$

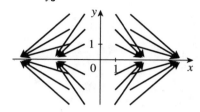

2. $\dfrac{x\mathbf{i} + y\mathbf{j}}{x^2 + y^2}$

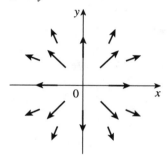

3. $\dfrac{1}{54}\left(10^{3/2} - 1\right)$

4. $\dfrac{1}{1215}\left[19\,(13)^{3/2} + 64\right]$

5. $\dfrac{3\sqrt{13}}{2}$

6. 48

7. 0

8. $\dfrac{32\sqrt{3} + 66}{5}$

9. $25\sin 1 - 1$

10. -1919

11. $-\dfrac{4}{3}$

12. $-\dfrac{4}{3}$

13. 0

14. $-\dfrac{\pi}{4}$

15. 0

16. π

17. (a) $xz\mathbf{i} - yz\mathbf{j} + y\mathbf{k}$

(b) $x\,(1 + y)$

18. (a) $-\sin x\,\mathbf{k}$

(b) $\cos x + 2z$

19. (a) $(3xe^y + 2ye^{yz})\mathbf{i} + (xe^{xz} - 3e^y)\mathbf{j}$

(b) $ze^{xz} - 2ze^{yz}$

20. (a) $5\mathbf{i} - 0\mathbf{j} - 3\mathbf{k}$

(b) -3

21. (a) $(e^{-y} + \ln z)\mathbf{i} - xe^y\mathbf{k}$

(b) $e^y + ze^{-y} + \dfrac{y}{z}$

22. (a) $-\dfrac{x}{z}\mathbf{i} + \left(xye^{xyz} + \dfrac{y}{z}\right)\mathbf{j} + [\cos(x - y) - xze^{xyz}]\,\mathbf{k}$

(b) $yze^{xyz} - \cos(x - y) + \dfrac{xy}{z^2}$

23. $x = x,\ y = y,\ z = -\sqrt{1 + x^2 + y^2},\ -1 \le x \le 1,$
$-3 \le y \le 3$

24. $x = x,\ y = 6 - 3x^2 - 2z^2,\ z = z,\ 3x^2 + 2z^2 \le 6$

25. $x = \sin\theta,\ y = y,\ z = \cos\theta,\ 0 \le \theta \le 2\pi,\ -1 \le y \le 3$

26. $x = r\cos\theta,\ y = r\sin\theta,\ z = 5,\ 0 \le r \le 4,$
$0 \le \theta \le 2\pi$

27. $\dfrac{1}{6}(11 - 10e)$

28. -1

29. $\dfrac{73}{6}\pi$

30. 108π

31. 128π

32. $\dfrac{7}{2}$

33. $\dfrac{4}{3}$

34. -4π

35. 8

36. 24

37. 0

38. $\dfrac{5}{24}$

39. $\dfrac{12}{5}\pi$

16 | SOLUTIONS TO SELECTED EXERCISES

1. $f(x, y) = x^2 - \frac{1}{2}y^2$, $\nabla f(x, y) = 2x\mathbf{i} - y\mathbf{j}$. The length of $\nabla f(x, y)$ is $\sqrt{4x^2 + y^2}$, and $\nabla f(x, y)$ terminates on the x-axis at the point $(3x, 0)$.

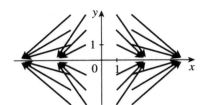

2. $f(x, y) = \ln\sqrt{x^2 + y^2} = \frac{1}{2}\ln(x^2 + y^2) \Rightarrow$

$\nabla f = \frac{1}{2}\nabla \ln(x^2 + y^2)$

$= \frac{x}{x^2 + y^2}\mathbf{i} + \frac{y}{x^2 + y^2}\mathbf{j} = \frac{x\mathbf{i} + y\mathbf{j}}{x^2 + y^2}$

The length of ∇f decreases as x and/or y increase and all the vectors "flow out" away from the origin.

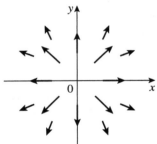

3. $\int_C x \, ds = \int_0^1 (t^3)\sqrt{9t^4 + 1} \, dt = \frac{1}{54}(9t^4 + 1)^{3/2}\Big|_0^1$

$= \frac{1}{54}(10^{3/2} - 1)$

4. $\int_C y \, ds = \int_0^1 (t^2)\sqrt{9t^4 + 4t^2} \, dt = \int_0^1 t^3\sqrt{9t^2 + 4} \, dt$

$= \int_0^1 3t^3\sqrt{t^2 + \left(\frac{2}{3}\right)^2} \, dt$

$= 3\left(\frac{1}{5}t^2 - \frac{8}{135}\right)\left(t^2 + \frac{4}{9}\right)^{3/2}\Big|_0^1$

$= \frac{19}{45}\left(\frac{13}{9}\right)^{3/2} + \frac{8}{45}\left(\frac{8}{27}\right)$

$= \frac{1}{1215}\left[19(13)^{3/2} + 64\right]$

5. The line is $3y - 2x = 5$, so $x = x$,

$y = \frac{1}{3}(2x + 5)$, $-1 \le x \le 2$. Then

$\int_C xy \, ds = \int_{-1}^2 \frac{1}{3}x(2x + 5) \cdot \frac{\sqrt{13}}{3} \, dx$

$= \frac{\sqrt{13}}{9}\int_{-1}^2 (2x^2 + 5x) \, dx$

$= \frac{\sqrt{13}}{9}\left(\frac{46}{3} - \frac{11}{6}\right) = \frac{3\sqrt{13}}{2}$

6. $x = x$, $y = x^2$, $-2 \le x \le 1$. Then

$\int_C (x - 2y^2) \, dy = \int_{-2}^1 (x - 2x^4)2x \, dx$

$= \int_{-2}^1 (2x^2 - 4x^5) \, dx$

$= \frac{2}{3}[x^3 - x^6]_{-2}^1 = 48$

7. Choosing y as the parameter, we have $x = y^4$, $y = y$, $-1 \le y \le 1$. Then

$\int_C \sin x \, dx = \int_{-1}^1 (\sin y^4)(4y^3) \, dy = -\cos y^4\big|_{-1}^1 = 0$.

8.

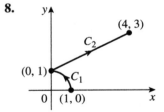

On C_1: $x = \cos t \Rightarrow dx = -\sin t \, dt$,

$y = \sin t \Rightarrow y = \cos t \, dt$, $0 \le t \le \frac{\pi}{2}$.

On C_2: $x = 4t \Rightarrow dx = 4 \, dt$,

$y = 2t + 1 \Rightarrow dy = 2 \, dt$, $0 \le t \le 1$. Then

$\int_C x\sqrt{y} \, dx + 2y\sqrt{x} \, dy$

$= \int_{C_1} x\sqrt{y} \, dx + 2y\sqrt{x} \, dy$

$+ \int_{C_2} x\sqrt{y} \, dx + 2y\sqrt{x} \, dy$

$$= \int_0^{\pi/2} \left[-\cos t \, (\sin t)^{3/2} + 2 \sin t \, (\cos t)^{3/2} \right] dt$$

$$+ \int_0^1 \left[16t\sqrt{2t+1} + 8\,(2t+1)\sqrt{t} \right] dt$$

$$= \left[-\frac{2}{5} (\sin t)^{5/2} - \frac{4}{5} (\cos t)^{5/2} \right]_0^{\pi/2} + \left[\frac{16}{3} t \, (2t+1)^{3/2} \right.$$

$$\left. - \frac{16}{15} (2t+1)^{5/2} + 8 \left(\frac{4}{5} t^{5/2} + \frac{2}{3} t^{3/2} \right) \right]_0^1$$

$$= \frac{2}{5} + \frac{16}{3} \cdot 3\sqrt{3} - \frac{16}{15} \cdot 3^2 \cdot \sqrt{3} + \frac{16}{15} + 8 \left(\frac{4}{5} + \frac{2}{3} \right)$$

$$= \frac{32\sqrt{3} + 66}{5}$$

9. Here $\mathbf{F}(x, y) = (2x \sin y)\mathbf{i} + (x^2 \cos y - 3y^2)\mathbf{j}$.
Then $f(x, y) = x^2 \sin y - y^3$ is a potential function
for $\mathbf{F}$, that is, $\nabla f = \mathbf{F}$ so $\mathbf{F}$ is conservative and thus
its line integral is independent of path. Hence

$$\int_C 2x \sin y \, dx + (x^2 \cos y - 3y^2) \, dy$$

$$= \int_C \mathbf{F} \cdot d\mathbf{r} = f(5, 1) - f(-1, 0) = 25 \sin 1 - 1$$

10. Here $\mathbf{F}(x, y) = (2y^2 - 12x^3 y^3)\mathbf{i} + (4xy - 9x^4 y^2)\mathbf{j}$.
Then $f(x, y) = 2xy^2 - 3x^4 y^3$ is a potential function
for $\mathbf{F}$, that is, $\nabla f = \mathbf{F}$. Hence $\mathbf{F}$ is conservative and
its line integral is independent of path.

$$\int_C (2y^2 - 12x^3 y^3) \, dx + (4xy - 9x^4 y^2) \, dy$$

$$= \int_C \mathbf{F} \cdot d\mathbf{r} = f(3, 2) - f(1, 1) = -1920 - (-1)$$

$$= -1919$$

11. $\displaystyle \oint_C xy \, dx + y^5 \, dy = \int_0^2 \int_0^{x/2} (0 - x) \, dy \, dx$

$$= \int_0^2 \left(-\frac{1}{2} x^2 \right) dx = -\frac{4}{3}$$

12. $\displaystyle \int_{-1}^1 \int_{-1}^1 (y^5 - x^2) \, dy \, dx = \int_{-1}^1 \left(-\frac{2}{3} \right) dx = -\frac{4}{3}$

13. $\displaystyle \iint_D (0 - 0) \, dA = 0$

14. $\displaystyle \iint_{x^2 + y^2 \le 1} (0 - x^2) \, dA = -\int_0^{2\pi} \int_0^1 r^3 \cos^2\theta \, dr \, d\theta$

$$= -\pi \left(\frac{1}{4} \right) = -\frac{\pi}{4}$$

15. $\displaystyle \iint_D (2x - 2x) \, dA = 0$

16. $\displaystyle \iint_D (2x - x) \, dA = \int_0^\pi \int_0^{\sin x} x \, dy \, dx = \int_0^\pi x \sin x \, dx$

$$= [-x \cos x + \sin x]_0^\pi = \pi$$

17. (a) $\text{curl } \mathbf{F} = \nabla \times \mathbf{F} = \begin{vmatrix} \mathbf{i} & \mathbf{j} & \mathbf{k} \\ \partial/\partial x & \partial/\partial x & \partial/\partial z \\ 0 & xy & xyz \end{vmatrix}$

$$= xz\mathbf{i} - yz\mathbf{j} + y\mathbf{k}$$

(b) $\text{div } \mathbf{F} = \nabla \cdot \mathbf{F} = \dfrac{\partial}{\partial x} (0) + \dfrac{\partial}{\partial y} (xy) + \dfrac{\partial}{\partial z} (xyz)$

$$= 0 + x + xy = x \, (1 + y)$$

18. (a) $\text{curl } \mathbf{F} = \nabla \times \mathbf{F} = \begin{vmatrix} \mathbf{i} & \mathbf{j} & \mathbf{k} \\ \partial/\partial x & \partial/\partial y & \partial/\partial z \\ \sin x & \cos x & z^2 \end{vmatrix}$

$$= (-\sin x + 0)\mathbf{k} = -\sin x \, \mathbf{k}$$

(b) $\text{div } \mathbf{F} = \nabla \cdot \mathbf{F}$

$$= \dfrac{\partial}{\partial x} (\sin x) + \dfrac{\partial}{\partial y} (\cos x) + \dfrac{\partial}{\partial z} (z^2)$$

$$= \cos x + 2z$$

19. (a) $\nabla \times \mathbf{F} = \begin{vmatrix} \mathbf{i} & \mathbf{j} & \mathbf{k} \\ \partial/\partial x & \partial/\partial y & \partial/\partial z \\ e^{xz} & -2e^{yz} & 3xe^y \end{vmatrix}$

$$= (3xe^y + 2ye^{yz})\mathbf{i} + (xe^{xz} - 3e^y)\mathbf{j}$$

(b) $\nabla \cdot \mathbf{F} = \dfrac{\partial}{\partial x}(e^{xz}) + \dfrac{\partial}{\partial y}(-2e^{yz}) + \dfrac{\partial}{\partial z}(3xe^y)$

$$= ze^{xz} - 2ze^{yz}$$

20. (a) $\nabla \times \mathbf{F} = \begin{vmatrix} \mathbf{i} & \mathbf{j} & \mathbf{k} \\ \partial/\partial x & \partial/\partial y & \partial/\partial z \\ x + 3y - 5z & z - 3y & 5x + 6y - z \end{vmatrix}$

$$= (6 - 1)\mathbf{i} + (5 - 5)\mathbf{j} + (0 - 3)\mathbf{k}$$

$$= 5\mathbf{i} - 0\mathbf{j} - 3\mathbf{k}$$

(b) $\nabla \cdot \mathbf{F} = \dfrac{\partial}{\partial x} (x + 3y - 5z) + \dfrac{\partial}{\partial y} (z - 3y)$

$$+ \dfrac{\partial}{\partial z} (5x + 6y - z)$$

$$= 1 - 3 - 1 = -3$$

21. (a) $\operatorname{curl} \mathbf{F} = \begin{vmatrix} \mathbf{i} & \mathbf{j} & \mathbf{k} \\ \partial/\partial x & \partial/\partial y & \partial/\partial z \\ xe^y & -ze^{-y} & y \ln z \end{vmatrix}$

$$= (e^{-y} + \ln z)\mathbf{i} - xe^y \mathbf{k}$$

(b) $\operatorname{div} \mathbf{F} = \dfrac{\partial}{\partial x}(xe^y) + \dfrac{\partial}{\partial y}(-ze^{-y}) + \dfrac{\partial}{\partial z}(y \ln z)$

$$= e^y + ze^{-y} + \dfrac{y}{z}$$

22. (a) $\nabla \times \mathbf{F} = \begin{vmatrix} \mathbf{i} & \mathbf{j} & \mathbf{k} \\ \partial/\partial x & \partial/\partial y & \partial/\partial z \\ e^{xyz} & \sin(x-y) & -xy/z \end{vmatrix}$

$$= -\dfrac{x}{z}\mathbf{i} + \left(xye^{xyz} + \dfrac{y}{z} \right)\mathbf{j}$$
$$+ (\cos(x-y) - xze^{xyz})\mathbf{k}$$

(b) $\nabla \cdot \mathbf{F} = \dfrac{\partial}{\partial x}(e^{xyz}) + \dfrac{\partial}{\partial y}\sin(x-y) + \dfrac{\partial}{\partial z}\left(-\dfrac{xy}{z}\right)$

$$= yze^{xyz} - \cos(x-y) + \dfrac{xy}{z^2}$$

23. Letting x and y be the parameters, parametric equations are $x = x$, $y = y$, $z = -\sqrt{1 + x^2 + y^2}$ (since the surface lies below the rectangle) where $-1 \le x \le 1$ and $-3 \le y \le 3$.
Alternate Solution: Using cylindrical coordinates, $x = r\cos\theta$, $y = r\sin\theta$, $z = -\sqrt{1 + r^2}$ where $-1 \le r\cos\theta \le 1$ and $-3 \le r\sin\theta \le 3$.

24. $x = x$, $y = 6 - 3x^2 - 2z^2$, $z = z$ where $3x^2 + 2z^2 \le 6$ since $y \ge 0$. Then the associated vector equation is $\mathbf{r}(x, z) = x\mathbf{i} + (6 - 3x^2 - 2z^2)\mathbf{j} + z\mathbf{k}$.

25. In cylindrical coordinates, parametric equations are $x = \sin\theta$, $y = y$, $z = \cos\theta$, $0 \le \theta \le 2\pi$, $-1 \le y \le 3$.

26. The surface is a disc with radius 4 and center $(0, 0, 5)$. Thus, $x = r\cos\theta$, $y = r\sin\theta$, $z = 5$ where $0 \le r \le 4$, $0 \le \theta \le 2\pi$ is a parametric representation of the surface.
Alternate Solution: In rectangular coordinates we could represent the surface as $x = x$, $y = y$, $z = 5$ where $0 \le x^2 + y^2 \le 16$.

27. $\mathbf{F}(\mathbf{r}(x, y)) = e^y\mathbf{i} + ye^x\mathbf{j} + x^2y\mathbf{k}$ and $\mathbf{r}_x \times \mathbf{r}_y = -2x\mathbf{i} - 2y\mathbf{j} + \mathbf{k}$. Then $\mathbf{F}(\mathbf{r}(x, y)) \cdot (\mathbf{r}_x \times \mathbf{r}_y) = -2xe^y - 2y^2e^x + x^2y$ and

$$\iint_S \mathbf{F} \cdot d\mathbf{S} = \int_0^1 \int_0^1 (-2xe^y - 2y^2e^x + x^2y)\, dx\, dy$$
$$= \int_0^1 \left(-e^y - 2ey^2 + \dfrac{1}{3}y + 2y^2 \right) dy$$
$$= \dfrac{1}{6}(11 - 10e)$$

28. $\mathbf{F}(\mathbf{r}(x, y)) = x^2y\mathbf{i} - 3xy^2\mathbf{j} + 4y^3\mathbf{k}$, $\mathbf{r}_y \times \mathbf{r}_x = 2x\mathbf{i} + 2y\mathbf{j} - \mathbf{k}$ (since downward), and $\mathbf{F}(\mathbf{r}(x, y)) \cdot (\mathbf{r}_x \times \mathbf{r}_y) = 2x^3y - 6xy^3 - 4y^3$. Hence

$$\iint_S \mathbf{F} \cdot d\mathbf{S} = \int_0^2 \int_0^1 (2x^3y - 6xy^3 - 4y^3)\, dy\, dx$$
$$= \int_0^2 \left(x^3 - \dfrac{3}{2}x - 1 \right) dx = -1$$

29. $\mathbf{r}_x \times \mathbf{r}_y = -\dfrac{x}{\sqrt{x^2 + y^2}}\mathbf{i} - \dfrac{y}{\sqrt{x^2 + y^2}}\mathbf{j} + \mathbf{k}$
(since upward) and

$$\mathbf{F}(\mathbf{r}(x, y)) \cdot (\mathbf{r}_x \times \mathbf{r}_y) = \dfrac{x^2 + y^2}{\sqrt{x^2 + y^2}} + x^2 + y^2$$

where $1 \le x^2 + y^2 \le 4$. Then

$$\iint_S \mathbf{F} \cdot d\mathbf{S} = \iint_{1 \le x^2 + y^2 \le 4} \left(\sqrt{x^2 + y^2} + x^2 + y^2 \right) dA$$
$$= \int_0^{2\pi} \int_1^2 (r + r^2)r\, dr\, d\theta = 2\pi\left(\dfrac{73}{12}\right) = \dfrac{73}{6}\pi$$

30. $\mathbf{F}(\mathbf{r}(\phi, \theta)) = 3\sin\phi\cos\theta\mathbf{i} + 3\sin\phi\sin\theta\mathbf{j} + 3\cos\phi\mathbf{k}$ and $\mathbf{r}_\phi \times \mathbf{r}_\theta = 9\sin^2\phi\cos\theta\mathbf{i} + 9\sin^2\phi\sin\theta\mathbf{j} + 9\sin\phi\cos\phi\mathbf{k}$. Then
$\mathbf{F}(\mathbf{r}(\phi, \theta)) \cdot (\mathbf{r}_\phi \times \mathbf{r}_\theta)$
$= 27\sin^3\phi\cos^2\theta + 27\sin^3\phi\sin^2\theta + 27\sin\phi\cos^2\phi$
$= 27\sin\phi$

and

$$\iint_S \mathbf{F} \cdot d\mathbf{S} = \int_0^{2\pi} \int_0^\pi 27\sin\phi\, d\phi\, d\theta$$
$$= (2\pi)(54) = 108\pi.$$

31. $\mathbf{F}(\mathbf{r}(\phi, \theta)) = -4\sin\phi\sin\theta\mathbf{i} + 4\sin\phi\cos\theta\mathbf{j} + 12\cos\phi\mathbf{k}$

and

$\mathbf{r}_\phi \times \mathbf{r}_\theta = 16\sin^2\phi\cos\theta\mathbf{i} + 16\sin^2\phi\sin\theta\mathbf{j} + 16\sin\phi\cos\phi\mathbf{k}$

Then

$\mathbf{F}(\mathbf{r}(\phi, \theta)) \cdot (\mathbf{r}_\phi \times \mathbf{r}_\theta)$
$= -64\sin^3\phi\sin\theta\cos\theta + 64\sin^3\phi\sin\theta\cos\theta + 192\sin\phi\cos^2\phi$
$= 192\sin\phi\cos^2\phi$

and

$$\iint_S \mathbf{F} \cdot d\mathbf{S} = \int_0^{2\pi} \int_0^{\pi/2} 192\sin\phi\cos^2\phi\, d\phi\, d\theta$$
$$= 2\pi\left[-64\cos^3\phi \right]_0^{\pi/2} = 128\pi$$

32. $\operatorname{curl}\mathbf{F} = 3x\mathbf{i} + (x - 3y)\mathbf{j} + 2y\mathbf{k}$,

$\mathbf{n} = \dfrac{1}{\sqrt{11}}(3\mathbf{i} + \mathbf{j} + \mathbf{k})$

and

$$\oint_C \mathbf{F}\cdot d\mathbf{r} = \iint_S \operatorname{curl}\mathbf{F}\cdot\mathbf{n}\, dS$$

$$= \int_0^1\int_0^{3-3x} \frac{1}{\sqrt{11}}\big[9x + (x - 3y)$$

$$+ 2y\big](\sqrt{11})\, dy\, dx$$

$$= \int_0^1\int_0^{3-3x}(10x - y)\, dy\, dx$$

$$= \int_0^1\left[10\,(3x - 3x^2) - \frac{1}{2}\,(3 - 3x)^2\right]dx$$

$$= \left[15x^2 - 10x^3 + \frac{3}{2}\,(1 - x^3)\right]_0^1 = \frac{7}{2}$$

33. The triangle is in the plane $2x + 2y + z = 2$ with

normal $\mathbf{n} = \dfrac{1}{3}(2\mathbf{i} + 2\mathbf{j} + \mathbf{k})$, $\operatorname{curl}\mathbf{F} = x\mathbf{i} + (2z - y)\mathbf{j}$,

$\operatorname{curl}\mathbf{F}\cdot\mathbf{n} = \dfrac{1}{3}(2x + 4z - 2y) = \dfrac{1}{3}(8 - 6x - 10y)$,

and $dS = 3\, dx\, dy$. So

$$\oint_C \mathbf{F}\cdot d\mathbf{r} = \iint_S \operatorname{curl}\mathbf{F}\cdot\mathbf{n}\, dS$$

$$= \int_0^1\int_0^{1-x}(8 - 6x - 10y)\, dy\, dx$$

$$= \int_0^1\big[8\,(1 - x) - 6\,(x - x^2) - 5\,(1 - x)^2\big]\, dx$$

$$= \left[8x - 7x^2 + 2x^3 + \frac{5}{3}\,(1 - x)^3\right]_0^1 = \frac{4}{3}$$

34. The curve of intersection is an ellipse in the plane

$z = x + 4$ with unit normal $\mathbf{n} = \dfrac{1}{\sqrt{2}}(-\mathbf{i} + \mathbf{k})$ and

$\operatorname{curl}\mathbf{F} = 5\mathbf{i} + 2\mathbf{j} + 4\mathbf{k}$ so $\operatorname{curl}\mathbf{F}\cdot\mathbf{n} = -\dfrac{1}{\sqrt{2}}$. Then

$$\oint_C \mathbf{F}\cdot d\mathbf{r} = -\iint_S \frac{1}{\sqrt{2}}\, dS$$

$$= -\frac{1}{\sqrt{2}}\cdot(\text{surface area of planar ellipse})$$

$$= -\frac{1}{\sqrt{2}}\,\pi\,(2)\,(2\sqrt{2}) = -4\pi$$

Recall that the area of an ellipse with semiaxes a
and b is πab.

35. $\operatorname{div}\mathbf{F} = \dfrac{\partial}{\partial x}\,(3y^2z^3) + \dfrac{\partial}{\partial y}\,(9x^2yz^2) + \dfrac{\partial}{\partial z}\,(4xy^2) = 9x^2z^2$

so by the Divergence Theorem,

$$\iint_S \mathbf{F}\cdot d\mathbf{S} = \iiint_E 9x^2z^2\, dV$$

$$= \int_{-1}^1\int_{-1}^1\int_{-1}^1 9x^2z^2\, dx\, dy\, dz = 8$$

36. $\operatorname{div}\mathbf{F} = \dfrac{\partial}{\partial x}\,(x^2y) + \dfrac{\partial}{\partial y}\,(-x^2z) + \dfrac{\partial}{\partial z}\,(z^2y) = 2xy + 2zy$

so by the Divergence Theorem,

$$\iint_S \mathbf{F}\cdot d\mathbf{S} = \iiint_E (2xy + 2yz)\, dV$$

$$= \int_0^1\int_0^2\int_0^3 (2xy + 2yz)\, dx\, dy\, dz = 24$$

37. $\operatorname{div}\mathbf{F} = \dfrac{\partial}{\partial x}(-xz) + \dfrac{\partial}{\partial y}(-yz) + \dfrac{\partial}{\partial z}(z^2)$

$$= -z - z + 2z = 0$$

so $\displaystyle\iint_S \mathbf{F}\cdot d\mathbf{S} = \iiint_E \operatorname{div}\mathbf{F}\, dV = \iiint_E 0\, dV = 0.$

38. $\displaystyle\iint_S \mathbf{F}\cdot d\mathbf{S} = \iiint_E (5y)\, dV$

$$= \int_0^1\int_0^{1-x}\int_0^{1-x-y} 5y\, dz\, dy\, dx$$

$$= \int_0^1\int_0^{1-x}\big[5\,(1 - x)\,y - 5y^2\big]\, dy\, dx$$

$$= \int_0^1\left[\frac{5}{2}\,(1 - x)^3 - \frac{5}{3}\,(1 - x)^3\right]dx = \frac{5}{24}$$

39. $\displaystyle\iint_S \mathbf{F}\cdot d\mathbf{S} = \iiint_E 3\,(x^2 + y^2 + z^2)\, dV$

$$= \int_0^{2\pi}\int_0^\pi\int_0^1 3\rho^4 \sin\phi\, d\rho\, d\phi\, d\theta$$

$$= 2\pi\int_0^\pi \frac{3}{5}\sin\phi\, d\phi = \frac{12}{5}\pi$$

17 | SECOND-ORDER DIFFERENTIAL EQUATIONS

1–8 ■ Solve the boundary-value problem, if possible.

1. $y'' + 4y' + 4y = 0$, $\quad y(0) = 0$, $\quad y(1) = 3$

2. $y'' + 5y' - 6y = 0$, $\quad y(0) = 0$, $\quad y(2) = 1$

3. $y'' + y = 0$, $\quad y(0) = 1$, $\quad y(\pi) = 0$

4. $y'' + 9y = 0$, $\quad y(0) = 1$, $\quad y(\pi/2) = 0$

5. $y'' - y' - 2y = 0$, $\quad y(-1) = 1$, $\quad y(1) = 0$

6. $y'' + 4y' + 3y = 0$, $\quad y(1) = 0$, $\quad y(3) = 2$

7. $y'' + 4y' + 13y = 0$, $\quad y(0) = 2$, $\quad y(\pi/2) = 1$

8. $y'' + 2y' + 5y = 0$, $\quad y(0) = 1$, $\quad y(\pi) = 2$

9–12 ■ Write a trial solution for the method of undetermined coefficients. Do not determine the coefficients.

9. $y'' + 2y' + 6y = x^4 e^{2x}$

10. $y'' + 6y' + 2y = x^3 + e^x \sin 2x$

11. $y'' - 2y' + 2y = e^x \cos x$

12. $y'' + 3y' = 1 + xe^{-3x}$

17 | ANSWERS TO SELECTED EXERCISES

1. $y = 3xe^{-2x+2}$

2. $y = (e^2 - e^{-12})^{-1}(e^x - e^{-6x})$

3. No solution

4. $y = \cos 3x$

5. $y = \dfrac{1}{e^6 - 1}\left[e^{5-x} - e^{2(1+x)}\right]$

6. $y = \dfrac{1}{e^4 - 1}(2e^{7-x} - 2e^{9-3x})$

7. $y = e^{-2x}(2\cos 3x - e^{\pi}\sin 3x)$

8. No solution

9. $y_p(x) = (Ax^4 + Bx^3 + Cx^2 + Dx + E)\,e^{2x}$

10. $y_{p1}(x) = Ax^3 + Bx^2 + Cx + D,$
$y_{p2}(x) = e^x(A\cos 2x + B\sin 2x)$

11. $y_p(x) = xe^x(A\cos x + B\sin x)$

12. $y_{p1}(x) = xA,\; y_{p2}(x) = x(Ax + B)\,e^{-3x}$

17 | SOLUTIONS TO SELECTED EXERCISES

1. $r^2 + 4r + 4 = (r+2)^2 = 0$ so the general solution is $y = c_1 e^{-2x} + c_2 x e^{-2x}$. Then $0 = y(0) = c_1$, $3 = y(1) = c_2 e^{-2}$ so $c_2 = 3e^2$ and the solution of the boundary-value problem is $y = 3x e^{-2x+2}$.

2. $r^2 + 5r - 6 = (r+6)(r-1) = 0$ so the general solution is $y = c_1 e^x + c_2 e^{-6x}$. Then $0 = y(0) = c_1 + c_2$ and $1 = y(2) = c_1 e^2 + c_2 e^{-12}$ so $c_2 = (e^{-12} - e^2)^{-1}$, $c_1 = -(e^{-12} - e^2)^{-1}$.
The solution of the boundary-value problem is $y = (e^2 - e^{-12})^{-1}(e^x - e^{-6x})$.

3. $r^2 + 1 = 0 \implies r = \pm i$ and the general solution is $y = c_1 \cos x + c_2 \sin x$. But $1 = y(0) = c_1$ and $0 = y(\pi) = -c_1$ so there is no solution.

4. $r^2 + 9 = 0 \implies r = \pm 3i$ and the general solution is $y = c_1 \cos 3x + c_2 \sin 3x$. But $1 = y(0) = c_1$ and $0 = y\left(\dfrac{\pi}{2}\right) = -c_2$, so the solution to the boundary-value problem is $y = \cos 3x$.

5. $r^2 - r - 2 = (r-2)(r+1) = 0$ so the general solution is $y = c_1 e^{-x} + c_2 e^{2x}$. Then $1 = y(-1) = c_1 e + c_2 e^{-2}$ and $0 = y(1) = c_1 e^{-1} + c_2 e^2$ so $c_1 = \dfrac{e^5}{e^6 - 1}$ and $c_2 = \dfrac{e^2}{1 - e^6}$ so the solution to the boundary-value problem is
$$y = \frac{e^5}{e^6 - 1} e^{-x} + \frac{e^2}{1 - e^6} e^{2x} = \frac{1}{e^6 - 1}\left[e^{5-x} - e^{2(1+x)} \right].$$

6. $r^2 + 4r + 3 = (r+3)(r+1) = 0$ so the general solution is $y = c_1 e^{-x} + c_2 e^{-3x}$.
Then $0 = y(1) = c_1 e^{-1} + c_2 e^{-3}$ and
$2 = y(3) = c_1 e^{-3} + c_2 e^{-9}$ so $c_1 = \dfrac{2e^7}{e^4 - 1}$ and

$c_2 = \dfrac{2e^9}{1 - e^4}$. Hence the solution to the boundary-value problem is $y = \dfrac{1}{e^4 - 1}(2e^{7-x} - 2e^{9-3x})$.

7. $r^2 + 4r + 13 = 0 \implies r = -2 \pm 3i$ and the general solution is $y = e^{-2x}(c_1 \cos 3x + c_2 \sin 3x)$.
But $2 = y(0) = c_1$ and $1 = y\left(\dfrac{\pi}{2}\right) = e^{-\pi}(-c_2)$, so the solution to the boundary-value problem is $y = e^{-2x}(2 \cos 3x - e^\pi \sin 3x)$.

8. $r^2 + 2r + 5 = 0 \implies r = -1 \pm 2i$ and the general solution is $y = e^{-x}(c_1 \cos 2x + c_2 \sin 2x)$. But $1 = y(0) = c_1$ and $2 = y(\pi) = e^{-\pi}(c_1)$ so there is no solution to the boundary-value problem.

9. Since the roots of the auxiliary equation are complex, we need only try $y_p(x) = (Ax^4 + Bx^3 + Cx^2 + Dx + E)e^{2x}$.

10. For $y'' + 6y' + 2y = x^3$, try $y_{p1}(x) = Ax^3 + Bx^2 + Cx + D$, and for $y'' + 6y' + 2y = e^x \sin 2x$, try $y_{p2}(x) = e^x(A \cos 2x + B \sin 2x)$.

11. Since $y_c(x) = e^x(c_1 \cos x + c_2 \sin x)$ we try $y_p(x) = xe^x(A \cos x + B \sin x)$.

12. Here $y_c(x) = c_1 + c_2 e^{-3x}$. For $y'' + 3y' = 1$, try $y_{p1}(x) = xA$, so that y_{p1} is not a solution of the complementary equation. For $y'' + 3y' = xe^{-3x}$ try $y_{p2}(x) = x(Ax + B)e^{-3x}$.